EPIDEMIOLOGY OF MENTAL DISORDER

A SYMPOSIUM ORGANIZED BY THE AMERICAN PSYCHI-
ATRIC ASSOCIATION TO COMMEMORATE THE CENTEN-
NIAL OF THE BIRTH OF EMIL KRAEPELIN, COSPONSORED
BY THE AMERICAN PUBLIC HEALTH ASSOCIATION, AND
HELD AT THE NEW YORK MEETING, DECEMBER 27–28,
1956

Edited by

Benjamin Pasamanick

Publication No. 60 of the

AMERICAN ASSOCIATION FOR THE ADVANCEMENT OF SCIENCE

Washington, D. C., 1959

Printed in the United States of America

Preface

It is particularly fitting that the centennial of the birth of Emil Kraepelin be celebrated by a symposium on the epidemiology of mental disorder. During the interim since his death, owing largely to the development of antibiotics and other chemotherapeutic specifics, medicine has been brought up against its last great obstacle, the chronic diseases. Of these, indubitably the most numerous and most destructive to the individual and society are the psychiatric disorders.

Kraepelin's greatest contribution to psychiatry was his construction of a rational and usable classification of mental diseases, the first step in the systematic investigation of the etiology of disease. It is painful to note that we have advanced little since his death and, indeed, in many areas of psychiatry have regressed to that prescientific level, the unsystematic statements of outstanding clinicians. By some, categorization of disease states has been decried as unnecessary and even harmful.

The epidemiology of mental disorder promises to offer us some of the etiologic leads we badly need in a field where, it is now evident, multifactorial causation is interwoven with environmental variables on every level of integration. We have become aware that the quick and easy answer in psychiatry will not be forthcoming, in contrast to what occurred in the era of the investigation of the acute infectious diseases. Research in this area will be extremely expensive in terms of time and money, will have to be exceedingly carefully planned to avoid leaving any loopholes unplugged and may, notwithstanding enormous expenditures of effort, be unrewarding. It is here that the epidemiologist can offer valuable and even indispensable assistance. By indicating which hypothesized etiologic relationships are actually present he can point to the most profitable direction for more definitive studies.

iii

The individuals who presented and discussed the papers in this volume probably comprise the majority of the investigators in this field. They come from the disciplines of psychiatry, psychology, sociology, public health, biostatistics, pediatrics, anthropology, genetics, and medicine. The studies reported range chronologically in the life cycle from conception to old age. Because the interdisciplinary approach to the epidemiology of mental disorder is relatively new, with much of its methodology still to be delineated and refined, it was hoped that discussion would be critical, constructive when feasible, and would avoid as much as possible the all too common practice of uttering platitudes. The reader must judge for himself whether or not these hopes were fulfilled. The participants were in agreement that discussion was sharp and perhaps at times cutting.

I am pleased to have this opportunity to express my deep gratitude to the participants in the Symposium and to the Milbank Fund for their financial aid toward transcribing the proceedings.

BENJAMIN PASAMANICK

Contributors

KATHERINE BERRY, Milbank Memorial Fund, New York City

E. I. BURDOCK, Biometrics Research, New York State Department of Mental Hygiene, New York City

FRANCES CHEEK, New Jersey Bureau of Research in Neurology and Psychiatry, Princeton, New Jersey

JOHN A. CLAUSEN, Laboratory of Socio-environmental Studies, National Institute of Mental Health, Bethesda, Maryland

E. Z. DAGER, Department of Sociology, Purdue University, Lafayette, Indiana

JOSEPH DOWNING, Mental Health Services Division, San Mateo County Department of Public Health and Welfare, San Mateo, California

EUGEN KAHN, M. D. Anderson Department of Psychiatry, College of Medicine, Baylor University, Houston, Texas

FRANZ J. KALLMAN, New York State Psychiatric Institute, New York City

HILDA KNOBLOCH, The Ohio State University College of Medicine, Columbus, Ohio

MELVIN L. KOHN, Laboratory of Socio-environmental Studies, National Institute of Mental Health, Bethesda, Maryland

DEAN B. KRUEGER, National Institutes of Health, Bethesda, Maryland

THOMAS LANGNER, Department of Psychiatry, Cornell University Medical School, New York City

PAUL W. LEMKAU, School of Hygiene and Public Health, The Johns Hopkins University, Baltimore, Maryland

ALLISTER MILES MACMILLAN (Deceased), Cornell University, Ithaca, New York

A. R. MANGUS, Department of Sociology and Anthropology, The Ohio State University, Columbus, Ohio

ISABEL MCCAFFREY, New York State Department of Mental Hygiene, Syracuse, New York

BENJAMIN PASAMANICK, Columbus Psychiatric Institute and Hospital, and The Ohio State University College of Medicine, Columbus, Ohio

JOHN D. RAINER, New York State Psychiatric Institute, New York City

DEAN W. ROBERTS, The National Society for Crippled Children and Adults, Chicago, Illinois

EUGENE ROGOT, National Institute of Neurological Diseases and Blindness, Bethesda, Maryland

LEO SROLE, Department of Psychiatry, Cornell University Medical School, New York City

SAMUEL SUTTON, Biometrics Research, New York State Department of Mental Hygiene, New York City

WINSLOW T. TOMPKINS, Beckley Memorial Hospital, Beckley, West Virginia

ROSABELLE PRICE WALKLEY, School of Hygiene and Public Health, The Johns Hopkins University, Baltimore, Maryland

DOROTHY G. WIEHL, Milbank Memorial Fund, New York City

DANIEL M. WILNER, School of Hygiene and Public Health, The Johns Hopkins University, Baltimore, Maryland

JOSEPH ZUBIN, New York State Department of Mental Hygiene, New York City

Discussants

ANNE ANASTASI, Department of Psychology, Fordham University, New York City

HERBERT G. BIRCH, Association for the Aid of Crippled Children, New York City

ISIDOR CHEIN, Department of Psychology, New York University, New York City

OSKAR DIETHELM, Department of Psychiatry, The New York Hospital, New York City

SIMON DINITZ, Department of Sociology and Anthropology, Ohio State University, Columbus, Ohio

ERNEST M. GRUENBERG, Milbank Memorial Fund, New York City

MORTON KRAMER, Biostatistics Branch, National Institute of Mental Health, Bethesda, Maryland

REMA LAPOUSE, Tulane University, New Orleans, Louisiana

ABRAHAM LILIENFELD, Division of Biostatistics and Epidemiology, Roswell Park Memorial Institute, Buffalo, New York

ALAN D. MILLER, Mental Health Services Section, U. S. Public Health Service, Denver, Colorado

MILTON TERRIS, Tulane University, New Orleans, Louisiana

Contents

The Emil Kraepelin Memorial Lecture

EUGEN KAHN

Department of Psychiatry
Baylor University College of Medicine, Houston, Texas

Emil Kraepelin was born on February 15, 1856, in Neu-Strelitz, the capital of the Grandduchy of Mecklenburg-Strelitz in northern Germany. He was born eight years after the not very effective democratic cloudburst in 1848. Meanwhile the democratic emotions had simmered down. Although it was the capital, Neu-Strelitz was like many of its sister capitals in the numerous independent German kingdoms, grandduchies, etc., a provincial town. With all his visions, works, and travels, Kraepelin always remained a Neu-Strelitzer, i.e., a provincial. I deem it appropriate to mention that Sigmund Freud also never ceased to be a provincial; in a sense he never grew beyond Freiberg in Moravia. Freud suffered under the same nationalism to which Kraepelin was patriotically dedicated. Kraepelin developed the conviction of the superiority of the German race and a somewhat adverse attitude toward the Jews whom he considered as dangerous to his German compatriots and to German science. Toward the end of his life he admitted that he had had relationships with many Jews and that he had held some of them in high esteem. He was politically a conservative, rather a monarchist.

Kraepelin grew up in modest circumstances. His father seems to have been an actor who specialized in the recitation of the works of Fritz Reuter, who was then a very much read and heard writer in Plattdeutsch, a northern German dialect. There

1

was a brother, Karl, highly admired by his younger brother. Karl became a well-known biologist (botanist). One gets the impression that their mother was the adored center of the family.

The Grandduchy of Mecklenburg-Strelitz (there was also a Grandduchy of Mecklenberg-Schwerin with its capital Schwerin) could not remain entirely untouched by the hot and cold wars due to the old rivalry between the empire of Austria and the kingdom of Prussia; one might just as well say: between the Roman Catholic house of Habsburg and the Lutheran house of Hohenzollern. When Kraepelin was ten years old, Prussia vanquished Austria and assumed the position of the leading German state. Under Prussian leadership the union of the German states conquered the French empire of Napoleon III, in the war 1870–71. On January 18, 1871, Wilhelm I, the then king of Prussia, whose right-hand man was the "iron chancellor" Bismarck, was proclaimed German emperor in Versailles. He was supposed to be *primus inter pares* of the rulers of all the states belonging to the German union, then called "Das deutsche Reich," the German Empire. There is no doubt about the tremendous enthusiasm among the German teen-agers of that time. It was scarcely incidental that Kraepelin, who became fifteen years old four weeks after the proclamation in Versailles, got himself engaged in 1871 to Miss Ina Schwabe, a young lady seven years his senior. Even then the plan of his life was laid out clearly: he would be a physician, preferably a professor. When he left Neu-Strelitz in 1874 to study medicine, the German Emipre was three years old. In other words, Kraepelin's late youth and early manhood coincided with the early years of his beloved empire.

He went to Leipzig where he served his first half year with the army. In the spring of 1875 he was already in Würzburg; there, in 1876, he passed the tentamen physicum, the examination in the preclinical disciplines. During the summer vacation of the year Kraepelin took a psychology course under Wilhelm Wundt (1840–1920) in Leipzig. Early in 1877 Professor Franz von

Rinecker (1811–83) called him back to Würzburg as an assistant in psychiatry. Rinecker, originally a professor of pharmacology, had an outspokenly scientific attitude; he took over the psychiatric clinic in 1863 and the clinic for syphilology and dermatology in 1872. He was a highly intelligent man who knew people and had administrative ability and a high sense of order; "his handwriting was unsurpassably clear and neat. . . . Due to the manysidedness of his scientific activity he had a very insufficient training in psychiatry which at that time was in its infancy anyway." However, he stimulated the interest in psychiatric problems and was the "progenitor" of a number of academic teachers. He must have had a high regard for young Kraepelin, who on his part always considered Rinecker as one of his most important teachers. The others were Wundt and Gudden.

In 1877, while serving on Rinecker's staff and continuing the study of medicine, Kraepelin won a reward with an essay "On the influence of acute diseases on the origination of mental diseases." In this paper, which was not published until 1881, Kraepelin discussed the factors of disposition and the external causal factors. He assumed, "The various stimuli on the one side and the changes of the nervous system on the other side produce the resulting symptom complex." Thoroughly aware of dealing with symptom complexes, he tried to establish two groups (Formenkreise) of these psychoses with many transitions: (1) states of agitation with depressive or manic beginning and (2) picture of a quiet depression with or without delusions. He regretfully wrote: "I must admit that it is still impossible to describe the psychoses accompanying infections according to really clinical views." As late as 1910 he expected that in the future "more profound laws as regards the relations between specificity of the toxic effect and the formation of the disease picture will be recognized." [1]

[1] Bonhoeffer, who described the exogenous reaction types, wrote in 1912 in his monograph *Infektionpsychosen:* "Kraepelin, in his new edition, has accepted my opinion in essential points, particularly as

When Kraepelin was working on this paper, it was not long since the psychicists had tried to derive the mental disorders from the psyche. Heinroth (1773–1843) held that insanity was due to sin and guilt. "Innocence does not become insane, only guilt does." Ideler had assumed that uncontrolled passions played the main role in the causation of mental disease, perhaps of all diseases. In an opposing camp the somaticists held the notion that the immortal soul could not get sick at all, but that pathological changes in the body were impeding the activities of the soul and its expressions. Outstanding somaticists were Nasse (1778–1852), a physiologist, and Jacobi (1775–1858). On the basis of their respective views both parties categorized mental disorders, going into all manner of detail. A mutual understanding was impossible as every psychiatrist of some rank—presumably some others, too—had his own list of mental disorders.

For decades German psychiatrists were preoccupied with speculations. During the same time French psychiatrists made minutious observations. The past master of ingenious description was Esquirol (1755–1826). French authors brought forth the classical description of general paresis (Beyle, 1822; Georget and Calmeil, 1826). Their picture of general paresis was for a long time regarded as the first and only "disease entity" in psychiatry.

In Germany Neumann (1814–84) stated: "There is only one kind of mental disease; we call it insanity." This led to the formulation of a unitary psychosis (Einheitspsychose), which

---

regards the impossibility of a clinical separation of the infectious deliria and psychoses due to exhaustion. However, he holds that after some time it will be possible to characterize the single infectious processes according to their psychic symptoms. He believes this especially in view of the extraordinary variety with which chemical effects influence the psyche as manifested in psychological experiments and in anatomical and physiological findings in the nervous system . . . I am convinced that the available data need be supplemented point for point; yet I presume that the future development of this problem will not necessarily support Kraepelin . . . I am certain that Kraepelin sees the etiological situation too simple notwithstanding the remark he makes on it."

took its characteristic course from the beginning to the end unless it healed or came to a standstill some time. The unitary psychosis was expected to have the following five stages: depression, agitation, confusion, paranoia (Verruecktheit), dementia.

In 1845, *The Pathology and Therapy of Psychic Disease* by Wilhelm Griesinger (1817–68) was published. This important book was built up on the axiom "Mental diseases are diseases of the brain." Obviously a promising contact with medicine at large, neurology in particular was the order of the day; neuropathology received some impetus. Griesinger's classification knew (1) depressions, (2) exaltations, and (3) conditions of psychic weakness; general paresis and epilepsy did not fit into this system; he considered them as complications. Schuele found that Griesinger's system was too predominantly psychological and did not do justice to general paresis. He paid homage to Morel who introduced the etiological principle in his classification, which looked as follows: (1) folies héréditaires, (2) folie par intoxication, (3) folie par transformation, (4) folies sympathiques, (5) folies idiopathiques, (6) démence, formes terminatives. However, the etiological view was not sufficient even to Morel himself.[2] The next step was done by Kahlbaum (1828–99), who was aware of the significance of the course of the sickness. Kahlbaum differentiated five classes: (1) vesania, closely related to the unitary psychosis it afflicts the whole personality; it may end with or without dementia; (2) vecordia does not afflict the whole personality but only "parts" of it; its course may be continuous, but it is unpredictable; (3) dysphrenia covers symptomatic psychosis in somatic diseases; (4) neophrenia concerns innate or early acquired disorders; (5) paraphrenia originates in transitional periods of the biographical development (puberty).

---

[2] Schuele made an observation foreshadowing multidimensional diagnosis: "If a drinker who has an inherited disposition and is ruining himself through sexual excesses is an epileptic, is his epilepsy based on heredity or alcoholism or sexuality?"

Later came Kahlbaum's catatonia and the hebephrenia of his associate Hecker as natural diseases.

Schuele made a circumstantial attempt to do better than all those he criticized. He, like Kahlbaum and several others of their contemporaries, had already come to see that melancholia and mania were only patterns, not diseases in their own right.[3] Schuele found "concrete psychological kinds of disease which at the same time we comprehend under the physiological-pathological category of certain pathological cerebral states (always, of course, only in the most general sense)." Schuele has two main categories of mental disorders, viz., those of the healthy, completely developed brain and those of the invalid brain. In the latter category, called "states of mental defect and degeneration," there are "many patients whose disease is not an acquired affliction but a defect of the Anlage"; this category reaches from microcephaly to periodic and circular insanity. In the first category "insanity is always acquired"; it comprehends everything from the "acute and subacute cerebral neurosis" to the "encephalitis syphilitica with psychic disturbances." The primary paranoia is considered a "mixtum compositum of healthy and morbid psychic life in which the perversions of elementary mental functions prevail over the pathological forms of reaction of healthy brain function." "Paranoia, the chronic psychic cerebral neurosis on degenerative basis and of primary neurotic origination," is a subgroup in the second category. Schuele's classification is an impressive example of the proceeding of a clinician who needs a system but cannot help discovering that with all natural groups and natural grouping nature refuses to be pigeonholed—at least in psychiatry. We may remember that Kraepelin notwithstanding his decisiveness and never tiring patience of grouping and regrouping was familiar with this frustrating experience.

[3] This is a characteristic remark of Schuele's: "Melancholia and mania are per se only patterns for which the pertinent cerebral state must be sought in order to give them nosological reality."

In the paper from which we started this long digression Kraepelin wrote: ["The most important achievement which the advance of scientific research has brought to psychiatry in our century is the firm foundation of the notion of the somatic basis of mental disorders."] Kraepelin never wavered in this profession to natural science behind which we may surmise the influence of his brother, of his teacher Wundt, and of Griesinger.

He passed the examen rigorosum for the degree of doctor of medicine in March and his final medical examination in July 1878. In the same year he became an assistant of Bernhard von Gudden (1824–88) in Munich. Gudden was particularly interested in neuropathology.

In 1880, presumably during the time he served his second half year with the army as a physician, Kraepelin wrote his remarkable essay "The abolition of the determinate sentence." In this essay he discussed theoretical and practical aspects of the criminal law and made a number of recommendations for its reform. Most of these recommendations have since been made as new and utterly progressive. As so far not all of them have been enacted, there is still a chance for several rediscoveries.

In 1882 Kraepelin went to Flechsig (1847–1929) in Leipzig. He could not agree with his chief's notions, and resigned his position at the clinic. Against Flechsig's wish he became a privat docent in the medical faculty of the University of Leipzig in 1882 through the energetic support of Wundt. He worked in Wundt's laboratory on psychopharmacological problems; he initiated the systematic research in this field and introduced it into psychiatry. Kraepelin wrote several pertinent papers before he published his pioneer book *On the Influence of Several Medicaments on Simple Psychic Processes* in 1892.

In 1882 Kraepelin published a study "On psychic weakness," in which he attempted "the critical analysis of pictures of mental disease into their elementary phenomena" in the sense of Wundt's psychology. He found two types of psychic weakness and called them anergesia and erethism, and elaborated that they were, as the Greek names tell, characterized by torpidity and excitability, respectively. He did not restrict either type to innate feeble mindedness, but explained that they occur also during and after a variety of psychoses. "Our types do not have any nosological validity, as little as the symptoms of anxiety or grandiosity. . . ."

About this time Kraepelin considered quitting psychiatry and devoting himself to physiological psychology since the opportunities in academic psychiatry did not appear to be good. Wundt dissuaded him from making this change as he, Wundt, then thought that the opportunities in experimental psychology were slim.

In 1883 Kraepelin's *Compendium of Psychiatry: For the Use of Students and Physicians* was published. He dedicated it to Bernhard von Gudden. All the later editions of this book and of Kraepelin's *Psychiatry: A Textbook for Students and Physicians* are dedicated to the memory of Gudden who perished in 1888 with the schizophrenic king Ludwig II of Bavaria. Kraepelin's never changing attitude toward Gudden, Wundt, and Rinecker are characteristic of him, no less than his devotion to natural science, which is intimately tied up with these personal loyalties. In the preface to the *Compendium* Kraepelin writes: "Nobody will expect anything new in a compendium. However, I have at least striven for a certain independence of the presentation as far as my own experiences permitted it." [He stated that psychic manifestations "are 'functions' of the brain, and that psychic disorders are diffuse diseases of the cerebral cortex . . .] The inner relationship between cerebral and psychic functions is so far physiologically not understood. [Indeed, we know only that this relationship exists and that it apparently follows certain laws."] The conclusion is that cerebral pathology and psychopathology must intimately cooperate "to discover the laws of the reciprocal relationships between somatic and psychic disturbances and thus to progress to a deeper understanding of the manifestations of insanity." The *Compendium*

is divided into a general and a special pathology and therapy
of insanity. In the first part, among other topics somatic and
psychic, external and internal causes are discussed in which
general and individual predisposition is elaborated on. Kraepelin
did not accept the concept of the unitary psychosis: "Experience
has not taught the regular course of the 'mental disease' "; he
observes "a very varied course" and many pictures; "according
to their course we must first divide the psychic disorders in
pathological processes and pathological states.[4] The first are
alterations which take their course in a given span of time; the
latter are characterized through permanent abnormal behavior
which may be due to evolutional inhibitions, innate (e.g., idiocy,
cretinism), or to the result of a preceding mental disease (secondary dementia)." The young psychiatrist is already nosologically
minded: "The definition and circumscription of separate forms
of disease is the next task of a special pathology of mental disorders." But where to find a unifying viewpoint? He would prefer
neuropathology; however he conjectured that "the great majority
of mental diseases are likely to be based on functional changes
which will remain inaccessible to anatomic research with the
possible exception of microchemical processes." For the present
(1883) the clinical-symptomatological view appeared to be the
best available for classification; it does, of course, "offer us
only symptom complexes, not diseases."

In the *Compendium,* Kraepelin refers to the picture of
hebephrenia as described by Kahlbaum and Hecker; he does
not mention Kahlbaum's classification to which, it is true, nobody
had paid much attention anyway, nor his catatonia. In later
editions, Kraepelin did full justice to both Kahlbaum and Hecker;
e.g., "Only through the clear distinction Kahlbaum's between
states and disease forms did a satisfactory clinical view become
possible at all" (1910).

The year 1883 saw Kraepelin again in Munich on Gudden's
staff where he once more became a privat docent. The academic

[4] Cf. Schuele.

outlook was still not favorable, hence Kraepelin became chief of staff (Oberarzt) in the mental hospital of Leubus in July 1884. This move enabled him to marry Miss Schwabe.

He had a dream in 1884 which he reported in 1886 in a paper on "Falsifications of recollection." "In November 1884, I dreamed about one of my closest friends who is short and has a black Vandyke beard. In my dream he appeared to me tall, slender and lean with a small blond mustachio. There was a maximal difference between fantasy and recollection; but I did not become conscious of it in the dream. Not for a moment did I doubt that this person was really that friend although this thought was not supported by any trait, but rather contradicted by every single fact." Kraepelin was sturdy, a little under middle size, and had a tendency toward corpulence (he was a rather good representative of Kretschmer's pyknic type); he wore a Vandyke beard which at this time was still dark.

From a paper "Concerning the psychology of the comical" (1884) I quote: "In the majority of instances the joke belongs to the conscious, intended comical; the joke 'is made.' There are, however, unconscious jokes [unbewusste Witze] which have a double effect since here the contrast between intention and effect, i.e., the comical situation is added to the contrasting ideas." Kraepelin tries to show "the intellectual contrast as the essential factor" in all kinds of the comical. He considered his paper "a small contribution to this interesting field of scientific aesthetics on the basis of physiological psychology."

In May 1885 he took over in the Saxonian capital Dresden, with its greater possibilities, the management of the mental hospital, a larger institution than the one in Leubus. A paper "On confusion" was probably written in Dresden. I shall not try to report all nor even to mention every one of Kraepelin's publications.

He had planned to be a professor at the age of thirty. At a time at which perhaps only he and Mrs. Kraepelin still expected it, it happened: in 1886 he was called to Dorpat as professor of psychiatry. Dorpat, which is now called Tartu, was a university town in Estonia, one of the then three Baltic grandduchies, of which the Tzar of Russia was the grandduke. In the Balticum the nobility, the intelligentsia, and other classes more or less dependent on them adhered to the German language and culture. The life in these provinces seems to have been under considerably less pressure than in Russia proper. Kraepelin obviously adjusted himself and his family well to the new surroundings. A number of papers on clinical, psychological, and psychopharmacological problems were written in Dorpat. Furthermore, the second and third editions of *Psychiatry,* which no longer was a compendium, appeared in 1887 and 1889. These editions, like the fourth (1893) are essentially built on symptom complexes. One feels some groping, though, toward a clinical classification in the sense of a nosology. General paresis always remains a group by itself. "Primary paranoia" becomes "paranoia." Chronic intoxications enter in the second and stay until the fourth edition. I shall not follow the changes in all details but restrict myself to a few observations on the evolution of the dementia praecox and the manic depressive psychosis in Kraepelin's system.

The term démence précoce was first used by Morel. The dementia praecox and the manic-depressive psychoses are Kraepelin's creations; these terms are used by Kraepelin first in his fourth and sixth editions respectively. In the two editions he wrote in Dorpat there are Wahnsinn and Verruecktheit in which one may see *nuclei* of a part of the disturbances later subsumed under dementia praecox.

In Kraepelin's book, mania, melancholia, periodic and circular psychoses get closer to each other, but they are unified only in the sixth edition as manic-depressive psychoses (1899). With several of our observations we have already anticipated a step into the happiest time of Kraepelin's life, his years in Heidelberg.

Kraepelin accepted a call to a professorship in Heidelberg in 1891. In Heidelberg he continued to observe and to collect clinical material. Impressed with the course of the diseases, he had accepted some views of Kahlbaum's. [Kraepelin had now come to the notion that natural groups of mental diseases might be established only on the basis of various factors, namely etiology, symptomatology, course, final state and pathological-anatomical findings.] Groups that would show a community of these factors might be considered disease entities. I do not know who first used this word. Kraepelin does not use it very often; he prefers terms like Formenkreis, Krankheitsform, klinische Einheit (group of disease forms, forms of disease, clinical entity). He always assumed that each of these groups, the grouping and classification of which could not be done but through clinical observation and follow-up, were likely to be due to a specific disease process (Krankheitsvorgang). [Originally he had had great hopes that neuropathology would play an outstanding role in defining the disease process, i.e., by finding out the damage done in the brain by the process.] I may say here that Kraepelin was aware of the limitations clinical work will always have. I think that the idea of the disease entity became for him a lodestar, an ideal which he did not expect ever to reach. It was a valuable working hypothesis, although its most far reaching effect, the establishment of the dementia praecox and the manic-depressive psychosis seems paradoxical since these disorders do not fulfill the five conditions or preconditions of a natural disease group, to say nothing of a disease entity. With all these contradictions and doubts, the establishment of these two disorders is the most important and the most impressive of many clinical achievements we owe to Kraepelin.

With increasing experience, aided by his associates in psychiatry and in the auxiliary sciences, he grouped and regrouped his growing material. He soon found and averred that not all cases in groups which seemed to belong together had the same course as, according to the quest for the disease entity, they ought to have. He tried to do justice to his material by forming small and large groups.

In the fifth edition of *Psychiatry* (1896), Kraepelin could write in a certain triumphant attitude: ["In the development of this book this edition signifies the last step from the symptomatic to the clinical view of mental disease."] He had come to distinguish two main classes: the "acquired mental disorders" and "the mental disorders on the basis of pathological constitution." [5] In the first class as a subgroup of metabolic diseases there are "processes of deterioration (dementia praecox, catatonias, dementia paranoides)." [6] To the mental disorders on the basis of pathological constitution belong as a group "constitutional mental disorders (periodic insanity, paranoia)."

In the sixth edition (1899) dementia praecox and the manic-depressive psychosis are groups of their own. The etiological principle, though by no means forgotten, is no longer used to separate two comprehensive groups. Paranoia, too, is now a group of its own.

In addition to the fourth, fifth, and sixth editions of his *Psychiatry,* Kraepelin published during the Heidelberg period the *Introduction into the Psychiatric Clinic,* which I shall deal with later, and a goodly number of papers, those on psychological problems being printed in the *Psychological Studies* which he founded and edited from 1895. He built up an excellent staff who put out numerous publications. In 1895 Nissl (1860–1919) took charge of the neuropathological laboratory. Aschaffenburg (1866–1942)[7] worked on clinical, later on forensic topics; he was professor of psychiatry in the University of Cologne faculty of medicine until he came to this country in 1934. Robert Gaupp

[5] Cf. Schuele.

[6] The three other subgroups were (*a*) myxedema, (*b*) cretinism, (*c*) dementia paralytica. In the eighth edition (second volume, 1910) general paresis is as it had been since the sixth edition (1899), a group of its own, with the clarification as regards serology and treatment; but it was preceded by a new group from now on (1910), namely syphilitic mental disorders.

[7] Aschaffenburg's most outstanding pupil is Kurt Schneider.

(1870–1953) went in 1900 from Breslau to Heidelberg; he had been on Carl Wernicke's staff (1848–1905). Wernicke was, in a sense, a "refined" successor of Griesinger. Kraepelin and Wernicke were in many ways psychiatric opponents, the more so as Kraepelin no longer believed in Griesinger's dogma "Mental diseases are brain diseases." There were on the staff in Heidelberg also Wilhelm Weygandt (1870–1939), later professor in Hamburg, and Karl Wilmanns (1873–1945). Wilmanns was Nissl's faithful chief of staff from 1904–18 and then himself professor from 1918–33.[8] These men and a number of others acquired outstanding reputations in psychiatry. They befriended a multitude of visitors and visiting foreign students; we remember Smith Ely Jelliffe and Charles Macfie Campbell, and we particularly salute Clarence B. Farrar. These were the years in which Kraepelin's work became known all over the civilized world and during which his classification, his nosology, was taken over by a great multitude of psychiatrists. Since its sixth edition his *Psychiatry* has not ceased to be the sturdy backbone of psychiatric clinical classifications.

Kraepelin and his family, Mrs. Kraepelin and their three daughters, were very fond of Heidelberg where he spent the prime of his life. When the call came from Munich, he could not but accept it (1903), for there was a completely new clinic with ample space for laboratories, with more patients, and more opportunities for his growing staff. "I did it with the feeling of sacrificing my own happiness to our science." Gaupp came along as chief of staff and Alzheimer (1864–1915), who had joined Kraepelin's staff in 1902, as chief of laboratories. Kraepelin insisted that the "laboratory men" on his staff keep up their interest and their participation in clinical psychiatry. Nissl and Alzheimer may not always have been pleased with this, but developments showed that their chief was right. In Heidelberg, after a short interregnum under Karl Bonhoeffer (1868–1948),

[8] H. W. Gruhle (1880–1958) was his chief of staff for years; he was later professor of psychiatry and neurology in Bonn.

Nissl acceded to the professorship in 1904. Alzheimer accepted the chair of psychiatry and neurology in Breslau in 1912.

Heidelberg was a charming old university town in the Grand-duchy of Baden whose inhabitants were proud of town and gown. It was a provincial town, similar in this respect to Neu-Strelitz and to Dorpat. The Kraepelins fitted in well. In Heidelberg a professor particularly opposed to alcohol might be looked upon as an eccentric, but with amusement rather than with hostility. There Kraepelin, notwithstanding his obligations as teacher, member of the faculty, and manager of his clinic, had time to pursue his own work. I did not hear him say it, but I think it likely that he said it in Munich: "It is good that I learned psychiatry in Heidelberg; I could not do it in Munich." It was the third time that he had come to live and to work in Munich, a city of metropolitan character and then the capital of the king-dom of Bavaria. He never felt at home there. He disliked the increasing administrative and faculty obligations and became more and more parsimonious with his time renouncing all social life outside his family. He had, it is true, always considered parties and meetings a waste of time.

As he was interested and active in alcohol research and in the abstinence movement, he was not welcome to the "alcohol trade" and its representatives, the breweries in Bavaria, in general, and in Munich, in particular. He had many a fight with them in which he showed a sarcastic humor; these fights probably amused him almost as much as they annoyed him. The section on alcohol-ism had become the largest part of the chapter "Intoxications" of *Psychiatry*. He described as "a peculiar form of alcoholic psychosis the "halluzinatorischen Wahnsinn der Trinker (Wer-nicke's acute Halluzinose der Tinker)"; this psychosis once in a while becomes chronic, then its "demarcation from certain syndromes of dementia praecox is very difficult." [9]

[9] Benedetti has shown in a monograph that one group of the pertinent patients deteriorate organically. The other group ends in schizophrenic paranoid dementia (1952).

We are back thus at the dementia praecox which in the sixth and seventh editions of *Psychiatry* contained the subgroups dementia simplex, hebephrenia, catatonia, and dementia paranoides. In the eighth edition several small subgroups are added to the dementia praecox, but certain paranoid forms are tentatively taken out of it and grouped under the name of paraphrenia. Both dementia praecox and paraphrenia were then subgroups of the endogenous dementias (1913). There were years when the problem of the classification of the paranoid psychoses was regarded one of the first clinical dignity. In a paper on paranoid diseases (1912) Kraepelin had explained "that the disease process of the dementia praecox can among many other pictures produce paranoid ones." Paranoid psychoses which commenced in later life and seemed to show some differences from dementia praecox were then characterized as paraphrenias with four subsubgroups, viz., paraphrenia systematica, expansive, confabulans, and phantastica. Kraepelin did not feel at all sure "whether and how far the paraphrenias can be maintained as an independent disease group," meaning whether they were due to a disease process different from the disease process assumed in dementia praecox.

In the eighth edition Kraepelin notes Eugen Bleuler's term "schizophrenia" and the terms suggested by a few other investigators. From then on he occasionally used Bleuler's term schizophrenia and its adjective schizophrenic. Since in several quarters the opinion seems to predominate that Bleuler was the creator of the schizophrenias, I call attention to his monograph's title: "Dementia praecox or the group of the schizophrenias." I quote from Bleuler:[10] "The whole idea of the dementia praecox stems from Kraepelin; we also owe the grouping and the characterization of the single symptoms almost

---

[10] It is fair to quote from Bleuler: "An important part of the attempt further to develop the pathology is nothing but the application of Freud's ideas on the dementia praecox." Here Bleuler could be sure of Kraepelin's hearty disagreement.

alone to him . . . The cradle of the concept is the fifth edition of Kraepelin's *Psychiatry* (1896)."

⌈The endogenous dementias Kraepelin now contrasted with paranoia, which he completely separated from all other paranoid psychoses and considered "abnormal developments occurring in constitutionally psychopathic persons under the influence of every day stimuli."⌉ In the third volume of the eighth edition of *Psychiatry*, Kraepelin explains that "There was a time when the paranoiacs in our mental hospitals were 70–80% of all cases." It is obvious that nowadays the diagnostic point of gravitation is with the schizophrenics; the majority of the formerly so-called paranoiacs would at present be diagnosed as schizophrenics, presumably paranoid schizophrenics. The reformulation of the paranoia concept by Kraepelin introduced the distinction of personality development from disease process into clinical psychiatry. This distinction led to numerous discussions; Karl Jaspers (1883–) dealt with it in his *General Psychopathology*.

In 1919 Kraepelin demonstrated several paranoid patients in a scientific conference of the Research Institute. When he asked Nissl what he thought about the first shown patient, Nissl responded with a shrug of his shoulders. Kraepelin then declared with a challenging glance at Nissl: "This is one of the cases I have described as paraphrenia systematica," whereupon Nissl said: "You can call it what you want," implying that the diagnosis of paranoid schizophrenia could be made as well. This apparent lack of interest in clinical differentiation in his own house made Kraepelin terribly angry. Perhaps he recognized too late that he better had not asked Nissl this question; he complained loudly and bitterly about such a clinically disinterested attitude. I never saw Kraepelin so angry. Nissl, who was a very kind man, had certainly meant no harm.[11]

[11] In the classification of the third edition of the *Introduction* (1916), dementia praecox and paraphrenias are two subgroups of the group "psychoses due to internal somatic disease processes." This may be a concession to the teachability of the material. On the first page of "The
(*Footnote continued on p. 18*)

When Kraepelin published the seventh edition of *Psychiatry* in 1904 in two volumes, like the sixth, he was at the peak of his career. Despite the burden of his position he was able to cover and to publish an astounding amount of scientific work. He had his clinic superbly organized, he was proud "that I myself became in the institution directed by me the most dispensable person." He was able to make full use of the university vacations, i.e., two months in the spring and three months in the summer. During the Munich period he realized a dream, namely the purchase and development of his beloved "place in the country." By European standards it was rather far from Munich, but not so far that the Kraepelin family could not occasionally make the trip on bicycles. The estate was in Suna on the Lago

---

endogenous dementias" in Volume II (1913) of the eighth edition of *Psychiatry* we read: "Under the designation of 'endogenous dementias' are comprehended here for the purpose of a merely provisional understanding a number of disease pictures whose reciprocal relationships are still unclear today. However, they have the common peculiarity that they originate without recognizable external stimuli on the basis of internal causes, and that in at least their great majority of cases end in a more or less clear-cut psychic invalidity. . . . I keep the question open whether or not these different forms are not founded on the same disease process with various points of attack and changing course."

Kraepelin used Bleuler's term schizophrenia only for his dementia praecox, not for the paraphrenias in the description of which he referred to Magnan's délire chronique a évolution systématisé.

Bleuler in the first edition of his *Textbook of Psychiatry* observes: "Not a few of the paranoid forms which I have, following the former notions of Kraepelin, subsumed here under the Dementia praecox, appear in their total exterior habitus to be quite different from the deteriorating random schizophrenic . . . It is very likely that among these cases there are forms which ought to be separated from the dementia praecox as we circumscribe it nowadays; whether later they will induce a widening of the concept of schizophrenia or whether they are something entirely different, the future may teach us" (1916).

Kraepelin wrote in the Preface to the ninth edition of *Psychiatry* about the endogenous dementias that "I have for the time being maintained the separate description of certain forms, which I designated paraphrenias in a somewhat altered demarcation although the justification to do so [i.e., to separate them from dementia praecox] is not indubitable" (1926).

Maggiore in northern Italy. Kraepelin, not interested in making money, frugal in his own needs, was, like Mrs. Kraepelin, a good householder. He thought that what he spent for his Suna estate was entirely out of proportion to his means, but it was worth it. Time to work without disturbance was a most vital need for him. "A source of inexhaustible pleasure is for me my garden in Italy with its southern flora." He did not like the cool north where he might "experience the winter like a grave disease." In Suna he did much of his work for publications during these years. He always returned refreshed and as eager as ever to check his old with new clinical observations. In the north as in the south he was true to his motto "Work is healthy," mindful of Wundt's saying "To give lectures and to write books keeps a man healthy." It appears as though Suna or rather his estate in Suna was the place of which he was fondest, although the people around and their language remained strange to him. He always felt at home with his family, but otherwise he did not seem to take root. In his paper "On uprooting" (1921), which is a contribution to social psychiatry, he stated "that a certain uprooting is a precondition of all development." I believe that this paper had a certain personal significance for Kraepelin, but I should not speculate about it.

I insert here a few remarks on the *Introduction into Clinical Psychiatry,* which was first written and published in 1901 in Heidelberg. The second and third editions appeared in Munich in 1905 and 1916. With this book Kraepelin wanted to give to the medical students what they in his opinion needed of clinical psychiatry. As in his *Psychiatry,* the language in the *Introduction* is simple, the case histories are very well chosen— they "do not want to be taken for scientific documents." In the third edition he makes several additions to the clinical lectures. The particularly interesting additions are (1) the classification of the mental diseases (1916) and (2) a chapter on "syndromes and forms of disease." One symptom never means much, but syndromes may show the way to "the disease processes which are

concealed behind them." Until we get a better grasp of the disease
processes, we must get along with clinical grouping which is
more than the mere comprehension of symptoms into syndromes
but less than the recognition of disease processes. There are a
few organic disorders which might be considered due to certain
disease processes, and there is "dementia praecox, schizophrenia," and the "manic depressive psychosis." According to
Kraepelin's explanation in the *Introduction,* it is possible to
interpret the syndromes if one observes them accurately as
belonging to different psychoses; the syndromes "are never completely alike, as the conditions under which they originate always
differ in certain essential points from each other." The reasoning
is obviously this: many mental disorders are due to disease processes which may elude us for a long time; until then we continue
the attempt to form disease groups; their classification is an
intermediate aim in the search for the disease processes.[12] Today
we know nothing about the disease processes in the endogenous
psychoses, nevertheless their establishment as clinical groups
was a remarkable advance. Mayer-Gross has forcibly expressed
this: "Kraepelin's approach was nosological . . . It is on the
basis of his work that we are now able to classify mental disorders
into three main classes, the organic psychoses, the endogenous
psychoses with known structural pathology, and the deviations
of personality and reactive states. Kraepelin's ideas proved
practical and fertile, although they required and received considerable consequent modification. Kraepelin himself recognized
this, and was always ready to change his theoretical point of
view. The nosological concept which he took from medicine has
proved too valuable to be entirely discarded, even by the most
fanatically 'psychodynamic' school."

The manic-depressive group has since its first appearance

---

[12] Johannes Lange: "Der Erforschung des Krankheitsvorganges dient
alle klinische Ordnungsarbeit." (All clinical classification aims at the
search for the disease process.) It has never been formulated more con-
cisely that clinical classification is not an aim in itself.

on Kraepelin's system (1899) maintained its place in psychiatry. Eugen Bleuler makes a historically and psychologically interesting observation when in his monograph he discusses the name of the disease: "One ought to think the original significance of the name [namely dementia praecox] is irrelevant since Kraepelin has elaborated in classical manner what he means by it. One talks after all about melancholia without being disturbed by the black bile . . . Kraepelin's 'periodic insanity' found many a door closed which was opened to the manic-depressive insanity since there were psychiatrists who could not tolerate the adjective 'periodic' for the designation of a disease which during a whole life may perhaps be manifested only a few times or even only once." Kraepelin has explained that French psychiatrists, among them mainly Falret and Baillarger, had in addition to mania and melancholia described "various courses of the manic-depressive psychosis," "manie and mélancholie intermittente, type régulier and irrégulier, folie alternante, folie a double forme, folie circulaire continnuée. I believe I have convinced myself that such tendencies for grouping necessarily must fail because of the irregularity of the disease." "The decisive moment for us, this must be emphasized over and again, is the fundamental and complete agreement of the general clinical disease picture." And finally: "During the course of the years, I have become more and more convinced that all the pictures mentioned are but manifestations of *one* disease process. It is possible, though, that later a number of sub-forms can be shaped or even that small groups may be completely separated. If this will happen it will, in my opinion, not be permissible to consider those symptoms as decisive which have been put into the foreground so far."

The master stroke of comprehending the manic-depressive psychosis as a form of disease due to *one* disease process became still more visible and incisive as Kraepelin subsumed to it the "Grundzustaende," i.e., the depressive, manic, irritable, and cyclothymic constitutions.

There were "border line fights" in which the melancholia

played about the same role in the shaping of the manic-depressive psychoses that the paranoid disorders played in the description and classification of the endogenous dementias. It repeatedly happened during the first and second decade of this century that a group of disease pictures changed place from the dementia praecox (or the endogenous dementias) to the manic-depressive psychoses and vice versa: there were manic-depressive disorders found in which paranoid and/or catatonic syndromes had occurred, and schizophrenias with manic and depressive symptomatology. Kraepelin pointed out that there was not only "an extraordinary widening but also considerable narrowing of our disease concept" in the manic-depressive group. He made a remark in this context which illuminates that he was not 'sold' to the notion of the 'disease entity.' "All these formations are based on the same disease process, but they are so different in their origination, their clinical syndromes, in their course and prognosis that one might talk of a group of diseases stemming from a common root with flowing transitions between the single forms rather than of a disease entity in the ordinary sense of the word." Briefly, the manic-depressive disorders are a disease group not a disease entity. To say it once more: Kraepelin never ceased to search for the unifying element in small as well as in large disease groups, viz.,[the disease process.]

The manic-depressive group and schizophrenia as we have come to discuss them here were printed in the third volume of the eighth edition of *Psychiatry* in 1913, the last year of the peaceful prewar era. In the same year the psychoanalytic congress was held in Munich which not only bespeaks the waxing expansion of Freud's teaching, but has a particular accentuation since there Freud and Jung saw each other the last time; the hostility in their drifting apart had become insuperable. The attitude of academic psychiatry toward Freud and his work was in general negative and, to express it mildly, impolite. However, descriptive psychiatry had had its high day, the interest in psychopathology grew rapidly and was in 1913 given a powerful push through the appearance of Karl Jaspers' *General Psychopathology* which in five editions (up to 1948) became a sort of bible to the German-speaking psychiatrists. The interest in the individual, in the person and his experiences, particularly in the meaning of these experiences, increased rapidly. The growing of Freud's school has been mentioned. Following Jaspers a more phenomenological approach replaced at least partly the merely symptomatological approach. Gaupp, the pupil of Wernicke and Kraepelin, had considerable merit in this development. In 1906 he went from Munich to Tübingen as professor. He was faithful to Kraepelin's teaching; he combined with an interest in the individual the desire to do psychotherapy. Kraepelin is the "grandsire" of Gaupp's most famous pupil, Ernst Kretschmer (1888–) whose "Body build and character" derived from observations on manic-depressive and schizophrenic patients, and who in his "The delusions of reference" described and analyzed patients diagnosed as paranoia in Kraepelin's sense.[13]

When Gaupp left for Tübingen, Alzheimer became chief of staff until 1909 when Ernst Ruedin (1874–1953) succeeded him in this office. Alzheimer was in charge of the neuroanatomical laboratories until he moved to Breslau. Ruedin introduced scientific genealogy into psychiatry. In 1912 Walter Spielmeyer (1879–1935) took over the neuroanatomical laboratories. Everything was in full swing at the clinic when the storm broke in 1914.

[13] The argument about paranoia is still alive. Kolle demonstrated (1931) on extensive clinical material that the patients with the diagnosis paranoia have considerable schizophrenic heredity and seem to begin and to take the course of paranoid schizophrenias. Recently Gruhle reemphasized this point. He subsumes "paranoia to schizophrenia in respect to origination, cause and final state"; he includes Gaupp's and Kretschmer's pertinent cases. Gruhle observes: "The description of the master which he gave of paranoia in 1904 could just as well be the description of paranoid schizophrenia." I share Kolle's and Gruhle's opinion concerning paranoia. The paraphrenias re-disappeared among the paranoid schizophrenias long ago. Incidentally, in 1904 Freud's *Psychopathology of Every Day Life* made its first appearance.

Kraepelin suffered gravely under the war and the German collapse; he resented deeply the political upheaval of November 1918. He agreed with the predominantly conservative trends in Bavaria; he said about the chief of government in Munich who was a solid and honest career official: "Mr. von Kahr knows what he wants." [14] During and several years after the war Suna was not accessible to Kraepelin; this hurt him very much, but even during those unhappy years his output of work was astonishing. He rejoiced when he could resume his regular pilgrimages to the south. He brought his plan of a research institute to fulfillment; the idea he probably conceived many years before.

The first publication concerning the research institute of which I know is a paper "Research institutes and universities" (1911). In May 1913, Kraepelin reported at the annual meeting of the German Association for Psychiatry on "the preparatory work for the foundation of a research institute for psychiatry. The institute shall not serve clinical research, but the study of the essence and origination of the mental diseases." He planned a "clinical-experimental department with a small ward and serological, chemical and psychological laboratories, an ana-tomic-histological department and a demographic-statistical de-partment for the study of degeneration." There should be a library, lecture rooms, and photographic facilities. He told the Association that he had written a detailed report which he sug-gested to submit to the Kaiser-Wilhelms-Gesellschaft, the then young German research institution for a variety of fields. The pertinent notice ends: "The assembly agrees in principle with this plan. The chairman thanks Mr. Kraepelin for his trouble." Owing to the receptivity of the Kaiser-Wilhelms-Gesellschaft, which later became the Max-Planck-Institut, and the under-standing and financial support of the American James Loeb, a former patient of Kraepelin's, the plan materialized. The re-

[14] Mr. von Kahr was murdered by the Nazis in 1933 after withstanding their growing power for many a year.

search institute was founded in 1917 and housed in Kraepelin's clinic.[15] He was able to win Korbinian Brodmann (1868–1918) and Nissl for the institute staff.[16] Spielmeyer, Felix Plaut, the serologist (1877–1940), and Ruedin[17] belonged for several years to the staffs of the institute and of the clinic. Later Franz Jahnel (1885–1951) a serologist, joined the institute group.

At the first public meeting of his institute on June 17, 1917, Kraepelin read a paper "One hundred years of psychiatry: A contribution to human civilization." Toward the end of the paper he briefly deals with the prevention of mental disease with particular emphasis on "hereditary degeneration, alcohol abuse and syphilis." He continues: "The great war through which we are living has taught us impressively that science was able to forge victorious arms for us against a world of enemies—should it be different in the battle against an inner enemy that threatens to ruin the bases of our existence?" From now on Kraepelin's papers appear under the flag of the research institute although he resigned from his professorship and the management of his clinic only in the spring of 1922.

In a paper "Goals and means of psychiatric research," read in the second public meeting of the institute, 1918, Kraepelin pays special tribute to Kahlbaum; in respect to Hecker's hebe-phrenia and Kahlbaum's catatonia, he observes: "With these two disease forms and with general paresis, which had been their model, the beginning was made for the discovery of real

[15] Only in 1928 was the institute's staff able to move into its own home.
[16] Brodmann and Nissl died in 1918 and 1919 respectively.
[17] Ruedin was chief of staff of the clinic until 1919. He remained on the institute's staff until 1925 when he went as professor to Basel (Switzerland) from where he returned after three years.
In 1919 George Stertz (1878–1959), equally interested in psychiatry and neurology, became clinical chief of staff. He was professor of psychiatry and neurology (1921–26) in Marburg and in Kiel (1926–37), and after years of involuntary retirement, in Munich (1946–52). The psychiatric clinic in Munich became the psychiatric and neurological clinic under Kraepelin's successor, Oswald Bumke (1877–1950). It is now the Nervenklinik under Kurt Kolle (1898–).

disease processes." We read there: "In addition to the efficient causes, the condition of the patient is for the origination of the disease, especially for the formation of the clinical picture of decisive importance. [This is the case particularly in the mental diseases since a very large proportion of them stem from pathological disposition which, it is true, is often mobilized through the impact of unfavorable living circumstances."]He stresses the importance of comparative psychiatry, the study of "the relationships between the formation of the pictures of mental disease and the psychology of various human groups." He notes that "the mental health of our people in each period of its existence" belongs to the "fundamental problems of our national existence." He is not discouraged through inner or outer difficulties, "What can be reached at all, will be reached through scientific knowledge or through liberating medical action."

The relationships between Kraepelin and the "alcoholic trade" had not improved. He spoke and wrote considerably for complete abstinence. His intransigence embittered his adversaries who tried to ridicule his personal attitude and to discredit his pertinent scientific work. No wonder they did not enjoy papers like "Alcoholism in Munich" (1906) or "The influence of alcohol on hitting the mark in shooting" (1916). A paper "Alcohol trade and science," published at the inopportune time of the fall of 1918, is interesting and entertaining. Kraepelin calls the "Defense union against the exaggerations of the abstinence movement" to task. This Union had suggested that a department for alcohol research should be a part of the research institute, but feared "That the research institute in Muenchen under the leadership of professor Kraepelin would in a not entirely fair manner put the alcohol as causal factor into the foreground." The union begged "His Majesty the King of Bavaria . . . to consider for this position only men who are scientifically unbiased as regards the damages alcohol does to health." Kraepelin's thirty-one pages are full of irony and sarcasm; he elaborates "that there can be only one truth and that is on our side. . . ."

Kraepelin's paper "The forms of psychotic manifestation," 1920, was repeatedly misinterpreted as a capitulation of the protagonist of the "disease entities," one had better say of the forms and groups of disease. It seems to me that the last sentences of this paper ought to make such a misunderstanding impossible: "The vistas due to such a view are encouraging despite the scantiness of our present knowledge. They might contribute to making easier our main task which is so immensely difficult, viz., the grouping of the clinical forms of disease." This corresponds with the attitude taken by Kraepelin in the third edition of his *Introduction* (1916).[18]

In "The riddle of paresis," 1925, Kraepelin discussed the particularities of this disease which could not neuropathologically and serologically be explained. He ends up: "Finally we can say proudly that most of the reported progress must be attributed to German investigators. The suppression by our enemies threatens to undo this source of our global prestige, too, since it robs us of the means without which science must atrophy. There are vital needs here the neglect of which would make poorer not only ourselves but all mankind. To protect them is the duty of all those who believe in a better future of our people and want to help in bringing it about."

In 1925 Kraepelin accompanied by Plaut visited this country. He wanted to collect material for comparative psychiatry. The American tour put a heavy strain on both travelers. Kraepelin, apparently convinced of his perfect health, exerted himself physically; I shall not forget Plaut's description of the ashen-looking Kraepelin emerging afoot from the Grand Canyon. Kraepelin was unimpressed with American psychiatry and did not mind letting his hosts know about it. Plaut, a gentleman of impeccable manners, worried about the older man's health and deportment.

Kraepelin was in the midst of preparations for the ninth edition of *Psychiatry* and for a research journey to India when

[18] See Kahn, *Gedenkblatt*.

in late summer 1926 he fell ill with indigestion in Suna. He returned to Munich where cardiac insufficiency, probably due to an old myocarditis, made him fatally ill. "It was a bitter and cruel dying which he bore with great patience and dignity." He died on October 7, 1926.

The preface to the second volume, the last one to appear,[19] is dated October 4, his forty-second wedding anniversary. Comparing the prefaces of the eighth and ninth editions one does not find any incisive changes. There are, however, a goodly number of minor changes: a word or a sentence dropped, sometimes replaced by a new one; a new sentence inserted, a word adapted. The dying master took pains to express himself as clearly as possible. In every respect he put his house in order. Once more he points out the vagueness of the group of the endogenous dementias; he deems it likely that they are manifestations of the same disease process. [Reemphasizing the inherited disposition in the manic-depressive group, he wants it understood that the significance of heredity led him to give to this group, to the endogenous dementias and to (genuine) epilepsy their particular place in his system.] He also thinks of "certain relationships [of the manic-depressive group] to the psychogenic disorders since psychic shocks not rarely precipitate the development of attacks of this disease." He maintains the opinion that the vast majority of schizophrenic patients end in the more or less characteristic dementia, but that there is a number of cases that come to a standstill and a few that must

---

[19] This volume appeared in 1927. The first volume of the ninth edition, general psychiatry, was taken over by Lange some time earlier since Kraepelin felt he would no longer be able to do justice to the enormous literature.

Johannes Lange (1891–1938) was, after his apprenticeship in Kraepelin's clinic, in charge of the psychiatric service of the general hospital Muenchen-Schwabing. This service was to be the clinical department of the research institute. Lange was professor of psychiatry and neurology from 1930 until his untimely death in 1938.

be adjudged as completely recovered.[20] In the manic-depressive group he deems it the rule that the patients recover from single and from repeated attacks. There are, however, patients who come scarcely or not at all out of a continued series of manic or/and depressive disturbances. Certain depressive states in late middle and later life are apt to become chronic, and, owing to added organic factors (arteriosclerotic, senile), do not fully recover.[21]

Jaspers states that Kraepelin's "concepts for the first time put psychiatric thought on common ground." Kraepelin's nosology is still, if here and there unwittingly and unwillingly, used, to say the least, in many psychiatric institutions. The work of more than one generation of psychiatrists would not have been possible without Kraepelin's achievements. Professor Yushi Uchimura says: "Modern German psychiatry seems to be influenced mainly by Jaspers. I opine, though, that Kraepelin was eminent in introducing many-sided scientific methods of investigation and of founding exact ways of observing psychic anomaly. Most important, he was the teacher of prominent

[20] *Psychiatry,* 8th edition, p. 867: "Concerning my former grouping of hebephrenic, catatonic and paranoid forms I had concluded that about 8% of the first and about 13% of the second group seem to recover fully while paranoid forms scarcely ever recuperate completely." After discussing the difficulties of establishing new statistical figures, he continues (p. 869): "At any rate there is a very great number of seemingly cured cases in which an incorrect diagnosis was made or where there is only a temporary improvement with a later relapse. On the other side one cannot deny the possibility of complete and permanent recovery in dementia praecox. If a disease process can stand still for 29 years, as I have observed it in a case, it may presumably come to complete restitution. . . ."

[21] *Psychiatry,* 8th edition, p. 1349: "Violent and long drawnout attacks of the manic-depressive psychosis can end in complete restitution of the former personality when they occur only once. There exists, however, the peril of the development of psychic invalidism after multiple attacks, possibly also in grave single attacks which last for many years and occur in later age. It is feasible that, vice versa, the development of permanent alterations is responsible for such courses of the disease."

researchers. One may doubt whether even Jaspers would have occurred without Kraepelin."

Kraepelin was a simple and modest man. He had, like all of us, his prejudices. He tried not to let them disturb his work, but he was not always able to hide them behind the front of courteous behavior. He had tendencies toward intolerance and autocracy. He wanted to say what he considered the truth. He appeared to be shy and was shy to a certain degree, but only a part of this shyness was real: it helped him to keep away from the nonsense of formalities and time-consuming social life. He certainly was not a gregarious person. He had an outspoken sense of dignity. He freely discussed scientific problems with all, even the youngest members of the staff, yet he remained always the professor, the chief. He desired to do right by everybody but was also anxious to protect his own rights in every respect. He loved his family, he loved nature and his buon retiro in Suna. And he loved his work. According to the frequent misuse of notions and words some people are likely to say that he was a compulsive worker. I prefer to say that he was dedicated to the task he had set himself to and that he was fortunate enough to achieve. If this is compulsive, I pray that our field may have more such compulsives.

Kraepelin had considerable self-discipline that shows in his work, in the clarity of his speech and writing. He despised twaddle. When told of any new statement or findings that were not and could not be proved, Kraepelin might say; "Where does Mr. X take this knowledge from?" He did not allow "speculations." He wanted to deal only with what he considered "facts." Hence psychopathological symptoms were registered and shown their place; there was no attempt at analyzing their meanings. I quote Jaspers: "The basic attitude of Kraepelin was somatic which he like most physicians considered the only medical one; it is not just number one, but absolute. There are excellent psychological discussions in his textbook, but he seems to have arrived at them against his own will: for him they are

expedients until experiment, microscope and test tube will suc-
ceed in objective examination of everything." It occurs to me
that a considerable number of our contemporary colleagues
find this attitude perfectly apropos.

I see him entering the classroom: he walks rather fast and
energetically, the right shoulder projects a bit as though he were
going to an attack. He sits down and puts his papers on the
table. With a familiar movement he swings his nickel-rimmed
pince nez, which is secured on a black cord, on his nose and
lets two students come down to interrogate the patient, who
meanwhile has taken his seat at the left side of the professor.
He may help the students in the examination; he is never mean
trying to trap a student with a trick question[22] as some teachers,
I understand, are still fond of doing. He may say a word when
the performance of a student is too far from justified expectations. The patient leaves the room. Kraepelin talks about him
and his disease. A few more patients come and go; so do the
examining students. At the end of the demonstration Kraepelin
gives a summary of the disease under discussion with special
attention to differential diagnosis.[23] When the two hours clinical
demonstration and discussion (the "noon clinic") are over, he
leaves the classroom in the same manner in which he entered it,
and, as in coming, passes through the adjoining examining room
without saying a word. But he can always be "held up," told
about a new case or any problem he and the staff are preoccupied with. In the daily conferences he orients himself about
the admissions and discharges, inquires about particular patients,
and makes the plan for the next clinic. He is accessible for every
sensible question and debate. A discussion may start between

[22] He was known for his seriousness and fairness as examiner in the
medical students' finals.
[23] He spoke clearly without any frills and fringes. He was no orator.
When he had to speak, to read a paper, before a large audience, he never
seemed to feel entirely at his ease. He claimed that it was a misfortune
to be a good speaker since oratory led from "facts" to speculation and
twaddle.

two or more staff members to which Kraepelin always listens
with interest. Once in a while he may make a joke or laugh
heartily when told a funny story. There is never any, not even
the remotest, profanity.

Kraepelin was a great teacher. He was especially aware of
the teaching value of his clinical classification. He never hesitated
to make changes in his system when new investigations seemed
to indicate their desirability. He could show some irritability
against colleagues who did not follow the changes he proposed.
Half jokingly he might remark that one or the other of his
former associates got stuck at the classification of a past edition
of *Psychiatry*.

It is noteworthy that academic teachers of the rank of H. W.
Gruhle (1880–1958) and Kurt Schneider (1887–)—W. Mayer-
Gross I quoted above—notwithstanding considerable differences
in their clinical and psychopathological approach agree that
"the epoch of Kraepelin is not over as yet." Gruhle goes so far
as to say: "I do not see the slightest reason to give up Kraepelin's
general viewpoint." He would regret it if the wide open Kraepelinian classification would be forgotten and symptomatological ir-
relevancies would again be toyed with.

We cannot do without some order. This order must be dis-
arranged again and again through disorder lest we grow com-
placent in an all too well-settled order. From the psychiatric
point of view there are the compulsive and the paranoic patients
who manifest an exaggerated sense of order with the tendency
to systematize certain of their experiences. Nature does not give
us the systems that we so badly need, but we see our systems *into*
nature and are thus able to find them in her. It is said *natura non
facit saltus*; this may be true in most instances. It happens,
though, that *nature facit saltus* and that we are unable to catch
up with these jumps as they do not fit in our systems. One might
say: a little systematization is helpful, too much of it can become
obstructive. A clinical system ought to serve our orientation
in an otherwise apparently chaotic material; it ought not be

used for the diagnostic burial of individual cases. This implies that a clinical system must be flexible, it must be adjusted to observations. Kraepelin's flexible classification was a successful one—so much so, indeed, that many, perhaps most, of our psychoanalytically oriented colleagues who do not brook much clinical psychiatry in general and still less Kraepelinian in particular do not tire to treat patients suffering from a disturbance whose "cradle" was the fifth edition of Kraepelin's *Psychiatry*. Not to forget the existential analysts who decided that there are manic-depressive and schizophrenic ways of existence.

[The backbone of Kraepelin's system can be seen in three categories[24] of mental disorder: (1) the organic psychoses, (2) the endogenous psychoses, and (3) the deviant personalities.] Kraepelin worked on all three categories and enhanced our knowledge. In the second category he created most relevant groups. Here essential changes have not been achieved since Kraepelin. Many authors have chiseled on the schizophrenias and on the manic-depressive psychoses, but Kraepelin's findings about them were verified. Recently Stevenson and Malzberg made pertinent statements based on a forty-year comparative study in the New York State mental hospital system. With the exception of the word hostility, now generally and generously used in psychopathology, there is nothing in this statement that does not correspond with Kraepelin's descriptions and thoughts about the schizophrenic and the manic-depressive group and the other smaller groups mentioned.[25]

In psychopathology Kraepelin's formulations have become antiquated. The elemental and experimental psychology of

[24] See Jaspers (1948) and Mayer-Gross (1950).
I might mention that there cannot be any waterproof separation or borderlines between the three categories; there occur all manner of combinations not only on the syndromal but also on the "categorical" level.
[25] Dr. George S. Stevenson was so kind as to let me have a copy of the release to the press with a sheet attached on the "symptoms of mental illness discussed in this release."

Wundt upon which they were founded was a great beginning, but it does not do justice to the problems as we see them now.

In clinical psychiatry Kraepelin's descriptions are classical. Their language is simple and what they convey can literally be "seen." Kraepelin opened a new era as regards the clinical classification of mental disorders. He put down the conditions under which such a disorder could be clinically demarcated as a "disease entity." Once more I want to say that Kraepelin did not use this word often. He preferred, particularly in later years, to talk and to write about groups of disease or forms of disease. It evolved that these groups and/or forms of disease did not follow the alleged rules for disease entities. In view of this undeniable fact it is the more remarkable that the groups of the manic-depressive psychoses and of the endogenous dementias became and remained clinically valid. Thirty years after Kraepelin's death there is no doubt as regards the clinical validity of the most important part of his psychiatric work. He was not unmindful of the personality and its surroundings, nor was he unaware of social factors. Yet he considered it the most urgent task to provide a solid nosological foundation for clinical psychiatry.

Kraepelin, like Freud, was a child of his time. It is not astonishing that much of their teaching is no longer up to date; in fact, it is astonishing that so much of their teaching still is useful notwithstanding the circumstance that the greater parts of their lives belonged to a historical period profoundly different from the present one. I hold that many arguments against either of them were due to a lack of understanding of these men in their time and in their environments. I also hold that, despite their insistence on the "it is so," neither Kraepelin nor Freud ever meant to imply "and it will be so in all eternity"; both made incisive changes in their teaching. None of their successors has carried on with their originality and enthusiasm the tasks with which they had commissioned themselves. It is to be regretted that in their time and in their environments there was no possibility for Kraepelin and Freud to get together. It goes almost beyond imagination what mutual understanding between them might have achieved. Kraepelin might have exercised a restricting influence on Freud's abundant imaginativeness, and Freud might have put colors into Kraepelin's sober unilinearity. More important: the Protestant German and the Jewish Austrian might have buried their mutual hostility with consequences reaching far beyond the personal destinies of these two men.

BIBLIOGRAPHY

Benedetti, G. *Die Alkoholhalluzinosen.* Stuttgart, 1952.

Bleuler, E. Dementia praecox oder die Gruppe der Schizophrenien. In *Handbuch der Psychiatrie,* edited by G. Aschaffenburg. Leipzig, 1911.

————. *Lehrbuch der Psychiatrie,* 1916.

Bonhoeffer, K. Die Psychosen im Gefolge von akuten Infektionen, Allgemeinerkrankungen und inneren Erkrankungen. In *Handbuch der Psychiatrie,* edited by G. Aschaffenburg. Leipzig, 1912.

deBoor, Wolfgang. *Psychiatrische Systematik: Ihre Entwicklung in Deutschland seit Kahlbaum.* Berlin, 1954.

————. *Pharmakopsychologie und Psychopathologie.* Berlin, 1956.

Farrar, C. B. I remember Nissl. *Am. J. Psychiat., 110,* 1954.

————. I remember Kraepelin. *Am. J. Psychiat., 113,* 1956.

Gaupp, Robert. Die Lehren Kraepelins in ihrer Bedeutung fuer die heutige Psychiatrie. *Z. ges. Neurol. Psychiat., 165,* 1939.

Griesinger, Wilhelm. *Die Pathologie und Therapie der psychischen Krankheiten.* Stuttgart, 1845; 4th edition, 1876.

Gruhle, H. W. Wernickes psychopathologische und klinische Lehren. *Nervenarzt, 26* (1955).

————. Emil Kraepelin's 100. Geburtstag. *Nervenarzt, 27* (1956).

Hecker, E. Die Hebephrenie. *Arch. pathol. Anat. u. Physiol., Virchow's, 52* (1871).

Jaspers, Karl. *Allgemeine Psychopathologie.* Berlin, 1913; 5th edition, 1948.

Jones, Ernest. *The Life and Work of Sigmund Freud.* New York, Vol. I, 1953; Vol. II, 1955; Vol. III, 1957.

Kahlbaum, L. K. *Die Gruppierung der psychischen Krankheiten und die Einteilung der Seelenstoerungen.* Danzig, 1863.

————. *Die Katatonie.* Berlin, 1874.

Kahn, Eugen. A marginal note on interpretation. *Am. J. Psychiat., 112* (1955).

————. Emil Kraepelin. Ein Gedenkblatt zum 100. Geburtstag. *Monatsschr. Psychiat. Neurol., 131* (1956).

————. Emil Kraepelin. 1856–1926–1956. *Am. J. Psychiat., 113* (1956).

Kolle, Kurt. Die primaere Paranoia. Leipzig, 1931.

————. Die endogenen Psychosen —das delphische Orakel der Psychiatrie. *Münch. med. Wochschr.,* 1955.

————. *Psychiatrie,* 4th edition. Munich, 1955.

————. Emil Kraepelin. In *Grosse Nervenaerzte,* edited by K. Kolle. Stuttgart, 1955.

————. Emil Kraepelin —Gedenken zum 100. Geburtstag. *Deut. med. Wochschr., 81* (1956).

Kraepelin, Emil. *Die Abschaffung des Strafmasses.* Stuttgart, 1880.

————. Ueber den Einfluss akuter Krankheiten auf die Entstehung der Geisteskrankheiten. *Arch. Psychiat., 11* (1881).

————. Ueber psychische Schwaeche. *Arch. Psychiat., 13* (1882).

————. Ueber die Einwirkung einiger medikamentoeser Stoffe auf die Dauer einfacher psychischer Vorgaenge. *Wundt's Philosoph. Studien, 1* (1883).

————. *Compendium der Psychiatrie.* Leipzig, 1883.

————. Zur Psychologie des Komischen. *Wundt's Philosoph. Studien, 2* (1884).

————. Ueber die Verwirrtheit. *Zentr. Nervenheilk. & Psychiat., 8* (1885).

————. Ueber Erinnerungsfaelschungen. *Arch. Psychiat. 17* (1886).

————. *Psychiatrie,* 2nd edition. Leipzig, 1887.

————. Bernhard von Gudden. *Münch. med. Wochschr.,* 1888.

————. Psychiatrie, 3rd edition. Leipzig, 1889.

————. Die Abgrenzung der Paranoia. *Neurol. Zentr.,* 1892.

————. *Ueber die Beeinflussung einfacher psychischer Vorgaenge durch einige Arzneimittel.* Jena, 1892.

————. *Psychiatrie,* 4th edition. Leipzig, 1893.

————. *Der psychologische Versuch in der Psychiatrie.* Leipzig, 1895.

————. Ueber die Wirkung der Theebestandteile auf koerperliche und geistige Arbeit. *Kraepelin's Psychol. Arbeiten, 1,* 1895.

————. *Psychiatrie,* 5th edition. Leipzig, 1896.

————. Neuere Untersuchungen ueber die psychische Wirkung des Alkohols. *Münch. med. Wochschr.,* 1899.

————. *Psychiatrie,* 6th edition. Leipzig, 1899 (2 vols.).

————. *Einfuehrung in die psychiatrische Klinik.* Leipzig, 1901.

————. Die Arbeitskurve. *Wundt's Philosoph. Studien,* 1902.

————. *Psychiatrie,* 7th edition. Leipzig, 1904 (2 vols.).

————. *Einfuehrung in die psychiatrische Klinik,* 2nd edition. Leipzig, 1905.

————. Der Alkoholismus in Muenchen. *Münch. med. Wochschr.,* 1906.

————. *Psychiatrie,* 8th edition, Vol. I. Leipzig, 1909.

————. *Psychiatrie,* 8th edition, Vol. II. Leipzig, 1910.

————. Forschungsinstitute und Hochschulen. *Süddeut. Monatsh.,* 1911.

————. Ueber paranoide Erkrankungen. *Z. ges. Neurol. Psychiat., 11* (1912).

————. *Psychiatrie,* 8th edition, Vol. III. Leipzig, 1913.

————. Bericht ueber die Vorarbeiten zur Errichtung eines Forschungsinstitutes fuer Psychiatrie. Jahresversammlung d. Dtsch. Vereins f. Psychiatrie. *Allgem. Z. Psychiat., 70* (1913).

————. *Psychiatrie,* 8th edition, Vol. IV. Leipzig, 1915.

————. *Einfuehrung in die klinische Psychiatrie.* 3rd edition. Leipzig, 1916.

————. Die Beeinflussung der Treffsicherheit beim Schiessen durch Alkohol. *Alkoholfrage, 12* (1916).

————. Hundert Jahre Psychiatrie. *Z. ges. Neurol. Psychiat., 38* (1917).

————. Alkoholgewerbe und Wissenschaft. Intern. Monatschr. zur Erforschung des Alkoholimus und Bekaempfung der Trinksitten, 1918.

————. Ziele und Wege der psychiatrischen Forschung. *Z. ges. Neurol. Psychiat., 42* (1918).

————. Die deutsche Forschungsanstalt fuer Psychiatrie. *Naturwissenschaften,* 1918.

————. *Die Forschungsanstalt fuer Psychiatrie und die deutschen Irrenaerzte.* Halle, 1918.

————. Krankenvorstellungen (Paranoide Erkrankungen und Dementia praecox) *Z. ges. Neurol. Psychiat.,* Ref. *18,* 1919.

————. Franz. Nissl. *Münch. med. Wochschr.,* 1919.

————. Die Erforschung psychischer Krankheitsformen. *Z. ges. Neurol. Psychiat., 51* (1919).

———. Wilhelm Wundt. *Z. ges. Neurol. Psychiat., 61* (1920).

———. Die Erscheinungsformen des Irreseins. *Z. ges. Neurol. Psychiat., 62* (1920).

———. Lebensschicksale deutscher Forscher. (Alzheimer, Brodmann, Nissl.) *Münch. med. Wochschr.,* 1920.

———. Krieg und Geistesstoerungen. *Münch. med. Wochschr.,* 1920.

———. Franz von Rinecker. In *Deutsche Irrenaerzte,* edited by Theodor Kirchhoff. Berlin, 1921.

———. Ueber Entwurzelung. *Z. ges. Neurol. Psychiat., 63* (1921).

———. Das Raetsel der Paralyse. *Naturwissenschaften,* 1925.

———. *Psychiatrie,* 9th edition, Vol. II. Leipzig, 1927.

Kretschmer, E. *Der sensitive Beziehungswahn.* Berlin, 1921; 3rd edition, 1950.

———. *Koerperbau und Charakter.* Berlin, 1921; 11th and 12th editions, 1936.

Lange, Johannes. Emil Kraepelin zu seinem 70. Geburtstage. *Münch. med. Wochschr.,* 1926.

———. Emil Kraepelin. *Münch. med. Wochschr.,* 1926.

———. Kraepelin-Lange—Allgemeine Psychiatrie. Kraepelin's *Psychiatrie,* 9th edition, Vol. I. Leipzig, 1927.

———. Die endogenen und reaktiven Gemuetserkrankungen und die manisch-depressive Konstitution. In *Handbuch der Geisteskrankheiten,* edited by O. Bumke, Berlin, 1928.

Mayer-Gross, W., *et al. Clinical Psychiatry.* London, 1954.

Plaut, F. Worte der Erinnerung an Emil Kraepelin. *Z. Neurol. Psychiat., 108* (1927).

Schneider. Kurt. *Fortschr. Neurol. Psychiat., 24* (1956) (ref. from Gruhle, 1956).

Schuele, Heinrich. Handbuch der Geisteskrankheiten. In *Handbuch der speciellen Pathologie und Therapie,* edited by H. v. Ziemssen. Leipzig, 1878.

Spielmeyer, W. Kraepelin und die naturwissenschaftlich-medizinische Forschung in der Psychiatry. *Z. Neurol. Psychiat., 108* (1927).

Stevenson, George S. News release A.M. and P.M. on November 30, 1956, on report based on study by Benjamin Malzberg; report delivered November 29, 1956, in Washington, D.C.

Weygandt, W. Emil Kraepelin. *Allgem. Z. Psychiat., 85* (1927).

Factors Related to Personality Change during the Second Decade in the Lives of Young People[1]

A. R. MANGUS AND E. Z. DAGER [2]

Institute on Child Development and Family Life,
The Ohio State University, Columbus

This paper reports some of the more significant findings from a study of personality change in boys and girls during an important period in their lives. These subjects were first contacted for research purposes in 1946 when they were about nine years old and in the third grade in school. Personality assessment procedures applied at that age were repeated, in part, nine years later (1955) at which time they were in the upper classes in high school.[3] In the interval between the two cross-sectional studies these young people had experienced the onset of puberty and the important changes associated with their adolescent

[1] This report is based upon findings of a cooperative program of mental health research sponsored by The Ohio State University and the Ohio State Department of Mental Hygiene and Correction. Cooperating units at the University included the Institute on Child Development and Family Life, the Rural Sociology section of the Department of Agricultural Economics and Rural Sociology, the Department of Sociology and Anthropology, and the University Development Fund. The research was financed with funds provided by the Development Fund and the State Department of Mental Hygiene and Correction.

[2] Present address: Department of Sociology, Purdue University, Lafayette, Indiana.

[3] A detailed report on this study is contained in *Social Factors in Personality Change,* by Edward Z. Dager. Unpublished Ph.D. dissertation, The Ohio State University, Columbus, Ohio, 1956.

development. Also the interlude between the two studies was one marked by the continuing impacts of the postwar period on American youths.

The study was undertaken with three major purposes in view: (1) to determine the rates and directions of personality change during this transitional period in the lives of modern youths, (2) to identify social factors associated with personality change in the subjects; (3) to develop bases for making valid inferences regarding factors governing the occurrence of favorable or unfavorable personality change in the subjects. This last aim represents an attempt to identify factors of etiological significance.

Access to the subjects was had through the public schools which they attended. These schools are located in a midwestern county outside the large metropolitan areas. The county of about 60,000 inhabitants is located in the eastern part of the midwest. Its population is about equally divided between rural and urban categories. The urban population is concentrated largely in two comparatively small cities. The rural population is predominantly nonfarm. About one-sixth of the total population in the county resides on farms, while about one-third lives in villages and in open-country nonfarm homes. All parts of this county are within commuting distance of a fairly large metropolitan center.

The point of departure is a test-retest population of 384 subjects. In 1946, when they were attending the third grade in school, these subjects participated in personality assessment procedures to estimate the varying levels of their mental health. One of the assessment instruments used at that time was a structured personality inventory—the California Test of Personality. This is an age-graded, standardized test designed to measure degrees of a subject's "personal, social and total adjustment." After a time lag of nine years, the appropriate form of this standardized inventory was again administered to all of the same students who were still in school and therefore accessible in the sample county. Comparable results were thereby obtained for these public school attendants at two different age levels.

The subjects included in the present study obviously do not constitute a representative sample of the cohort of children initially studied at the third grade level. In fact, the number of retested students was about one-half the number of third graders included in the earlier study. This rather high rate of attrition is due to the fact that many boys and girls dropped out of school for various reasons before reaching the upper grades, while others moved away from the research area. There is no ready means of access to those who drop out of school or move to other localities. The basic test-retest population is believed to be typical of those young people who continue their studies from elementary grades through high school in a representative county.

Methods

To accomplish the aims of this study, the well-known group comparison method encompassing a normative, ecological, or epidemiological (1) perspective is combined with a clinical or case study, (2) approach to mental health research. The normative approach requires the collection of two kinds of objective facts: those that are descriptive of the subject's cultural and subcultural environment, and those that pertain to the subject himself such as his age, sex, and intelligence. The case study approach requires the collection of data descriptive of the subject's perceptual and conceptual experiences. Such data pertain to the personal meanings of events and changes that occur in his world and to his conception of himself in relation to these events.

One major difficulty in a study of this kind centers in the establishment of a satisfactory criterion of personality change in healthy or in unhealthy dimensions. For purposes of the present research, differences between standard scores derived from the two administrations of the California Test of Personality for each subject were used as the criterion variable. These differences, called discrepancy scores, are obtained by simple subtraction so that those having positive algebraic signs represent favorable personality change and those having negative signs represent unfavorable change. Admittedly, these variable discrepancy scores do not provide a completely satisfactory basis of judgment. They are used because they represent the best diagnostic data obtainable for the population of concern here.

For purposes of showing patterns and directions of personality change, the basic population of subjects was initially classified into five criterion groups, on the basis of discrepancy scores as follows:

1. Those whose discrepancy scores ranged from 11 to 26.
2. Those with scores from 6 through 10.
3. Those with scores centering around zero and ranging from minus 5 to plus 5.
4. Those with scores from minus 6 through minus 10.
5. Those whose discrepancy scores ranged downward from minus 11 to minus 22.

Categories 1 and 5 contain the extreme changers in positive and in negative directions. These subjects have discrepancy scores of such magnitudes that they are all acceptable at at least a 5% level of confidence, and the confidence level is much greater for most of them. Categories 2 and 4 contain the less extreme changers. Their discrepancy scores, both positive and negative, are too small to provide acceptable levels of confidence in their reliability. Finally category 3 contains the relatively stable group of nonchanging subjects.

For a more intensive study of factors associated with personality change two subsamples of the basic test-retest population were selected. These subsamples consisted of 30 subjects having the highest discrepancy scores and of another 30 having the lowest scores. These represent two contrasting criterion groups, those who showed the greatest advances in the direction of mental health and those who showed the greatest regression in the opposite direction. The subsample of upwardly mobile subjects are designated the H group. As a group these subjects ranked very low on the scale of personality test scores in 1946 but had advanced to a relatively high level in 1955. The opposite was true for the other subsample, which includes subjects who regressed from high levels of test scores in 1946 to very low levels at the time of retest. This downwardly mobile category is labeled the L group.

The great magnitude of the personality changes indicated for these criterion groups is reflected in the shifts in their mean percentile scores on the California Test of Personality from 1946 to 1955. The average percentile score for the high, or H group, rose from about 22 in 1946 to a high of about 78 at the time of retest. Conversely, the L group declined in average percentile score from a high of around 66 in 1946 to a low of about 22 nine years later (Table I).

TABLE I

Mean Percentile Scores on California Test of Personality for Criterion Groups, 1946 and 1955

(CR = critical ratio of difference in scores)

Type of Group	Total Adjustment			Personal Adjustment			Social Adjustment		
	1946	1955	CR	1946	1955	CR	1946	1955	CR
H group	21.5	77.9	18.4	20.7	79.3	18.4	22.7	76.1	13.9
L group	65.6	22.3	10.1	61.5	23.0	7.9	69.1	23.3	10.1

For these contrasting subsamples, extensive data collection procedures were undertaken. These procedures included a research interview with a lengthy interview schedule, a projective test in the form of an incomplete sentence blank, and the collection of written autobiographies prepared by each subject.

Factors associated with personality change are identified as those that significantly discriminate between the two contrasting criterion groups; that is, between those who progressed in the direction of mental health (H group) and those who regressed toward mental ill health (L group). The technique is essentially that of dividing the research subjects into risk categories in order to determine the differential chances of personality change in various subgroups.

This technique of identifying external factors associated with positive or negative personality change does not establish these factors as causal. Characteristics associated with change do not have any necessary etiological significance. The associated factor may be a consequent rather than an antecedent of personality change or it may be merely a concomitant of change and only incidentally or remotely related to it.

In accord with the theoretical approach assumed here, the immediate and direct causes of personality and behavioral change are to be found in the internal perceptual field of the individual. Exploration of this field is carried on with clinical or case study methods.

In order to have a better basis for etiological inferences, a further screening of subjects was undertaken. For this purpose 10 subjects were selected at random from each of the two contrasting groups described above. An additional subsample of 10 was selected from the nonchangers. With these 30 subjects, intensive interviewing was carried out. These interviews were tape recorded, and the interview transcriptions were used as one way of exploring the subject's perceptual world of meaning.

Patterns and Rates of Personality Change

Rates and directions of personality change among the students who were subjects of the present study have been determined for the entire test-retest population. This determination is based on discrepancy scores representing changes in personality test performance between the test and retest dates. On the basis of the criterion variable, consisting of discrepancy scores, the basic population is classified into criterion groups and these are compared with respect to residence, intelligence, age and sex of the subjects comprising this population.

Considering the population as a whole, there was a decided tendency for the subjects to be upwardly mobile on the scale to measure personality change. That is, the group as a whole had higher average scores in 1955 than in 1946. This is assumed to be indicative of general improvements in the level of personality health as the subjects progressed from the third, to the twelfth grade in school.

For purposes of portraying the incidence and directions of personality change, the following summary is presented:

Of each 100 subjects in the test-retest population:

     14.1 had discrepancy scores of 11 to 26
     19.7 had discrepancy scores of 6 to 10
     50.0 had discrepancy scores ranging from −5 to 5
      7.6 had discrepancy scores of −6 to −10
      8.6 had discrepancy scores of −11 to −22

On the basis of these findings, several conclusions are indicated. First, 50% of the population remained comparatively stable with respect to personality test performance. Second, nearly 20% showed moderate improvement in personality test scores but insufficient to give confidence in statistical significance. About 14% showed increase in test scores of such magnitude as to assure their statistical significance. Third, nearly 8% of the subjects had discrepancy scores that indicated some decline in levels of personality health, while nearly 9% showed extreme decline of rather certain statistical significance.

Age, Sex, and Intelligence as Factors

The 1946 study showed that the average level of personality adjustment was higher for girls than boys, higher for the brighter than for the duller students, and much higher for those in a grade normal for their age than for the overaged pupils. In view of these findings it seems reasonable to expect that these groups representing differential advantage and disadvantage in a cross-sectional study might show similar differentials with respect to change in personal and social adjustment over a period of time. Such was not the case, however. The present study shows that the pattern and rate of personality change as reflected in discrepancy scores was nearly identical for boys and girls. Hence, sex is apparently not a factor in change.

The present study also indicates that the direction and rate of personality change is independent of the level of intelligence represented among students who progress to the senior level in high school. The IQ's for these subjects ranged from a low of around 90 to a high of 140 and over with a median of 114. Those with higher levels of intelligence showed approximately the same pattern of personality change as did those with lower IQ's.

Again, while there was some variation in age (from 17 to 19 years) among the subjects in the test-retest population, age was not significantly related to personality change.

Location of School as Factor in Personality Change

The schools which the subjects of this study were attending in 1955 were of three types. The majority (206) were attending high schools located in one or another of the cities in the research area. The remainder were either attending schools located in villages large enough to have their own separate school districts or they were attending county schools located in small villages or in open country districts.

The present study shows that the type of school attended is a significant factor in personality change among the students. Those attending the rural schools (county and village) present a different pattern of change than that presented by those in the city schools. The difference favors those in the rural schools (Table II).

TABLE II

Discrepancy Scores for Subjects Attending Urban and Rural Schools, 1955

(Chi square = 17.50; P < 0.01)

Score	Number			Per Cent		
	Total	Urban	Rural	Total	Urban	Rural
11 and over	54	21	33	14.1	10.2	18.5
6 to 10	76	40	36	19.7	19.4	20.2
−5 to 5	192	98	94	50.0	47.6	52.9
−6 to −10	29	22	7	7.6	10.7	3.9
−11 and less	33	25	8	8.6	12.1	4.5
Total	384	206	178	100.0	100.0	100.0

Factors Associated with Personality Change

Personality change, as measured by the criterion variable used in this study, is presumed to be a function of changes in contingent variables which operate independently. These independent variables are of two major types. First, are those that operate in the environment that is external to the individual but which have an impact upon him. These are events and conditions that impinge upon the person in ways significant to his personal and social functioning. Second, are the factors that operate within the person's internal frame of reference. These consist of the concepts and meanings that the person attaches to things and events in the external world.

At this point, major concern is with findings from a study of external, or objective, factors associated with personality change. One aim of the present study was to carry out an extensive exploration of the objective worlds of the research subjects in order to identify the external factors associated or unassociated with personality change. In order to implement this aim it was necessary to select sample groups since the basic test-retest population was too large to permit intensive study of all individuals in it. Hence, extensive investigation and exploration was applied to the H group of 30 subjects who were upwardly mobile on the scale of personality change and to the L group of 30 subjects who were downwardly mobile on this same scale.

In the effort to identify external factors related to personality change in the subjects of this study, a contingency technique was used. Accordingly, extensive data collection procedures were applied to the 60 subjects included in the criterion groups described above. In gathering the data direct interviews were had with each subject. These subjects, already classified into two equal categories on the basis of personality test discrepancy scores, were cross-classified in contingency tables on the basis of numerous independent variables of potential significance. These contingency tables were then subjected to statistical tests to identify those which included factors significantly related to personality change.

Having noted the striking reversals in measured levels of personality adjustment in the H and L groups and the contingency method of analysis, we turn now to reporting some important findings with regard to external factors in personality change.

Among the numerous objective factors tested for their possible association with personality change in the subjects of this study, some were found to be fairly closely associated, others were only weakly associated, while many proved to be quite unrelated to personality change. Those showing considerable intensity of association pertain to migration, to family life, and to participation in group life.

Number of Schools Attended

There has been much speculation as to whether mobility is a favorable or unfavorable factor in the personality development of young people. In this study mobility was measured in terms of the number of different schools attended by the student subjects during the research period of nine years. It was found that less than one-half of the students had remained continuously in one school. The majority had changed schools at least once, and some had changed as many as four or more times. It seems like a reasonable hypothesis that the discontinuities contingent upon repeated change of schools may be reflected in adverse changes in the migrant student's personality.

To test this assumption a contingency table was constructed. Accordingly the research subjects in each of the contrasting criterion groups were divided according to whether they had continued in one particular school or whether they had attended two or more separate schools. The results show that the number of schools attended by the students is a significant factor in their personality change. Stability with respect to number of schools attended is associated with favorable personality change while mobility is associated with regressive change during the research period (Table III).

TABLE III

School Mobility and Personality Change

$(C = 0.33;$ chi square $= 7.17;$ $P < 0.01)$

Type of Group	Total	Observed Frequency		Expected Frequency	
		One school	Two or more schools	One school	Two or more schools
H group	30	16	14	11	19
L group	30	6	24	11	19
Both groups	60	22	38	22	38

The contingency table is constructed to show how the frequency with which subjects actually fall into the four categories represented (observed frequency) compares with the frequencies expected on the basis of a chance distribution. The significance of the association between school mobility and personality change is measured in terms of the well-known chi square test, and the intensity of the association is measured in terms of a contingency coefficient (C).[3] In this instance a chi square value of

[3] $C = \sqrt{\text{Chi square}/(N + \text{Chi square})}$

the magnitude of 7.17 could occur by chance alone less than once in a hundred repeat studies. The association therefore, is considered statistically significant and is measured by a contingency coefficient of 0.33.

On the basis of this finding, it is concluded that school mobility is associated significantly with personality change in an unfavorable direction and that school stability is associated with positive personality change. A more adequate way to state this conclusion is to say that the mobile students are subject to greater risks of adverse personality change, and that the nonmobile students have increased chances of changing in the direction of mental health.

A rationale for this association may be suggested. It seems likely that the more mobile students face differential risks of failure in finding continuing peer group support for their changing self-conceptions and that this introduces them to disorganizing stresses which are reflected in their personality test scores.

Broken Homes

Another objectively measurable contingency factor assumed to be associated with personality change is that of broken homes. Of the 60 students in the two contrasting criterion groups, 18 were living in homes broken by death, divorce, or separation, or in homes under the threat of being broken by divorce. A contingency table based on this classification showed that a much larger proportion of subjects in the L group lived in broken homes than was true of the H group (Table IV). Here the intensity of the association is measured by a contingency coefficient of 0.37. The association is sufficiently strong that it could be expected to occur by chance less than one time in a hundred.

It seems evident that a break or threatened break in an adolescent's or preadolescent's family poses a major threat to his personality organization.

TABLE IV

Broken Homes and Personality Change

(C = 0.37; chi square = 9.60; P < 0.01)

Type of Group	Total	Observed		Expected	
		Broken	Not broken	Broken	Not broken
H group	30	3	27	9	21
L group	30	15	15	9	21
Both groups	60	18	42	18	42

Affiliation with Community Organizations

A third factor rather closely associated with personality change in youths is that of membership in various community organizations. Nearly twice as many subjects in the H group had joined two or more formal membership organizations as had those in the L group. Hence, the joiners and nonjoiners represent strikingly different risk groups with respect to unfavorable personality change (Table V).

TABLE V

Number of Organizational Affiliations and Personality Change

(C = 0.35; chi square = 8.29; P < 0.01)

Type of Group	Total	Observed		Expected	
		One or none	Two or more	One or none	Two or more
H group	30	7	23	12.5	17.5
L group	30	18	12	12.5	17.5
Both groups	60	25	35	25	35

Affiliation or nonaffiliation by young people with community groups is not to be interpreted as a cause of their favorable or unfavorable personality change. It may be interpreted as a consequent of change rather than as a significant antecedent to it.

Other Factors

Of the many additional external factors tested for their possible association with personality change, only a few were found to be significant. Space does not allow for a full discussion of these factors. Suffice it to say that the chances of favorable change appear to be significantly greater and the risks of unfavorable change significantly less: (1) for those students who were living in rural homes, than for those residing in a city; (2) for those whose fathers were employed in jobs of high occupational prestige, than for those whose fathers were in the low-status occupations; (3) for those whose families were upwardly mobile in the social and occupational class structure, than for those whose families remained stable or were downwardly mobile.

Etiology of Personality Change

All basic research disciplines have as their ultimate objective the prediction and control of the central variables with which they are concerned. To accomplish such an objective purely descriptive study is supplemented by studies designed to explain the origins and changes of phenomena of research concern. In the present study a first step is that of describing personality change as measured by an available criterion, and of describing the factors associated with personality change in a population of subjects. Beyond this descriptive phase there is the etiological problem of explaining this change in terms of those necessary and sufficient factors which govern its occurrence and its direction.

According to the view taken here, the causal factors in personality and behavioral change in the direction of mental health or its opposite, do not reside exclusively in events and changed circumstances in the environment that is external to the person who experiences the change. On the contrary the essential causes probably reside in the meanings that those events and circumstances have for the subject. In support of this view is a readily observable fact that there is no known objective social or personal factor that exerts a constant influence on all individuals exposed to it. Each subject invests the event with his own personal meaning and reacts accordingly. In the present study, for example, each subject had experienced the well-known adolescent growth spurt, and most girls had reached or neared their adult height at the time of retest. This is a factor that has an impact on all, but which exerts differential effects on personality development. The girl whose accelerated growth is outpaced by her male companions will respond very differently to her new look than will the girl whose new height places her in the embarrassing position of being inches taller than the boy she had dreamed of marrying.

This strongly suggests that mental health research of etiological significance will need to move beyond normative studies of comparative populations and group averages to a clinical, case, or personal approach. In any study of personality change, objective facts and events, as agreed upon by competent external observers, are important research concerns, but only those that directly impinge upon the subject to effect changes in his perceptual field of meanings. This does not mean that the individual can be understood when isolated from the social systems in which he participates. He must be understood as a person with significant ties with other persons in his life. The ways he perceives objective events, the meanings they have for him, and the feelings he has about them seem to derive, not from the events themselves, but from the socially derived norms by which he interprets them. This suggests the need for an interpersonal approach to mental health research.

The interpersonal approach to the study of mental health and mental illness takes as its conceptual point of departure, an organizing and directing theory of personality and behavior. *Personality is seen as a person's varied and more or less enduring conceptions of himself together with all of his predispositions to act in ways consistent with those self conceptions.* A basic set of self conceptions have as anchorage points in the external world the various statuses or positions which the person occupies in those interpersonal situations in which he participates. These social statuses consist basically of expected behaviors in the form of obligations and privileges which devolve upon the occupants of those statuses. Carried into action, these behavioral expectations are viewed as social roles. Internalized in the person, they constitute his social self, the core of his personality. Also included in the person's self are his conceptions of his various qualities, traits, or attributes together with the evaluations he has learned to place upon these through his interaction with significant other people in his life.

According to this view, personality change in the direction of mental health or ill health is governed largely by changes in the subject's self concepts and in the attitudes that support those concepts. If this view is adopted, then the proper study of mental health is not exclusively a study of populations and group averages, but a study of the factors that govern healthy or unhealthy change in the subject's conceptual self which is a social self. These factors are seen as residing in the subject's perceptual field of meanings attached to things and events in his world. This interpersonal approach views the subject not as a biological organism or as a statistical unit but as a person without significance except in relation to other persons.

In an attempt to implement this approach to the study of etiological factors in personality change several kinds of data were collected in efforts to explore the subject's personal field of meaning. Information collected in this internal frame of reference includes, in addition to responses to separate items in the personality inventory, the subject's written responses to stimulus items in an incomplete sentence blank, written autobiographies, transcripts of electrically recorded interviews, and records of direct answers to certain questionnaire items. Complete analyses of these data is a task for the future but some preliminary findings may serve to illustrate the utility of the approach.

Personality Inventory Items

The significance of the personal or interpersonal frame of reference as an approach to the study of personality and mental health is neatly illustrated in findings derived from analyses of separate items in the California Test of Personality. The items in this inventory are presented to the subject in the form of questions. Each question contains an explicit or implied self reference item though disguises are made to avoid the arousal of defensive reactions in the subject. With the inventory of questions the subject taking the test is required to record his self perceptions and meanings by simple "yes" or "no" answers.

There are 80 separate items that are directly comparable in the inventories administered to the subjects of the present study in 1946 and again in 1955. An analysis of these items identifies 23 that are highly diagnostic of overall change in personality test scores. These items were identified in terms of their efficiency in differentiating between the H group and the L group of subjects as defined earlier.

One of these discriminating items, for example, is stated in the question: "Do you sometimes feel like leaving home for good?" The favorable response is obviously "no" and the unfavorable response is obviously "yes." With respect to this item, it is found that more than one-half of the subjects in each of the criterion groups reversed their answers from "yes" to "no" or from "no" to "yes" upon retest in 1955. Revealing was the fact that all subjects who changed their response from unfavorable (yes) to favorable (no) were in the H group. Conversely all who reversed their responses from favorable to unfavorable ones, with one exception, were in the L group. Similar are the findings based on the analyses of 22 other inventory items.

It is noted that the item referred to above might be restated to make more explicit its self reference implication. For example,

"Do you perceive yourself as an unloved, unwanted, or rejected person at home?" From this perspective many of the subjects in the H group are seen as changing their perceptions of themselves from that of rejected to that of accepted persons. The opposite change is seen for those in the L group. The explanation of such changes in self perceptions and meanings in terms of their necessary and sufficient antecedents seems to constitute the major problem of etiology in mental health research.

Some of the other inventory items that were found to be highly diagnostic of favorable or unfavorable change in subjects' overall personality test scores are listed below.

> Have you often wished that you had different parents than you have?
>
> Are certain people so unreasonable that you can't help but hate them?
>
> Do you have many problems that cause you a great deal of worry?
>
> Do you feel that people usually think well of you?

The self reference implications of each of these items seem fairly obvious.

Schedule Items

Some items in the interview schedule used in the present study asked the subject for his perception or evaluation of external events or situations. These items were in contrast with others which asked for objective descriptions of events in terms subject to verification by any competent observer. These perceptual or evaluative items were analyzed by means of the contingency technique as were the external factors described earlier.

One evaluative question, for example, asked for an appraisal by the subject of the changes in the economic status of his family. The results for the two extreme criterion groups are interesting (Table VI). Subjects in the H group generally perceived improvements, while those in the L group overwhelmingly perceived no

TABLE VI

Perceived Change in Economic Status of the Family and Personality
Change

$(C = 0.43;$ chi square $= 13.61;$ P $< 0.01)$

Type of Group	Total	Observed		Expected	
		Improved	Not improved	Improved	Not improved
H group	30	19	11	12	18
L group	30	5	25	12	18
Both groups	60	24	36	24	36

improvements in the economic condition of their respective families. Whether improvement actually occurred seems less important to favorable personality change than whether the subject himself views the situation as improved.

Other subjective reactions by the subjects that were found to be significantly related to positive or negative changes in their personality test scores include: (1) change in the subject's evaluation of the desirability of his neighborhood as a place to live; (2) change in the subject's perception of his opportunities to participate in social activities; (3) change in the subject's perception of his physical health; (4) changes in the subject's feelings about school as he advanced from elementary, to junior high, and to senior high school.

Sentence Completion Data

The personal field to be explored for etiological factors in personality change presumably consists of the meanings of events, past, present, and anticipated, for the subject. The important external events are presumed to be those that have favorable or unfavorable impacts on the social self. How are such objective events or changes to be identified?

One way to locate relevant events in the life of a subject is to test all those factors that might conceivably have pertinent impacts upon his self concepts. Such a procedure would require tremendous effort and might prove wasteful and inefficient if not impossible from a practical standpoint. A more efficient procedure is one by which the researcher allows himself to be guided by the persons who are the subjects for research. Presumably no one is better informed about significant facts in a person's life after, say age 10, than is that person himself.

Following this suggestion of self identification of significant events, an incomplete sentence blank was used with subjects in the present study. The stimulus phrases of the incomplete sentences were: "My greatest worries . . . ," "My bitterest disappointments . . . ," "My happiest times . . . ," "My unhappiest times . . . ," "My future. . . ."

The kind of responses obtained by this method is illustrated by a girl who experienced a decided downward change in her personality test scores between 1946 and 1955:

"For some strange reason, my happiest times seem to be when I am not at home."

"I have a particular aunt who is rather mean and hateful, and people are always comparing me to her."

"Another worry of mine is the fact that boys seem to treat me as they would a sister."

"I get unhappy and sorry for myself when I think of my younger days."

"A religious letdown I had last August seems to have changed my outlook on ministers and religion." The minister "told me he didn't think I had the Christian background to teach a class."

Interview Transcripts

The written autobiography and the research interview transcript are useful methods of exploring a subject's personal field of meanings of events. Electrically recorded interviews of varying degrees of depth were taken for 30 subjects included in the present study. Not all of these have been transcribed, and only a few have been analyzed completely. It is evident however, that these transcripts are potentially revealing of changes in perceptions of self in relation to changing situations.

In one interview, for example, the subject revealed that the most significant event in his recent life was an automobile accident as a result of which he was held responsible for the death of another person. This traumatic experience, together with a variety of other events contingent upon it, appeared to be basic as an etiological factor in an outstanding decline in his personality test scores. In another instance a girl in the criterion group representing unfavorable personality change identified a basic conflict. She was living under constant stress at the time of interview. This was apparently a result of disparity between her emerging conception of herself at 18 as an independent adult and her parents' treatment of her as still a child.

Many other examples might be cited to show how the immediate etiological factors in personality change reside within the subject's relatively unique personal field of meanings. The point seems clear, however, and further elaboration seems unnecessary.

Summary and Conclusion

The present study pertains to changes in levels of mental health among public school students at two different age levels. This dual cross-sectional study of the same subjects was carried out with three major objectives in view.

1. To determine rates and directions of personality change, the criterion being discrepancies between test and retest standard scores provided by a structured personality inventory.

2. To identify factors associated with personality change through use of the contingency technique of testing various factors for their power to discriminate between two criterion groups representing extreme change in the direction of mental health and extreme change in the opposite direction.

3. To explore the prospects for research designed to determine the direct etiological factors in personality change.

The times of the two cross-sectional studies were 1946 and

1955. The subjects were in the third grade in school in an eastern Midwest county at the time of the original test and were in the upper grades in high school when retested. The basic test-retest population contained 384 subjects. These were successively screened into smaller subpopulations for varying intensities of data collection activities.

Results show that 14.1% of the subjects changed significantly upward in their personality test scores while 8.6% moved downward to significantly lower levels of mental health. These rates and directions of change were about the same regardless of sex, age, or IQ of the subjects.

Factors significantly associated with personality change included place of residence, mobility, occupation of subjects' fathers, broken homes, and degrees of participation in community organizations. Evidence indicates that the immediate causal factors in personality change reside in the personal field of meanings of events for the subject. Significant events are those that have important impacts on the subject's conceptions of himself.

It is concluded that ecological or epidemiological studies that rely exclusively on a normative approach, comparing subpopulations in terms of group averages, are useful for descriptive purposes and for suggesting hypotheses for further research, but they have only limited utility for explaining the causes of personality change in the direction of mental illness or mental health. For explanatory purposes the normative approach must be superseded by the personal approach utilizing clinical or case study techniques and intensive diagnosis of persons as members of social groups.

REFERENCES

1. Gilliam, Alexander G. Epidemiology in noncommunicable disease. *Public Health Reports.* (*U.S.*), *69,* 907–913 (1954).
2. Snygg, Donald, and Arthur W. Combs. *Individual Behavior.*

Harper and Brothers, New York, 1949. Chap. 10, Diagnosis and Research.

DISCUSSION

DR. E. M. GRUENBERG: There are two outstanding characteristics of this paper which I wish to re-emphasize. These make the paper worthy of very careful attention by all of those interested in developing a better understanding of the conditions which favor mental ill health and of those which favor mental health. The first concerns the questions to which the study is addressed. So often when one wishes to engage in serious discussion with people on complicated and important issues, it is really necessary to say, "I don't agree with your question." Thus, when a person asks us which is more likely to produce schizophrenia, spanking a child when he has done something very wrong or not spanking him, the only sensible answer is to say in one way or another that the question is wrong. Hence, it is a great pleasure to be able to discuss a paper where the question is so obviously right and important and has been so well stated. To refresh your minds I will read again the statement of the three major purposes: (1) to determine the rates and directions of personality change during this transition period in the lives of modern youths; (2) to identify social factors associated with personality change in the subjects; (3) to develop bases for making valid inferences regarding factors governing the occurrence of favorable or unfavorable personality change.

These questions make a lot of sense. It would be highly desirable to have answers to them. Every day practical and vital judgments must be made by school and child welfare administrators which are guided, at least implicitly, by assumptions regarding the answers to these three questions. If we could answer them with assurance and transmit our answers to those whom we have made responsible for our youths, we could do great good for the mental health of the next generation.

The second outstanding feature of this paper, in my opinion, is the collection of data on the same children at two points in time of a nine-year interval. In spite of the fact that I do not believe these data provide answers to the questions posed, I do believe that the data will be of real value to us if they are used to answer some other questions.

Why do I say that Mangus and Dager have not answered the important questions they have asked? I think that my discussion will be most useful if I simply list the faults I have to find with this report. This is not a very polite thing to do, but I believe it is necessary. It is a serious effort to define areas of disagreement regarding research and research reporting so that the maximum benefit can be acquired from each piece of investigation. I would not, obviously, take the trouble to state these faults unless I thought them to be prevalent in the whole field of mental health research. In my own work, I have tried desperately hard to avoid them, not always, I fear, with complete success.

1. The California Personality Test and its use. My comments have to do with the way the test is used in the analysis. In the first place, the test comes in two forms, an elementary and an advanced form. Both forms contain 144 questions to be answered "yes" or "no"; 80 of the questions are worded identically in the two forms. The authors give no references, and I have not been able to locate literature which examines the comparability of performance on the two forms. This could readily be investigated, but, from the data available in the manual which accompanies the test and from the absence of references, I assume it has not yet been done. Hence, I find fault with assuming that the two forms of the test are "comparable." I think they need to be compared. Secondly, reference is made to "standard scores." I am at a loss to understand how the discrepancy scores, which are the algebraic differences between two standard scores, could so frequently be over 10. I am assured by Dr. Mangus that by standard score the authors do mean scores divided by the standard deviation of the mean score achieved by a standard population, but it is extraordinary, to say the least, to have 22% of a population score more than five standard deviations from the mean on at least one of two tests. Such a peculiar distribution of scores raises serious questions which need to be examined. Thirdly, although it is stated that the group had better mental health in 1955 than in 1946, absolutely no evidence on this point is forthcoming. Unless there is independent evidence that the advanced form of the test and elementary form of the test are quantitatively as well as qualitatively identical, the higher average scores in 1955 cannot be interpreted this way. It seems to me that one might be able to say that this group in 1955 scored higher than the Los Angeles school children who took the standardizing test to a greater degree than the same group did in 1955. But this could

obviously have been due to a number of other things than an improvement in mental health of the group which was tested twice.

2. We are told that the county where these studies are made is fairly representative. To a person in my position this is a meaningless statement. I cannot imagine what kind of data exist to support this statement.

3. "Regress" is used to describe the children whose 1955 score was lower than their 1946 score. It is pretty obvious that "decline" is meant. I assume that there is no evidence that these children had, before 1946, scores as low as their 1955 scores.

4. In Table V, percentile scores are indicated. But interpretation depends on knowing whether the percentiles were computed on the basis of the scores obtained in the present study or whether they are percentile positions in relation to the Los Angeles school population used by the authors of the test.

5. At one point, the authors state the "theoretical approach assumed here is that the immediate and direct causes of personality and behavioral change are to be found in the internal perceptual field of the individual." This is certainly a legitimate *assumption* and I have no quarrel with it. However, in the Summary and Conclusions, it is stated that *"Evidence* indicates that the immediate causal factors in personality change reside in the personal field of meanings of events for the subjects." This is not acceptable. No evidence can possibly be collected to support an assumption in the strict sense of these terms. I submit that the paper does not contain any evidence for or against this statement.

6. It is stated that *"sex* is apparently not a factor in change," that "change is independent of the level of *intelligence,"* and that *"age* was not significantly related to personality change." These are what I would call *pseudonegative* findings. The data might support each when analyzed separately and yet not support all three simultaneously. I have made, for my own edification, a table showing how IQ and sex combined could be important factors, assuming that the association between IQ and change in boys is in the opposite direction from its association with change in girls. Until the data are fully analyzed, keeping such obvious possibilities in mind, one does not seem justified in stating these negative findings.

7. Contrariwise, I think this study contains some *pseudopositive* findings. The association of predominant positive change with rurality, school placement stability, intact homes, multiple affiliations, fathers in high status occupations, upwardly mobile families are

cases in point. The data may indicate all these associations, but the methods used in the analysis only permit us to conclude that at least one exists in the data. Actually, the information given us does not even support one association; the contingency coefficients we have seen could be due to the opposite association; that is, that negative change is associated with downward mobility. Because the entire body of data is confined to children who had either positive or negative change, we only know how these children differ from the children who did not change.

8. Although I do not think it necessary to argue with the assumption that changes in personality are produced only by the children's change in self concept, though I do not think the assumption advisable, it seems to me that this has led the authors to ignore the possibility that changes in personality might produce changes in conscious perceptions of the self and of the environment (which could account for their interview data patterning).

9. I now come to the last and main fault. This fault might be suggested by calling the study a pseudoprospective study. Quoting from the paper, we find that in essence this is what it says.

"The subjects included in the present study obviously do not constitute a representative sample of the cohort of children initially studied at the third grade level. In fact, the number of students was about one-half the number of third graders included in the earlier study . . . The basic test-retest population is believed to be typical of those young people who continue their studies from elementary grades through high school in a representative county."

What this means is that the raw data of the study have to do with the difference between present test performance and test performance nine years previously of a sample of high school children. The data can distinguish children who had previously scored lower from those who had previously scored higher than their present score. We can conclude from the data presented that those who had previously scored higher differ in other important respects from those who had previously scored lower, and the analysis in those terms seems to me to be justified. But we must remember that this is the analog of asking whether cancer patients smoke more than noncancer patients: the only kind of question which can be asked when the sample is drawn on the basis of whether or not the event under investigation has occurred. As was quite properly pointed out when the first associations between having cancer and having been a smoker were published, this is a clue. It must, however, be confirmed by prospective studies in which the likelihood of developing cancer among smokers is compared to the likelihood of developing cancer among nonsmokers. This is much harder, but it has been done. Here we must say that the questions which have been asked about children who had changed from a low to a high score, as contrasted to children who changed from a high to a low score, is the reciprocal of the question to which the investigators addressed themselves initially. Initially they wanted to know whether children with factor A change upward more than children without factor A. But they have data on whether factor A is more or less common among the children who changed upward than among the children who changed downward. To get what they want, they must, having samples of children with factor A and another without A, find out which group changes upward more. If one assumes that the half of the children who dropped out of the 1946 sample were distributed in just the same way, with respect to all the variables studied, as the children who were in the 1955 sample, we are all right. But no one can reasonably make this assumption; we know too much about the characteristics of the children who drop out of school altogether. The present study shows us that the children who change schools within a county are different from the children who stay in the same school; how much more different might not the children be who moved out of the county altogether? (Parenthetically, I should remark that for this reason the 1955 sample is not representative of the 1955 high school population since it excludes in-migrants to the county.) In order to study the children who, say, come from broken homes, we must know about the children who come from broken homes. Perhaps the data underestimate the amount of change which occurs in such children, but it must be admitted that that may distort it. Perhaps those who make a positive adaptation to broken homes tend to drop out of school and leave only those who make a negative adjustment to this disruptive event. The same may, of course, be said of all the variables. We do not know how much the patterns reported reflect differential rates of dropping out of school (or leaving the county) and how much they reflect associations between changes in test performance and the variables studied.

In conclusion, let me say that the failure to provide definite answers to the very important questions asked is not entirely the failure of the authors of this study. In my opinion it reflects the failure of an entire field of research to develop the tools necessary to answer important questions. I do not see how these questions can be answered with existing tools. After all, if we see a child trying to cut down a great oak tree with a pen knife, we do not criticize him for failing to fell the tree. In my opinion, we in the mental health field are like children with pen knives surrounded by grown ups with power saws and axes. Personally, I'm going to try to get my hands at least on a hatchet before I tackle any big trees.

DR. MORTON KRAMER: There is only one point that I would like to point to and that is in the final paragraph of Dr. Mangus' paper, where he stated:

"It is concluded that ecological or epidemiological studies that rely exclusively on a normative approach, comparing subpopulations in terms of group averages, are useful for descriptive purposes and for suggesting hypotheses for further research but have only limited utility for explaining the causes of personality change in the direction of mental illness or mental health."

I would think that that was a very well accepted principle in epidemiological research, namely that these studies are done to get suggestions for hypotheses which can later be tested in more tightly designed studies in the laboratory or in the communities. This is the approach that has usually been used by most of us in epidemiological studies.

DR. J. ZUBIN: I think Dr. Gruenberg's slashing attack on psychology tests is well earned.

I would like to say that psychologists have passed way beyond the inventory approach to personality. I would like to say that they have gone on to bigger and better things with the TAT and Rorschach. Even those, however, have now been found very difficult to employ in personality measurement.

There is one reason why those techniques do not work, and that is a very simple one. Those techniques are nothing else than inventory of deviations, inventory of things of which the person shrinks away from the norm. They don't do anything with the assets of the person.

If, instead of asking a person whether he wanted to get away from home or not, you asked him about the kind of home he lived in and the reason for his desire to run away, then perhaps you might make some sense from it all.

DR. PAUL HOCH: I may add that I think Dr. Mangus arrived at that conclusion. He said that some of the scores should be supplemented by the clinical case approach. I think that the study showed quite clearly, which Dr. Mangus emphasized, that some of the scores should be clinically evaluated and possibly substantiated, not in the mind of the examiner, but in the minds of the people who are tested.

DR. MANGUS: Owing to the limitation of time, there is very little that I need to say here regarding the points that have been made. However, I will appreciate an opportunity to prepare a formal counter discussion for publication purposes. Such a counter statement seems most necessary since obvious misunderstandings are apparent in several points made by Dr. Gruenberg in his discussion.

I would like to say that we did not have any misgivings about the limitation of the California Test of Personality in its uses here. It was used because we did have a baseline established by this particular test in 1946, and we did not have any baseline established on any other kind of foundation than this one, so that this was an attempt, of course, to work with data and information that could be attained, admittedly, in rough form.

But with the tremendous variations that we found in the tests which we think are roughly comparable, I think we would agree that there are some questions about the precise comparability of the two forms of the test. We tried to check that, of course, with item analyses which were not reported in this paper, detailed item analyses on the basis of the 80 items that were the same, or approximately the same in the test.

The only other comment that I need to make here is once again to emphasize the point that was made by the discussant at the end of the paper. Although this is a stage in empirical research in the field of personality development that probably is somewhat primitive, we are now developing new methods and new techniques. Those new methods and new techniques were applied now, as of 1955.

It is hoped that somebody ten years from now will use this new baseline, established by these new techniques in 1955, to come out with a more definitive set of data on personality change during the next decade in the lives of these young people.

COUNTER DISCUSSION

A. R. MANGUS and E. Z. DAGER

Although Dr. Gruenberg presented a searching analysis of this paper, he seems to have misunderstood some parts and to have misinterpreted some others. From his description it appears that the *Manual for the California Test of Personality** which he obtained was an inappropriate or obsolete form, since the appropriate one for the tests used in this study does explain standardization procedures and does list standard scores for given percentiles, although it makes no claim for comparability.

In the study reported here standard scores are used to provide test score equivalents and to provide a basis for comparison between tests. They were not intended to be used as standard deviations, as the discussant assumed, and were *not* used that way. As to comparability, the item analysis of the 80 items which were identical or nearly so on both tests was evidence enough to justify the assumption that the two tests were roughly comparable. Moreover, all forms of the test are age-graded and show high reliability, and clinical evidence cited in the appropriate *manuals* indicates some degree of validity as the measurement of mental health. All this notwithstanding, the tests were used to ascertain the personality adjustment of the individual, *not as a final criterion,* but as a takeoff point for further research, which research, in fact, tended to corroborate the initial discrepancies between scores in the two time periods.

Criticisms six and seven concern so-called pseudopositive and pseudonegative findings which Dr. Gruenberg feels should not be stated. Granted, further analyses of the data can and should be made, most research workers must work within the limits of time, money, and circumstances. Nevertheless, as long as procedures are clearly stated, it is not only warranted, but imperative that all findings of any significance be reported. This has been done.

Dr. Gruenberg's last comments, taken purely from a statistical point of view, as they were, would stand unchallenged if he had not ignored the total context in which the study was made. His last criticisms do not take away from the basic conclusions of the study primarily because he made no reference to either the theoretical base for the study or the qualitative data that were used to augment the statistical data. It is at this precise point wherein the value of this research lies. It goes beyond the straight epidemiological researches in the field of mental health and attempts to maintain an integral cohesiveness between both quantitative and qualitative data together with theory.

* *Manual: California Test of Personality.* All Levels Kindergarten to Adult. Forms AA and BB. Published by California Test Bureau, 5916 Hollywood Blvd., Los Angeles 28, California.

Relation of Schizophrenia to the Social Structure of a Small City

JOHN A. CLAUSEN AND MELVIN L. KOHN

Laboratory of Socio-environmental Studies,
National Institute of Mental Health, Bethesda, Maryland

Despite the cumulative frequency of schizophrenia in mental hospital populations, its incidence in the general population is relatively low. This is undoubtedly one of the reasons why studies of the distribution of schizophrenia have most often been done within large populations—states or large cities. From an impressive number and variety of sources has come evidence that the distribution of schizophrenia in these populations is not random, but is associated with low socio-economic status and a variety of other social correlates (1–4). For example, the ecological research of Faris and Dunham (1) in Chicago during the 1930's demonstrated that lower status areas of the city sent to mental hospitals, where they were diagnosed as schizophrenic, much higher proportions of their residents than did middle and upper status areas. The more recent work by Redlich and Hollingshead (4) in New Haven has shown very great differences in the prevalence of treated schizophrenia among social classes delineated on the basis of area of residence, occupation, and educational level.

The present report is an analysis of the distribution of schizophrenia, as indexed by hospitalization, in Hagerstown, Maryland, a far smaller city than those previously studied (approximately 36,000 population.)[1] Hagerstown is an industrial and trading center located at the junction of three major railroads, a major east-west highway and a less important north-south highway, in northwestern Maryland. It has a large aircraft plant and several smaller factories. It is an old and settled community, though the war years brought an influx of workers to the aircraft plant. On the whole, however, the population has been relatively stable in recent decades, with an average annual increase slightly under 1% per year since 1920. The majority of in-migrants during the war years were from nearby counties of Pennsylvania and West Virginia and did not represent a different cultural group from the old inhabitants. The population is remarkably homogeneous—preponderantly white, Protestant, and native-born.

For our analysis of the distribution of schizophrenia in this city, we secured basic background data for all persons from Hagerstown and the surrounding Washington County hospitalized as first admissions at any public or private mental hospital within the state of Maryland in the years 1940 through 1952.[2] The designation of patients in our sample was greatly facilitated by the fact that the state of Maryland maintains a central file on all

[1] Our primary intent in the Hagerstown research was to compare the social experiences of schizophrenics with those of normal persons from the same social background in order to test hypotheses on the possible role of social isolation and of parent-child interaction in the development of schizophrenia. This part of the research has been reported in "Social Isolation and Schizophrenia," *American Sociological Review, 20,* 265–73 (1955), and "Parental Authority Behavior and Schizophrenia," *American Journal of Orthopsychiatry, 26,* 297–313 (1956).

In addition, we hoped not only to characterize the distribution of schizophrenia among strata of the local population but also to interpret it through analysis of the residential and occupational histories of the schizophrenic patients who came from this community.

[2] Throughout this discussion we shall be dealing with rates of illness *as indexed by hospitalization,* and *not* with the "true" incidence of disease. We have discussed the problems of interpreting ecological data based on hospitalization rates in "The Ecological Approach in Social Psychiatry," *American Journal of Sociology, 60,* 140–51 (1954).

hospitalizations for mental illness within the state. For the county as a whole, we secured data on 550 first admissions for psychotic disorders and for acute and chronic brain disorders. Detailed data from hospital records were secured only for the group conventionally referred to as the "functional psychoses" and designated in the present American Psychiatric Association nomenclature as "psychotic disorders," that is, schizophrenia, manic depressive psychoses, involutional psychoses and paranoia. Here our population amounted to 222 cases for the whole county, of which 112 were contributed by the population within the city

TABLE I

Total Cases and Average Annual Rates (Per 100,000 Population Aged 15–65) of First Hospitalization for Specified Psychoses, Washington County, Maryland, 1940–52

	County Total		Hagerstown City		Remainder of County	
	No.	Rate	No.	Rate	No.	Rate
Schizophrenia	128	19.5	62	19.4	66	19.5
Involutional psychosis	57	8.7	31	9.7	26	7.7
Manic-depressive psychosis	33	5.0	17	5.3	16	4.7
Paranoia	4	0.6	2	0.6	2	0.6
Total	222	33.8	112	35.0	110	32.5
Population base	50,596		24,590		26,006	

limits of Hagerstown (Table I). Differences in rates of hospitalization by type of disorder between the city population and the population of the remainder of the county are minimal. The rate of hospitalization for schizophrenia (19.4 per 100,000 population aged 15–64) is, however, lower than that found for Chicago by Faris and Dunham, 34.6 per 100,000 adult population (1, p. 46), but about the same as the rate found for Providence, Rhode Island, based on 1930 population of 253,000 (1, p. 147). The Hagerstown rate is thus a bit above the rate of 16 per 100,000

reported by Belknap and Jaco for Austin, Texas, based on 1949
population of 129,500 (5).

Ecological and Occupational Rates

To analyze the distribution of hospitalizations for schizophrenia in the Hagerstown population, we obtained the addresses
of all schizophrenic patients at the time of first hospitalization and
verified these by a thorough search of hospital case records, commitment records, and city directories. These were then plotted
on a map of the city. In order to secure relatively stable rates of
so infrequently occurring a phenomenon as schizophrenia, it was
necessary to base rates on rather large population segments; consequently, we had to combine the 50-odd Census enumeration
districts into a small number of aggregate areas. This we did on
the basis of an index of socio-economic status which combines the
average value of owner-occupied homes in the district with the
average rent paid for rented homes, the relative importance of
the two being determined by the proportion of homes owner-occupied. Districts were grouped into five broad strata, and the
average annual rate of first admissions for schizophrenia during
the period 1940–52 computed for each of these strata. The
resulting distribution of rates does not differ significantly from a
chance distribution; nor is there any tendency for the lower
socio-economic strata to manifest higher rates than do the middle and upper strata (Table II).[3]

These strata do not represent contiguous geographical areas.
Nevertheless, modifications in the method of grouping districts,
in order to take contiguity of districts and patterns of land use
into consideration, still did not yield significant differences in

[3] The 5% level has been used as the criterion of statistical significance
throughout this paper. In general, the chi square test has been used.
When evaluating the significance of differences between patient and
control groups, we have used the method suggested by McNemar for
comparisons between samples whose means are intercorrelated. See
Quinn McNemar, *Psychological Statistics,* John Wiley and Sons, New
York, 1949, pp. 71–82.

TABLE II

Average Annual Rates of First Hospital Admission for Schizophrenia by Area of Residence (Hagerstown to All Mental Hospitals in Maryland, 1940–52)

Area	Score on Rent-Value Index[a]	Population Aged 15–64	Number of Cases, 1940–52[b]	Average Annual Rate, 1940–52, per 100,000 Population Aged 15–64
I	0.50—0.69	5259	13	19.0
II	0.70—0.89	6429	13	15.6
III	0.90—1.09	5792	16	21.2
IV	1.10—1.29	3624	8	17.0
V	1.30+	3423	9	20.2

[a] A score of 1.0 is the median value for the city of Hagerstown.
[b] Excluding three ambiguous cases.

area rates. Nor did the regrouping of districts according to other possible indices of socio-economic status or computing separate series of rates for the earlier and later halves of the time period produce significant differences in area rates.

This is, of course, markedly divergent from the findings of ecological studies in larger cities. It is not, however, by any means as solid a finding as the results reported for larger cities. There is, for example, a much greater problem of delineating homogeneous areas in a small city. The "natural areas" of a small city are often infinitesimal—a few apartment houses wedged between a commercial area and a railroad, a thin line of brick homes trailing out along a "pike," a slum back of the city's residential street with the greatest prestige. Even the enumeration districts, the smallest for which population data are available, are far from homogeneous. Combinations of districts, using only an index of cost of housing, are necessarily even more heterogeneous.

In addition, rates for so small a city are subject to considerable fluctuation for a number of reasons unrelated to the core of the problem. To illustrate: in 1949 a very small (30-bed) private mental hospital, run under religious auspices, opened near

Hagerstown. The average annual number of Washington County patients who were hospitalized in any mental hospital with a diagnosis in the "functional" category increased from 14 to 25 with the opening of these new facilities (Table III). Before 1949,

TABLE III

Average Annual Number of First Admissions to Mental Hospitals from Washington County before and after the Opening of a New Private Hospital in 1949

(Diagnoses "Functional Psychoses")

	1940–48	1949–52
Public hospitals	10	5
New private hospital	—	17
Other private hospitals	4	3
Total	14	25

two-thirds of the Hagerstown patients went to public hospitals; after 1949, two-thirds went to the new hospital. Prior to 1949, only relatively well-to-do families sent members who were mentally ill to a private hospital. From 1949 on, many families who probably would previously have sent an ill member to the State Hospital, or kept him home, now managed to send him to the local private hospital which had modest rates.

Along with the change in the pattern of hospitalization went a change in the diagnostic labels applied to those individuals hospitalized. Relatively fewer were labeled schizophrenic; relatively more were labeled manic depressive or involutional.[4] The effect of such a small addition to available treatment facilities would be relatively minor if we were dealing with large numbers of cases. But when one is dealing with a small community and

[4] Moreover, even for patients diagnosed as schizophrenic, the average duration of initial hospitalization was much shorter for those going to the private hospital than for those hospitalized in the public mental hospital which serves Hagerstown—despite the evidence that a few years earlier these patients would have gone to the State Hospital.

few cases, even minor changes threaten the stability of rates and change their meaning.

We have also examined consistency of diagnosis for all patients admitted to Maryland hospitals on more than one occasion. Of course, patients do change, and changed diagnoses would in those instances reflect changes in the patient's behavior. However, if we compare the experiences of patients who return to the *same* hospital to those of patients who enter *another* hospital, we do get a rough estimate of consistency. There should be no more change in diagnosis on subsequent admissions to different hospitals than to the same hospital *if* diagnosis were consistent from hospital to hospital. This, however, is not the case (Table IV). We find considerably less consistency on admission to another hospital than on readmission to the same hospital.[5]

In view of the evidence from many sources that schizophrenia, manic-depressive psychoses and organic psychoses are very differently related to social structure, such shifts in diagnosis cause severe difficulties for epidemiological studies though they may be less critical when one is comparing experiences of patients and controls.

Furthermore, the population of a city the size of Hagerstown produces so few cases of schizophrenia per year that only very considerable differences in rates of hospitalization would be statistically significant. Given areas of the same population as the five that we have delineated, it would be necessary for rates to vary by more than a range of 15 to 35 cases per 100,000 population in order for the distribution of rates to differ significantly from chance expectations. The distribution of rates that we actually did find for Hagerstown would occasionally occur even if there were in fact substantial differences in incidence of schizophrenia in the different areas of the city.

[5] Further analysis shows that there is greater consistency in rediagnosis of females than of males, of older persons than of younger, of persons whose first admission was to a public hospital than of persons whose first admission was to a private hospital, and of persons diagnosed schizophrenic on first admission than of persons diagnosed manic-depressive.

TABLE IV

Consistency of Diagnostic Labeling among Patients with Two or More
Hospital Admissions

(Patients hospitalized from Washington County, Md., 1940–52, with
diagnosis in "functional psychoses" group)

	Patients Who Returned to Same Hospital, %	Patients Who Entered Different Hospitals, %
Diagnosis the same on all admissions	58	17
Diagnosis within same major syndrome (e.g., schizophrenia) on all admissions	19	11
Diagnoses all within the "functional psychoses" group	8	22
Diagnoses sometimes in "functional psychoses" group, sometimes not	15	50
Total	100	100
Number of cases	*26*	*18*

Nevertheless, the lack of any apparent *trend* in rates suggests
that *substantial* differences do *not* indeed exist. By contrast, our
much smaller sample of manic depressive patients does show a
departure from random distribution just significant at the 5%
level: the rate in areas four and five is more than three times that
in areas one and two.

This evidence of nonassociation between rates of schizophrenia
and socio-economic status is reinforced by our discovery that
rates of schizophrenia do not vary significantly by *occupational
group* either: the average annual rate per 100,000 professional,
technical, and managerial persons is 21.3; for operatives, service
workers, and laborers 21.7. Here, too, the small number of cases
necessitates cautious interpretation. But at least the occupational
rates are not obscured by the technical difficulties that make
ecological analysis so complicated in a city of this size. We

cannot help but be impressed by the lack of even a trend toward higher rates in the lower-status occupations. Moreover, the lack of differences would be most unlikely if the occupational differentials found to exist in larger cities were true of this population. To explain: we computed the number of cases of schizophrenia that would have been expected in each major occupational group in Hagerstown if the rates obtained by Clark for occupational groups in Chicago had prevailed. The actual distribution we found would occur less than once in a thousand times if the Chicago rates had been applicable.

Social Mobility

There remains the possibility that our results are an artifact of instability in the social status of the Hagerstown patients. The rates of hospitalization are based, after all, on the social status of the patients *at time of* hospitalization; they would be appreciably different if the patients had been particularly mobile (either upwardly or downwardly) in the years preceding hospitalization.

Our data on social mobility were secured by direct interview of the patients (or close relatives) and a group of control subjects from the same social backgrounds. Each patient was matched with a normal control on the basis of age, sex, and occupation (or father's occupation) as of a period well before the onset of illness—on the average, 16 years before hospitalization. In addition to individual pairing on these characteristics, overall frequencies were balanced with respect to family composition and area of residence.

Both patients and controls were asked, in the course of structured interviews, for complete occupational and residential histories. These data were checked against past city directories; consistency was almost uniformly high.

There is abundant evidence that Hagerstown schizophrenics have changed their places of residence and their jobs far more frequently than have normal persons of comparable background.

Forty-two per cent of the schizophrenics have had histories of intermittent employment or a succession of short jobs, as compared to only 8% of the normal controls. At least 55% of the schizophrenics have changed their place of residence more frequently than have their paired controls, while no more than 32% of the controls have moved more frequently than have the patients with whom they were paired.[6]

But the frequent occupational shifts did not entail changes in occupational status: *none* of the schizophrenics moved consistently downward in occupational status from the time of first steady employment until hospitalization, 8% fluctuated in occupational level, and only 16% moved upward. This record is approximately equal to that of the normal controls (Table V).[7]

Nor did the schizophrenics move to different status neighborhoods in the period preceding hospitalization: 80% lived in the same status neighborhood at the time of hospitalization as five years earlier; 12% had moved to lower status neighborhoods, while 8% had moved to higher. This pattern does not differ appreciably from that of the controls, 85% of whom lived in the same status neighborhood, 6% had moved to lower, and 9% to higher. Comparisons as of ten, fifteen, and twenty years

[6] This comparison understates the degree to which schizophrenics differ from their paired controls, for we treat every instance where an originally selected control moved from the Hagerstown area prior to the patient's hospitalization *as if* that control were more mobile than the patient.

It should be added that though the schizophrenics showed considerably greater residence-to-residence and city-to-city mobility than did the controls for the entire period from birth to hospitalization, they were not significantly more mobile *during childhood and adolescence* than were the controls. For this reason it does not appear likely that residential mobility has been a significant factor in the development of illness.

[7] This comparison considers the patient's occupational history to date of first hospitalization, and his control's history to that same date. In the case of married women who did not work after marriage, the evaluation is based on their occupational history to date of marriage, *provided* they worked more than six months.

Separate comparisons of male and female respondents yield findings similar to the above.

TABLE V

Occupational Mobility of Schizophrenics and Controls[a]

	Schizophrenics, %	Paired Controls, %
Never employed, or total work history of less than 6 months	18	21
All jobs on same occupational level	64	59
Consistent downward mobility	—	2
Consistent upward mobility	8	16
Fluctuations in occupational level	8	2
Inadequate data	2	—
Total	100	100
Number of cases	*62*	*62*

[a] Occupational levels are defined as the occupational classes used by the Bureau of the Census in the 1950 decennial census.

prior to hospitalization yield the same conclusion: the residential mobility of the schizophrenics has not been different from that of normal persons of similar background.

Even when we compare the socio-economic status of each respondent to that of his father, we do not find significant differences between the schizophrenics and their paired controls (Table VI). The 44 younger schizophrenics had been paired with

TABLE VI

"Intergenerational Mobility": A Comparison of Respondents' Occupational Statuses to Those of Their Parents

	Schizophrenics, %	Paired Controls, %
Occupational status higher than parents'	34	30
Occupational status equal to that of parents'	43	52
Occupational status lower than parents'	23	18
Total	100	100
Number of cases	*44*	*44*

their controls on the basis of their *fathers'* occupations. Thus the "intergenerational mobility" of these normal controls gives us a basis for estimating what degree of upward or downward mobility from the status of their fathers might normally be expected of persons of their particular socio-economic background. By comparison to this standard, the proportion of schizophrenics who fell from their fathers' occupational status, as well as the proportion who rose, do not differ significantly from normal expectations.[8]

Our conclusion must be, then, that there is no evidence of unusual upward or downward social mobility in the occupational and residential histories of these schizophrenic patients.

Interpretation

Let us summarize the data briefly.

1. There is no apparent relationship between the socio-economic levels of areas of the city and the rates of hospitalization for schizophrenia from these areas. Patients hospitalized for manic-depressive psychoses, on the other hand, tend to come disproportionately from higher status neighborhoods.

2. Rates of hospitalization for schizophrenia by major occupational groups in Hagerstown do not differ significantly from a chance distribution. On the other hand, they differ significantly from the distribution obtained by Clark in his study of occupational variations in rates of schizophrenia in Chicago.

3. There is no evidence of upward or downward social mobility, during the period preceding initial hospitalization, among patients hospitalized for schizophrenia from Hagerstown.

We cannot offer an unequivocal interpretation of these findings, for the data are themselves inconclusive in a number of respects. Several alternative interpretations of the Hagerstown data have some plausibility.

----

[8] In this comparison, the occupational status of married women has been based on their husbands' occupations.

1. There may be a tendency toward concentration of schizophrenics in the lower status segments of the population which is obscured because of (*a*) chance fluctuations in the small number of cases available and (*b*) the impossibility in a small city of delineating relatively homogeneous areas which are distinctly different in social conditions. The lack of any apparent relationship with occupation and the fact that the distribution of manic-depressive patients (though based on a far smaller number of cases) does show a significant relationship with socio-economic status lead us to feel that this interpretation is not sufficient.

2. There may be an appreciable association between socioeconomic status and the incidence of schizophrenia (as evidenced by rates of hospitalization) that has been obscured by out-migration of lower status schizophrenics to larger cities. Such out-migration would tend to increase rates of schizophrenia at lower class levels in those larger cities while lowering the rates in Hagerstown. Our data, unfortunately, do not bear directly on this possibility.

3. A third alternative is that high correlations between area of residence and rates of schizophrenia noted in larger cities may be largely a resultant of the "drift" of incipient schizophrenics into deteriorated areas where the unsuccessful tend to collect. The lack of such "collecting areas" in Hagerstown and the absence of downward drift there would account for the lack of ecological differentials. We feel that there may be a modicum of such effect, but both our own data and the studies of others dispute the assumption of downward drift (6).

4. It may be that the use of hospitalization as an index has obscured a real correlation between incidence and socio-economic status (or, conversely, that use of this index has produced spurious correlations in studies of larger cities). Such would be the case if lower status schizophrenics were less likely than higher status schizophrenics to be hospitalized in Hagerstown, or if the reverse were true in larger cities. Research on this point is badly needed. It is certain that some schizophrenics manage to get

along in sheltered settings for years or even decades. The question is: is there a difference between Hagerstown and larger cities in the probability that a lower status person who manifests schizophrenic symptoms will be hospitalized? We do not have the data to answer, but it is relevant that Hagerstown does have relatively good access to both public and private mental hospitals.

5. A final alternative is that there may in fact be a less direct relationship between socio-economic status, as indexed by area of residence and occupation, and rates of schizophrenia in cities the size of Hagerstown than in larger urban centers. While the other alternatives cannot be ruled out, we should like to explore this one in some detail.

We suggest that there may be a direct relationship between the size of the city and the *degree* to which rates of schizophrenia correlate with such indices of socio-economic status as area of residence and occupational level. A metropolis like Chicago produces strikingly high correlations. Smaller cities, such as Peoria, Kansas City, Milwaukee, and Omaha produce far lower correlations. The populations of these cities in 1930 were 105,-000; 400,000; 578,000; and 214,000 respectively (2). Schroeder in his study of the distribution of mental illness in Peoria, Illinois, found only a slight (nonsignificant) tendency for schizophrenia to correlate with residential area. He felt that his figures "should not be taken as evidence that there is not the . . . tendency for schizophrenia to concentrate, since there were only 193 cases available for study" (2, p. 46). Granting the difficulty of delineating homogeneous areas, we wonder at the lack of significant patterning with this number of cases. Note, too, that Frumkin's data for the state of Ohio (combining rural and urban admissions) show far less striking differences between *occupational groups* than Clark found for Chicago (7).

Finally, a city as small as Hagerstown produces no discernible correlation at all. It seems likely, then, that the social phenomena indexed by occupation and area of residence in

Hagerstown may be quite different from those indexed by the same items in a larger city. To be sure, in any size community in the United States, area of residence and occupation tend to be among our primary indices of social status. But perhaps more than this is involved.

Our participant-observation experiences in Hagerstown, though not very systematic, do suggest respects in which Hagerstown may differ from larger cities. It appears that the class structure of Hagerstown is not as highly differentiated as that of larger cities; in particular, there appears to be a relative absence of extremes, and social interaction appears to be less dependent on class position than in larger cities.

Hagerstown has its elite neighborhoods and its run-down neighborhoods, as has any older city. But with one or two exceptions these are rather small neighborhoods, which constitute parts of enumeration districts, or overlap several enumeration districts. This means that the different areas of the city do not represent a wide range of distinctly different living conditions. There are slum areas, but they are not large, nor are they as economically depressed as the skid rows of larger cities. Their children attend the same public schools as do the children from a fair variety of other residential settings.

Occupational status may likewise have a rather different meaning for social interaction in a community the size of Hagerstown than in a larger city. Unquestionably, status considerations are fully as important in social interaction here as elsewhere. But our observations lead us to believe that several non-job factors influence social interaction to a greater extent here than in the metropolis. These include the persistence of school associations into adult life and length of residence (and of one's family's residence) in the community. The very stability of Hagerstown's population implies, too, that members of one's extended family are likely to be rather close at hand; and such associations are also likely to cut across class lines. In addition, Hagerstown seems to have an unusual number of tightly bound religious groups (including the Mennonite, the Brethren, and a score of small fundamentalist churches); membership in any of these may imply as much about an individual's social participation as does his occupational status. Again, it would appear that we do not have the extremes that are found in larger cities—the professionals and proprietors are smaller operators, the blue collar workers are on the whole more integrated into neighborhood and community.

This interpretation is frankly conjectural. It was not our primary aim in this research to study local social structure. We naively assumed that we would find the usual correlations and we wished to examine these in the context of individual life histories of patients and controls. Perhaps at some later date we shall return to this community and secure the data needed to test the hypothetical interpretation offered above. Whether we do so or not, however, we feel that our negative findings pose a question to which much more attention might fruitfully be addressed. In the constellation of attitudes, values, behaviors, and relationships that are generally indexed by socio-economic status—by occupation, education, area of residence—what are the factors that are crucially related to the development of schizophrenia?

Conclusion

In conclusion, we would like to urge that epidemiological research in the smaller community not be neglected simply because it poses methodological difficulties. Highly intensive studies of the small community may help to delineate the psychologically most relevant aspects of social structure. But even crude correlational studies may have some value if a number of communities are studied, especially if several instances *each* of a variety of community types are included. If this is done, one can pool data on occupational groups and overcome the problem of few cases. More intensive work in such communities can then be focused upon the problematic aspects of observed differences in their rates of schizophrenia.

In any event, we hope that future investigators will be less inclined than we were to assume that we would find the same patterns that prevailed in larger cities.

Acknowledgment

The authors are indebted to the Maryland State Department of Mental Hygiene, and its Commissioner, Dr. Clifton Perkins, for making available its patient-files, granting access to patients at state hospitals, and aiding our research with a grant-in-aid; to the hospitals of the state of Maryland, especially Springfield State Hospital and Brooklane Farm Hospital for contributing their case records, and enabling us to interview their patients and former patients; to the physicians of Washington County for aid in arranging interviews and in providing valuable data; and to the Public Health Methods Division of the United States Public Health Service (especially Dr. Philip Lawrence, Chief of the Familial Studies Unit in Hagerstown) for granting access to their files of Morbidity Studies (basic to our control-group selection) and for valuable suggestions and aid in the field work.

REFERENCES

1. Faris, Robert E. L., and H. Warren Dunham. *Mental Disorders in Urban Areas*. University of Chicago Press, Chicago, Ill., 1939.
2. Schroeder, Clarence W. Mental disorders in cities. *Am. J. Sociol., 48,* 40–48 (1942).
3. Clark, Robert E. Psychoses, income, and occupational prestige. *Am. J. Sociol., 54,* 433–40 (1949).
4. Hollingshead, August B., and Frederick C. Redlich. Social stratification and psychiatric disorders. *Am. Sociol. Rev., 18,* 163–69 (1953).
5. Belknap, Ivan, and E. Gartley Jaco. The epidemiology of mental disorders in a political-type city. (Based on 1949 population of 129,500.) In *Interrelations between the Social Environment and Psychiatric Disorders*. Milbank Memorial Fund, New York, 1953. Page 237.

6. Hollingshead, August B., and Frederick C. Redlich. Social stratification and schizophrenia. *Am. Sociol. Rev., 19,* 302–306 (1954).
7. Frumkin, Robert M. Occupation and major mental disorders. In *Mental Health and Mental Disorder,* edited by Arnold Rose. W. W. Norton, New York, 1955.

DISCUSSION

DR. HERBERT G. BIRCH: It seems to me that in Dr. Clausen's paper we have an excellent example of attempting to apply existing methodologies to a most important and extremely complex problem. Whenever that happens, I am afraid that we must ask: (1) Is the question that is asked one which is capable of being answered by the research which is projected or carried out? (2) To what degree can we proceed to attempt to answer a question with methods that are not adequate for the problem?

I would say that in Dr. Clausen's research we find certain shifts of conception that I would like to mark at this moment. In the opening paragraphs of the paper, we have a discussion of, first, hospital admission rates of schizophrenics in a given community. As we proceed in the paper, a discussion appears to develop which bases itself upon the notion that we are dealing with the discussion of frequency of schizophrenics in this community.

I think that we have two entirely different problems. We certainly may be able to deal from the data with the first admission of schizophrenics in state hospitals, or in the private hospital in the later period, but we are unjustified, I think, in making the assumption that the frequency with which schizophrenia exists in any subpopulation is directly inducible, or is something which may be directly extrapolated from first admission data. I would like to suggest that perhaps some of the differences in presumed frequency of schizophrenia admissions in Chicago and Providence, as compared with Austin, Texas, and with Hagerstown, Maryland, may be the consequence not of a different rate, a difference in the rate with which schizophrenia is distributed in a population, but may be a consequence of quite different factors: (1) the availability of hospital care and (2), the difficulties that stand between a patient and admission to a mental hospital.

For example, in some states (if I recall correctly Maryland may be one of them) a jailing is necessary prior to an admission to a state hospital and commitment procedures on voluntary and other bases are not the same. Consequently, first admissions for schizo-phrenia, particularly in cases of young people who may be in schizo-phrenic panic at a given point, may be quite different in different communities in accordance with the social admission practices in these communities.

A second factor which has to be considered if we are to develop some ideas of comparative incidence of disorders in population, if, once again, we use as a basis hospital admission rates, is the attitude in the population toward hospital admission. (1) To what degree does the community function to retain within it individuals who are behaviorally aberrant? (2) To what degree is admission to a hospital considered to be a disgraceful and completely disruptive event? (3) To what degree is a state hospital viewed as an asylum rather than as a hospital? This attitude of the population is a general problem which I feel influences frequencies with which first admis-sions will occur, or even subsequent readmissions to hospitals.

I have somewhat the feeling in this area of work that I used to have when I was a comparative psychologist and was working al-most entirely with the lower organism, namely, that just as the comparative psychologist fell in love with the white rat and made this white rat the ubiquitous subject of almost all his investigations, people who are working in the epidemiological field, in the epidemiology of mental health and mental disease, have fallen in love with hospital admission rates and have made these rates the basis for most of their investigations.

If we follow the chart of comparative psychological investigation, we find that from 1900 to 1920, as contrasted with the number of animals studied from 1920 to 1940, some 15% of the studies in the earlier period were done on the white rats, and that in the later period, almost 90% of the studies were done on this organism.

Why is it chosen? (1) It is not representative of organisms in general. (2) It has cultures which are not specifically explored. (3) It is an animal that is cheaper and easier to maintain in large popu-lation. It is easy to obtain subjects, and I suspect that it is this last consideration which jointly has created the guinea pig, the white rat, and the first hospital admission rate as the chosen, but not neces-sarily the optimal, devices for investigation in the area of psychology and of physiological functions.

It is clear, I think, as we look at some of the data reported by Dr. Clausen, that the instant a new private hospital was opened in the Hagerstown community, the rate of schizophrenia in the com-munity was altered.

Now, I don't think that the social influence of a new hospital facility is to create a doubling of the incidence of psychosis in any community. I think that rather more individuals who are psychotic may receive hospitalization. If we use the hospitalization data as our primary population data, we inevitably come to conclusions that reflect the level of medical care and not the level of the incidence of the disorder. I suggest that these are two quite different indicators. One is an indicator of the degree to which society has provided adequate facilities for the handling and for the care of sick people. The other is a question concerning the number of sick people we may find exist in a community.

I think that to a certain extent Dr. Clausen's data give us information on the degree to which the society can handle sick people or has provided facilities for their management, rather than data on the incidence of a disorder in a population.

A few other points: If I think of Dr. Zuerling's study, it seems that schizophrenia is not necessarily such an infrequently occurring phenomenon as the hospitalization data would suggest. If I recall a study of his on patients in surgical wards in the Mid-west, the frequency of psychoses and the frequency of schizophrenia within this group of surgical patients was very, very much higher than the 33 per hundred thousand rate reported for Chicago, or the 21.7 reported for Hagerstown by Dr. Clausen.

The rates move at points, at least in this population, at better than 10% in certain instances, and we have to ask the question of which variety of data provides us with information on the frequency of the occurrence of the disorder. It seems that a first hospitalization represents an initial or, rather, a single index which, unless all its weaknesses are explored, can give us an erroneous notion of the frequency of the disorder itself. Furthermore, it is doubtful whether schizophrenic breakdown and hospitalization are identical with schizophrenia, with schizophrenia as a symptom complex or as a disease.

To what degree do we begin to have data upon individuals who are developing to a point which may at some time in their life histories require hospitalization? The existence of tuberculosis does not coincide, and the incidence of tuberculosis is not identical with the data on the number of deaths from tuberculosis. If we consider first hospital admissions in a sense as mortality figures, we would not conclude incidence of disorder as such from the mortality figure, especially when such a figure involves a poor reporting of the disorder itself.

To turn to another point altogether: I am in temperamental

agreement with Dr. Clausen on the lack of specific socio-economic determinants in the frequency of schizophrenia in his first hospitalization data. And I have suspected for some time that when we get distributions of data in the psychosis which are simply linked to such a linear index as socio-economic status, we are getting data that are not immediately interpretable. I don't think that we can conclude from the Chicago data that because there is a higher incidence of schizophrenia in lower economic status sections of the population, or lower socio-economic status sections, that that suggests that we have data which indicate an increased frequency of this disorder with lowered socio-economic status.

I think that in large urban communities lower socio-economic status is a function not merely of the occupation of the individual but is a function of the ethnic group to which this individual belongs, the period of residence in the community as such in a family sense; the degree to which the individual is first, second, third, or fourth generation Chicagoan or American; the national group to which the individual belongs, and the totality of social forms and social interrelations that have been established for the individual in communities.

I think that it is fairly well known as a sociological phenomenon that stability of in-group organization is in part a function of the stability of the group itself, so that an old established group may have patterns of organization, patterns of social interrelations that are not at all present in newly come groups or in groups that derive from multi-national backgrounds and are in nonhomogeneous circumstances.

I think that Dr. Clausen's population, as he described it, exhibits an extremely slow rate of change for an urban community because it probably is a more stable group in a social sense and a relatively homogeneous group in a social cultural sense. In such a group, I think that some of the studies that the people in New York State have been doing in Syracuse may provide more relevant conceptualizations about the variables that are involved than the simple use of socio-economic data as such. There they have found that the characteristics of social integration of the individual, independently of the specific socio-economic class, in many instances is a more important variable in determining frequency of disorders in a segment of the population than the usual rate.

I think that in this area of research we are confronted over and over again with the use of what we could call usual and available indices. To return to that point: We have socio-economic indices in terms of occupation and census tract. We have geographic indices within the terms, again, of census. We have hospitalization rates, which are materials already collected for us by agencies outside of our own control. We have a whole body of data to which it is most tempting to apply our analytical tools. However, it should never be forgotten that these data were not collected for us. They were not collected with the intention that they would be used to determine the distribution of psychological disorders in populations. The variables which they explore, the information which they accumulate, may often be irrelevant in that form to the phenomenon which we wish to consider.

It seems to me that the preliminary character of the investigations of distributions of mental disorders in populations on the basis of such indicators has too often been called tentative; it has too often been called preliminary; it has too often been referred to as exploration. It almost seems as though the method of exploration has become the method of choice in the investigation of some of these problems, that the preliminary method, because of the ease with which it may be utilized, has become the desirable method for investigation.

Dorn, in an extremely interesting paper delivered some years ago, points over and over again to the inadequacies of this type of survey method. He propounds alternate methods, including case finding studies, investigations of whole communities, longitudinal investigations of the development of disorders in selected populations, for all of which we have the tools.

The problem then of the degree to which an investigation of a problem with the tools which we have available can be adequate is the use of some of these more expensive instruments. They provide us with more data.

DR. MORTON KRAMER: I would like to direct a question to Dr. Clausen. In discussing the occupational differences, it seemed to me that males and females were combined. Is there any suggestion as to what happens to the occupational differences by your strata, if females were excluded? I don't know whether they were housewives or employed in other types of occupations. Also, would there be any indication about differences in mobility in the patients, as to whether they were females or males?

Dr. Birch has raised some questions about the inadequacy of hospital data and things that they do not show. That is true. There has been one study, recently published by Bert Kaplan and Robert Reed, which investigated the incidence of nonhospitalized psychoses in the Boston area.

Interestingly enough, this study revealed that the incidence of the nonhospitalized psychosis was greater in the upper socio-economic classes, in the wealthy group, than in the lower classes living in the slum area.

I think there is need for more studies of this type so we can get more information on the incidence of psychosis in the nonhospitalized group.

I cannot help but come back to one of the other comments that Dr. Birch made about the inadequacy of hospital data. I am sure Dr. Clausen will have some comments to make on this, too. Although some of us who are engaged in some types of epidemiological research realize that many of the aspects of these data that we have are very inadequate, I think it would be very helpful to us if the psychiatrists and the psychologists would develop screening techniques to detect in the general population individuals who have schizophrenia.

Dr. Birch did refer to the early data on tuberculosis. I must point out that one of the early case finding techniques in tuberculosis was not dissimilar from one that has been used in mental illness, namely the Framingham demonstration, done around 1917. It came up with a ratio of deaths from tuberculosis to active cases that was used until the 1930's to estimate the total number of cases in a community from its tuberculosis deaths. Unfortunately, we don't have even a good ratio of hospitalized first admissions or first attacks from schizophrenia.

People working in TB did get away from the use of some of these inadequate tools which did yield some very useful results for use over the years in the control of tuberculosis. For example, the tuberculin test was used to detect people who had TB infection. It would be helpful if the psychiatrists could develop a test that could be used to discover who in a community may be a latent schizophrenic or even an active one.

DR. J. DOWNING: I would like to ask about the socio-economic index. In Syracuse we, too, have troubles. We have been wondering whether it is possible to develop a more meaningful one, whether you have any ideas of which paths to take.

DR. P. V. LEMKAU: Do you have any data comparing the number of single person families in Hagerstown, in Chicago, and the other large city studies? One has a suspicion that the lower socio-economic group in Hagerstown may be a family group with what might be fewer individuals pushed out of their families. This might make the difference.

DR. PAUL HOCH: I was much interested in Dr. Clausen's work

because I was always suspicious about the results of the Chicago study, and also about the results of the Yale study. I must say that I was not only suspicious that the studies did not show the true picture, but I was appalled at the lack of clinical sophistication in the conduct of these studies.

One of the projects which probably could be suggested to the Public Health Service would be an epidemiological study of schizophrenics on Park Avenue in New York City—to turn from the low economic to the high economic. Park Avenue has not only a large concentration of people with a lot of money but also has the largest concentration of psychiatrists of this country. What do you think the psychiatrists do there? These psychiatrists are taking care of quite a number of schizophrenia patients in this group, who may or may not be diagnosed schizophrenias.

What you already found in Hagerstown, which you can find in any community, including any of the private institutions, is that the private institution, if it can, will label a patient differently from schizophrenia.

Another point that you brought out of interest to us is the drop in manic-depressive psychoses in the institutions, not because for some the diagnosis was different but because, where there are those who can afford it, they like to have those people treated outside. Now depressions and manic episodes are treated on the outside and, of course, in a low economic situation, the patient is admitted to the state hospital.

Finally, I would like very much to endorse what Dr. Birch said; that is, that hospitalization is no true index of the number of schizophrenics in the community. The number of schizophrenics in the community is very large and we have a very large untapped reservoir. If you would build facilities, either clinics or hospitals, to receive them, we very easily would be increasing the rate of hospitalization. This is especially true in underprivileged countries, which are now beginning to put in psychiatric facilities. Whereas they formerly claimed that they had no psychotic patients, their culture being such that it didn't produce schizophrenia, as soon as a hospital is built it is filled, and immediately they are made to build another hospital.

We are full of fallacies here, based on starvations and on some prejudicial ideas. I believe that some such research as Dr. Clausen and many others are carrying out will probably lead to a better understanding.

One more remark, this on the so-called first admission to hospitals. Since the diagnosis of schizophrenia only becomes official when the person is admitted to a hospital; when somebody signs the commitment, the person then becomes schizophrenic.

I am sure that a great deal of attention should be paid to an epidemiological investigation of schizophrenic individuals in the communities. I think, however, that we should try to establish a diagnosis of schizophrenia which does not depend on an administrative or legal stamp.

Dr. J. A. Clausen: First, let me say that I quite agree with Dr. Birch as to the inadequacy of hospitalization rates as expressions of the true incidence of schizophrenia. In our paper, Dr. Kohn and I speak of "the distribution of schizophrenia *as indexed by hospitalization.*" We have attempted to analyze not only the relationships between this index and social status but also the variation in the index associated with a change in available treatment services. One reason for selecting a control group of normal subjects from backgrounds comparable to those of the schizophrenics was to afford a more valid basis for examining data on current social status and on mobility than would be afforded by gross rates relative to the general population. The critical question from the standpoint of our investigation is not whether we have located all schizophrenics in the community but whether our group of hospitalized cases is markedly biased as to social status. Acknowledging that we cannot give an unequivocal answer to this question, I would nevertheless argue that it is worth while to learn as much as possible about those schizophrenics who are regarded by their families and associates as sick enough to require hospitalization.

I am in full agreement with Dr. Birch that we need more data on how patients come to the hospital. In another study, conducted with patients hospitalized in St. Elizabeths Hospital in Washington, we have been attempting to get such data. We took patients soon after they turned up in the hospital, and we attempted to find out how they got there—through what steps of recognition in the family or on the job they were channeled toward various treatment services or other community resources before arriving at the hospital. A preliminary report of this research is contained in our paper "Paths to the Mental Hospital" published in the *Journal of Social Issues* in 1955. Such data need to be obtained at a much earlier point than when the patient comes to the hospital so that one can ascertain alternatives to hospitalization.

I am not sure what Dr. Birch regards as the ax that will fell the prize timbers for the house of epidemiological knowledge. The more I have seen of attempts to assess the true incidence of specific mental diseases, the more skeptical I have become of the adequacy of our concepts and methods. If the diagnosis of schizophrenia is difficult to establish when the patient is under study in a hospital, how much more difficult is it by any combination of psychiatric examination and psychological tests of a cross section of a community! The studies that have attempted to assess true incidence or prevalence in recent years have to a large extent relied not only upon the present condition of the patient but also on reports of past episodes of behavior, and the indices used are subject to many of the same questions of selective bias, I think, that hospitalization itself is. When one comes up with an index of lifetime prevalence, for example, saying that sometime during this individual's life he had an episode that may now be recorded as schizophrenia, we are treading on awfully dangerous ground. The factors that lead to perception and reporting of such episodes are just as significant and perhaps even more difficult to get at than are those that influence the likelihood of one's being hospitalized.

To turn to Dr. Downing's question about socio-economic indexes, there is little that I can say briefly. I believe that an index combining area of residence, occupation, and years of schooling is probably the most widely used for social status. This is not always the same as socio-*economic* status, particularly with what has happened with wages of blue collar workers in recent years. Perhaps we sociologists are not entirely realistic in cross-community applications of some of our indices.

To answer Dr. Kramer's question on occupational differences, there was no tendency for differences among levels to emerge when we confined attention to males exclusively. In the case of females, most had been employed at one time, although at the time of the study I think the majority were housewives. Whether we used the husband's occupation or the wife's occupation when she was employed, again we found no tendency toward associations with occupational status.

I certainly have the same impression that Dr. Lemkau has, that single persons are relatively more rare in Hagerstown than in larger cities. It is not a good collecting place for the detached individual, but here, as I mentioned, we can only conjecture. Our data do not give us an adequate baseline for the total population.

As to Dr. Hoch's suggestion that the Public Health Service ought to study schizophrenia on Park Avenue, I would suggest that somebody other than the Public Health Service had better do it.

Complications of Pregnancy among Prenatal Patients Reporting Previous Nervous Illness[1]

DOROTHY G. WIEHL, KATHARINE BERRY,
Milbank Memorial Fund, New York

AND WINSLOW T. TOMPKINS
Beckley Memorial Hospital, Beckley, West Virginia

Although pregnancy is a normal physiological process, it is often accompanied by much anxiety. The relation between this anxiety and emotional stress and the occurrence of various complications has been receiving considerable attention in recent years from both obstetricians and psychiatrists. On the assumption that women who had a history of nervous breakdown or nervous illness would have an increased likelihood of emotional disorders during pregnancy, a study of the course and outcome of pregnancies among such a group seemed to be a possible approach to obtaining some evidence on the interrelation between the occurrence of complications and emotional factors.

Data for the study were available from records collected for 1,570 prenatal patients who had been asked early in the prenatal period if they had ever had a nervous breakdown. These prenatal patients were given clinic care and delivered on ward service at the Philadelphia Lying-In Hospital between 1947 and 1953. Some women had more than one pregnancy during these years and the population comprises 1,411 women. This popula-

[1] Maternal and Newborn Nutrition Studies at Philadelphia Lying-In Hospital. Maternal Studies V. Studies I–IV in Proceedings of the 1954 Annual Conference of the Milbank Memorial Fund, 1955.

tion was the subject of an experimental investigation of the relation of nutrition to pregnancy and has been described in previous reports (1). The characteristics of the population relevant to this report may be summarized briefly.

The 1,570 prenatal patients were supervised in special prenatal clinics and delivered as routine ward patients. They included all married women who registered at the hospital and made their first prenatal visit before the 17th week of gestation, with the exception of patients with chronic heart or kidney disease, or essential hypertension or syphilis. Patients with hyperemesis gravidarum also are excluded. In addition, patients whose pregnancies terminated at less than 28 weeks of gestation and any who had multiple births have not been included. Twin pregnancies have greater than average risk of complications, and records for abortion cases frequently were incomplete.

Seventy four per cent of the patients were white and 26% Negro. The white population was predominantly Italian, about two-thirds of all white women being of Italian stock.

Information concerning history of previous nervous breakdown was included on a special personal history record which was taken by a clerk in the prenatal clinic independently of the personal history data recorded by the physician examining in the clinic. The clerk asked each patient if she had ever had a nervous breakdown; and, if the patient reported either breakdown or nervous illness, the time of occurrence was to be reported. No other specific information about the nervous illness was asked, but some of the women reported stressful events or special conditions associated with its occurrence. These explanations were recorded. Many of the patients characterized their illness as "not a breakdown," and reported "verge of a breakdown," "very nervous," or just "nervousness," even though under medical care for "nerves."

There was no follow-up questioning of these patients by any professionally trained person to seek further information, and no attempt has been made to classify the nervous illnesses reported or to screen out those that were not primarily nervous disorders.

Sixty-two white women and 19 Negroes gave a history of nervous illness. Their own descriptions of the illnesses or the circumstances of their occurrences are tabulated in Table I. Two women reported shock treatment, 3 gave a history of chorea, 1 reported paralysis for one week, and 1 said she "lost the use of her left side"; all others reported nervous breakdown or

TABLE I

Previous Nervous Illness Reported by Pregnant Women and Associated Events or Conditions, and Medical Care Reported

Type of Illness and Associated Conditions	Number of White Women Reporting		Number of Negro Women Reporting	
	Nervous illness	With M.D. care[a]	Nervous illness	With M.D. care[a]
Total cases	62	48	19	14
Chorea	3	3		
Shock treatment	2	2		
Paralysis (temporary)	1	1	1	1
Nervous breakdown or nervousness	56	42	18	13
No associated condition	31	24	11	7
Condition or event	25	18	7	6
Death[b]	5	3	2	1
Illness in family	2	1		
Marital problem[c]	6	3		
Illness of self				
Postoperative	4	4		
Ulcer, G-I	3	3		
Other	3	2	1	1
After birth of live infant[d]	1	1	4	4
Overwork	1	1		

[a] Three white women and no Negro women specified no medical care.
[b] One white woman reported death of mother and desertion by husband who took the son.
[c] Includes one "broken romance," happy marriage later.
[d] Death of infant and one abortion are included with deaths.

simply nervousness. Eight cases had been hospitalized for treatment for nervousness, but the type of hospital was not specified. Severity and duration of the nervous illness is not known but, as shown in Table I, three-fourths of the women reported some medical care and only three stated they had no medical care. Probably all but these three had had some care.

One-fifth of the white women attributed their nervous illness to a death or illness in the family or to marital problems, and one-sixth of them associated it with some other illness. One-half of the white women did not mention any associated event. Negro women, on the other hand, did not report marital problems or illness, but two gave a death as a contributing event (both were infant deaths), and four reported that the nervous breakdown followed the birth of a child. Since these were spontaneous explanations given to a white interviewer, the emphasis on childbirth and infant death by Negroes may reflect willingness to talk about this problem and avoidance of marital problems. Certainly, reporting of events and circumstances was incomplete, and other information on the records for both white and Negro women suggests associated circumstances; for example, two white women had married at age 13 and had nervous breakdowns within one or two years, and premarital pregnancies, desertion and divorce, and recent infant deaths were reported but not associated by the informant with the nervousness. Obviously, no interpretation of cause and effect is possible. The event may be a precipitating factor, or the nervous illness may have been responsible for the event, as in the case of physical illness and break-up of the marriage.

It is evident, and important to remember, that the nervous illnesses reported by these women are very heterogeneous with respect to type of illness, severity, duration, and probability of complete recovery. The interval of time since the illness occurred also varied greatly; a few were recent and still present, and a few occurred more than ten years ago. These women form a group only in that they had previously experienced illness which had been diagnosed as nervousness or in which nervousness was a dominant symptom.

Frequency of Nervous Illness

The 81 women with a reported history of nervous illness are 5.7% of the total population of 1,411 women. Among white women, the percentage is 5.9 and among Negroes the percentage is 5.2. These, of course, are cumulative percentages for the life history up to the age of reporting, which varied from 15 to 45 years, with a median age of about 25 years. If the rates for history of nervous illness are examined by 5-year age periods, among white women the maximum reported percentage is 7.9 for the age group 25 to 29 years, and after this the rate declines again. Among Negroes, the age-specific rates are erratic because of small numbers, but the same tendency is shown, and at ages 25 to 29 years the percentage is 7.0 (Table II).

TABLE II

Percentage of Women with History of Nervous Illness and Percentage of Prenatal Patients at Specific Ages Who Reported Nervous Illness[a]

| | Reported History of Nervous Illness | | | | | |
| | Per cent of patients | | Number of patients | | Number of patients | |
Age Group	White	Negro	White	Negro	White	Negro
Total women	5.9	5.2	62	19	1,044	367
Total prenatal patients	5.8	5.2	67	21	1,163	407
Under 20 years	2.9	8.3	3	3	103	36
20–24	5.6	2.0	25	3	448	148
25–29	7.9	7.0	28	9	357	128
30–34	4.3	5.8	8	4	188	69
35+	4.5	7.7	3	2	67	26

[a] Nervous illness is counted only if reported at interview for the specific pregnancy. Four white women with illness reported at one pregnancy failed to report previous nervous illness at five later pregnancies, and one Negro did not report at a later pregnancy.

The most probable interpretation of lower percentages at the older ages is that the older women failed to report illnesses occurring a long time ago. This interpretation is confirmed by a tabulation of the interval of time between the reported age at which illness occurred and the patient's age at the time of interview. Of the 11 cases of nervous illness reported by white women aged 30 or older, only three had occurred more than 5 years before the interview, and only one occurred before age 25. It is unlikely that these older women had been nearly free of nervous illness before age 25.

Age-specific incidence rates for 5-year age periods were computed based on the population interviewed at that age or in the next older 5-year age period and on the nervous illnesses reported as occurring within the specific 5-year age period (Table III). The age-specific incidence is highest at age 20 to 24 years among white women (3.1%), decreases slightly at ages 25 to 29, and is only 1.6% at age 30 to 34 years.

From the age-specific rates an expected cumulative percentage for history for nervous illness is shown in Table III. The estimated cumulative percentages up to age 30 are slightly higher than the reported percentages, 8.4 and 7.5 for white women and Negroes, respectively. Over 30 years of age, the reported cumulative percentages are only about one-half the estimated cumulative percentages if these older women had about the same life experience that the younger women report. At ages 30 to 34, the estimated cumulative percentages for history of nervous illness are 10.1 and 9.8 for whites and Negroes respectively, compared with the reported 4.3 and 5.8%. If the white women who reported nervous illness at the time of an earlier pregnancy but did not report the illness at a later pregnancy are included, the known cumulative percentage is 5.3 compared with the estimated 10.1%.

This underreporting of earlier nervous illnesses means that the group of prenatal patients with a history of nervous illness does not include all such patients, especially at the older ages.

TABLE III

Incidence of Nervous Illness Reported for 5-Year Age Groups and
Estimated Cumulative Percentage for Women in Specified Age Group

Age at Time of Interview, Years	Age at Time of Illness, Years	Number of Women[a]		Per Cent with Illness at Specified Age[b]		Cumulated Percentage	
		White	Negro	White	Negro	White	Negro
Under 20 20–24	Under 20 Under 20	544	180	2.76	3.26	2.76	3.26
20–24 25–29	20–24 20–24	740	261	3.11	1.53	5.87	4.79
25–29 30–34	25–29 25–29	510	182	2.55	2.74	8.42	7.53
30–34 35–44	30–34 30–34	243	89	1.65	2.25	10.07	9.78
35–44	35–44	65	25	1.54	4.00	11.61	13.78

[a] Women with more than one pregnancy within the 10-year age period
for age at interview are counted only once.
[b] The average age for the 5-year age specific incidence rates is higher
than the midpoint since the population includes persons in the next higher
age group but is somewhat lower than the upper limit of the age interval.

It also means that the population classified as *without* history of
illness does include some patients who had had illness. However,
the unreported illnesses are mostly those that occurred a long
time previously. Approximately three-fourths of reported illnesses
occurred within 5 years of the current pregnancy. Therefore, this
is a study of pregnancy among women with a fairly recent illness
from nervousness.

Outcome of Previous Pregnancies

Before the outcome of the current pregnancy is discussed, it is
of interest to compare the pregnancy histories of the multigravida
patients reporting nervous illness with those of the total population.

There were 56 patients with nervous illness who had had 124 previous pregnancies, or 2.2 pregnancies per patient. In the total sample, there were 861 multigravida patients with an average of 1.8 previous pregnancies per patient. By using the rates in the total sample for premature births, perinatal deaths and abortions among whites and among Negroes, the expected number of each was computed for the "nervous" patients. As shown in Table IV, among white patients, there was no significant difference between the expected number and the actual number of premature births, abortions, or perinatal deaths (stillbirths plus neonatal deaths). Among the Negroes, those with a history of nervous illness had nearly twice as many premature births[2] as expected but, owing to small numbers, this difference is not statistically significant. Neonatal mortality was significantly higher than expected (P < 0.01), and stillbirths were equal to the expected. Total perinatal mortality, therefore, was higher than expected (5 vs. 2.28); but the excess was of marginal significance (P = 0.05–0.06).

Frequency of Prenatal Complications

As previously mentioned, these prenatal patients attended clinic the first time before the 17th week of gestation; most of them attended not later than the 14th week. Revisits were made at three-week intervals until the last two months, when return visits were at two-week intervals and sometimes weekly. At each visit, the clinic physician recorded observations commonly made for prenatal patients, including nausea and vomiting, edema, blood pressure, weight gain, and a number of subjective symptoms.

Nausea and vomiting is, of course, a frequent complication or complaint early in pregnancy. The incidence of nausea and/or

---

[2] In these tabulations of previous pregnancies, multiple births have been excluded since premature births by weight and perinatal deaths occur at a higher rate among multiple births than among single births.

TABLE IV

Outcome of Previous Pregnancies of Multigravida Patients with History of Nervous Illness Compared with Expected Outcome Estimated from Rates for Total Patients

Outcome of Pregnancy	Previous Pregnancies for All Patients		Women with History of Nervous Illness		Ratio of Reported to Expected
	Number	Per cent of total	Number reported	Expected number	
Total pregnancies	1,534		124		
Premature birth[a]	101	6.58	11	8.16	1.35
Perinatal mortality	59	3.85	8	4.77	1.68
Neonatal death	32	2.09	7	2.59	2.70[b]
Stillbirth	27	1.76	1	2.18	0.46
Abortion	220	14.34	15	17.78	0.84
White patients total pregnancies	1,087		89		
Premature birth	53	4.88	4	4.34	0.92
Perinatal mortality	30	2.76	3	2.46	1.22
Neonatal death	17	1.56	3	1.39	2.16
Stillbirth	13	1.20	0	1.07	
Abortion	135	12.42	10	11.05	0.90
Negro patients total pregnancies	447		35		
Premature birth	48	10.74	7	3.76	1.86[c]
Perinatal mortality	29	6.49	5	2.28	2.19[c]
Neonatal death	15	3.36	4	1.18	3.39[b]
Stillbirth	14	3.13	1	1.10	0.91
Abortion	85	19.02	5	6.66	0.75

[a] Premature by birth weight standard of 5.5 lb or less.
[b] Excess is statistically significant, P < 0.01.
[c] Excess is not statistically significant, P = 0.05–0.10.

vomiting is shown in Table V for patients with and without nervous illness classified by color and age. In this group of 1,570 patients, 80% had reported some nausea and vomiting during the first few months. For the 94 prenatal patients with a history of nervousness, 86% had some nausea and vomiting.

TABLE V

Early Nausea and Vomiting among Prenatal Patients Classified According to Their History of Nervous Illness and According to Color and Age

Population and Nervous History	Number of Patients	Per Cent of Patients with Specified Nausea and Vomiting				
		Total	Severe	Moderate	Slight	None
All patients						
No nervousness	1,476	100.0	8.0	30.2	41.7	20.1
Nervousness	94	100.0	10.6	31.9	43.6	13.8
Under 25 years						
No nervousness	700	100.0	7.9	31.7	42.0	18.4
Nervousness	35	100.0	20.0[a]	17.1	54.3	8.6
25 years or older						
No nervousness	776	100.0	8.1	28.9	41.4	21.6
Nervousness	59	100.0	5.1	40.7	37.3	16.9
White patients						
No nervousness	1,091	100.0	7.4	31.1	41.1	20.4
Nervousness	72	100.0	8.3	29.2	48.6	13.9
Under 25 years						
No nervousness	523	100.0	7.5	33.3	40.9	18.4
Nervousness	28	100.0	17.9[b]	14.3	60.7	7.1
25 years or older						
No nervousness	568	100.0	7.4	29.0	41.2	22.4
Nervousness	44	100.0	2.3	38.6	40.9	18.2
Negro patients						
No nervousness	385	100.0	9.6	27.8	43.4	19.2
Nervousness	22	100.0	18.2	40.9	27.3	13.6
Under 25 years						
No nervousness	177	100.0	9.0	27.1	45.2	18.6
Nervousness	7	100.0	28.6	28.6	28.6	14.3
25 years or older						
No nervousness	208	100.0	10.1	28.4	41.8	19.7
Nervousness	15	100.0	13.3	46.7	26.7	13.3

[a] Significantly higher, P = 0.01–0.02.
[b] Significantly higher, P = 0.02–0.05.

This difference is not statistically significant, and there was little difference in the frequency of nausea and vomiting classified as moderate or severe.

When patients were classified by *age,* severe nausea and vomiting was much more frequent among those under 25 years of age who had a history of nervous illness, 20% compared with 8% for patients of the same age not reporting nervous illness. This difference is statistically significant (P = 0.01–0.02). At ages 25 and over, patients with and without previous nervous illness reported similar amounts of nausea and vomiting.

Among the white patients, those under 25 years of age with a history of nervous illness had significantly more nausea and vomiting rated severe than patients in the same age group having no history of nervous illness. At older ages there was no significant difference. Among the Negro patients, only 22 had a history of nervous illness, and for these both severe and moderate nausea and vomiting were more frequent than among the other Negro patients. For severe plus moderate nausea and vomiting, the excess among Negro patients with nervousness is of borderline significance (P = 0.05–0.06). The excess of severe cases was chiefly at the younger ages and of moderate cases was at the older ages.

Nausea and vomiting ceases for the majority of prenatal patients before the latter half of pregnancy, but occasional attacks of nausea or vomiting are reported by a considerable number of patients. In this group, 19% had some nausea or vomiting after 20 weeks of gestation. All but two patients with late nausea had had early nausea and vomiting. As shown in Table VI, nausea and vomiting late in pregnancy was reported by patients with a history of nervous illness very significantly more often than by other patients. The percentages of patients with late nausea were 39 and 18 for the nervous and non-nervous patients, respectively.

A higher rate for late nausea and vomiting among the nervous patients is found for those under age 25 years and among older patients. It is also found for patients having their first baby, their second baby, and births of higher order. For each of these subgroups, age and order of birth, the percentage of prenatal patients with late nausea and vomiting is significantly higher for those with a history of illness than for those with no history of

TABLE VI

Nausea and/or Vomiting in Second Half of Pregnancy for Patients without and Patients with History of Nervous Illness

Population Group and Nervous History	All Patients			White Patients			Negro Patients		
		With N-V			With N-V			With N-V	
	Total	No.	Per cent	Total	No.	Per cent	Total	No.	Per cent
All patients									
No nervousness	1,476	269	18.2	1,091	190	17.4	385	79	20.5
Nervousness	94	37	39.4^a	72	29	40.3^a	22	8	36.4
Under 25 years									
No nervousness	700	123	17.6	523	85	16.3	177	38	21.5
Nervousness	35	14	40.0^a	28	12	42.9^a	7	2	28.6
25 years or older									
No nervousness	776	146	18.8	568	105	18.5	208	41	19.7
Nervousness	59	23	39.0^a	44	17	38.6^a	15	6	40.0
Para 0									
No nervousness	682	121	17.7	506	85	16.8	176	36	20.5
Nervousness	30	13	43.3^a	22	10	45.5^a	8	3	37.5
Para 1									
No nervousness	489	81	16.6	364	57	15.7	125	24	19.2
Nervousness	35	12	34.3^a	26	10	38.5^a	9	2	22.2
Para 2+									
No nervousness	305	67	22.0	221	48	21.7	84	19	22.6
Nervousness	29	12	41.4^b	24	9	37.5	5	3	60.0

^{a} Significantly higher, P < 0.01.
^{b} Significantly higher, P = 0.01–0.02.

nervous illness. Among white patients only, those with nervousness had a higher rate for late nausea at each age and for each order of birth, and the excess was statistically significant except for para two or higher. Negro patients showed the same tendency for late nausea to be higher when there was history of nervousness, but because of small numbers the differences are not statistically significant.

Since there was little difference between the patients with and those without nervousness with respect to early nausea and vomiting, the higher rates for the nervous group later in pregnancy perhaps are indicative of less ability to adjust to pregnancy or of an increasing emotional anxiety as pregnancy progressed.

Except for the nausea and vomiting, patients with a history of nervousness had no excessive frequency of prenatal complications or signs of metabolic imbalance. No cases of eclampsia or pre-eclampsia were diagnosed among the 94 patients, although two or three might have been expected since the rate for the total population was 2.6%. The frequency of edema or elevated blood pressure was approximately the same for the patients with and those without history of nervous illness. It should be remembered that all patients with essential hypertension had been excluded from the population. An analysis of the gain in weight by tri-mesters and for the total pregnancy period did not reveal any significant differences between the nervous patients and the others.

Two of the 94 patients with a history of nervous illness (both white patients) exhibited marked symptoms of nervous illness during the prenatal period. One was hospitalized and diagnosed as "cardiac neurosis." She had reported hospitalization for a nervous breakdown four years before this pregnancy. The other patient was "depressed, almost psychotic" according to a note on her record by the clinic physician. She had reported only treatment for nerves when interviewed by the clinic clerk. There were four patients among the 1,476 who did not report any history of nervous illness for whom a psychiatric illness was noted One was classified as conversion hysteria, one as psychotic, one as immature personality, and one as acute reactive depression. On a rate basis, the 2.1% for cases among the 94 prenatal patients with a history of nervous illness is 8 times the rate (0.27%) for patients with no previous history reported.

Labor and Delivery

Premature babies, that is babies weighing 5.5 pounds or less at birth, were born to 7 of the 94 patients with a history of nervous illness and the percentage (7.4) is not significantly higher than for the total group with 6.2% premature babies

TABLE VII

Premature Births by Weight among Patients with No History and with Reported History of Nervous Illness

Population Group and History of Nervousness	All Patients			White Patients			Negro Patients		
		Birth weight 5.5 lb or less			Birth weight 5.5 lb or less			Birth weight 5.5 lb or less	
	Total	No.	Per cent	Total	No.	Per cent	Total	No.	Per cent
Total patients									
No nervousness	1,476	91	6.2	1,091	47	4.3	385	44	11.4
Nervousness	94	7	7.4	72	6	8.3	22	1	4.6
Under 30 years									
No nervousness	1,146	64	5.6	850	33	3.9	296	31	10.4
Nervousness	74	7	9.5	58	6	10.3[a]	16	1	6.3
30 years or older									
No nervousness	330	27	8.2	241	14	5.8	89	13	14.6
Nervousness	20	0	0	14	0	0	6	0	0
Para 0									
No nervousness	682	49	7.2	506	27	5.3	176	22	12.5
Nervousness	30	4	13.3	22	3	13.6	8	1	12.5
Para 1									
No nervousness	489	25	5.1	364	13	3.6	125	12	9.6
Nervousness	35	3	8.6	26	3	11.5[a]	9	0	0
Para 2+									
No nervousness	305	17	5.6	221	7	3.2	84	10	11.9
Nervousness	29	0	0	24	0	0	5	0	0

[a] Significantly higher, P = 0.01–0.05.

(Table VII). All the premature births to patients with nervousness were to women under 30 years of age and were either first or second births. For the women under 30 years of age, the premature birth rates were 9.5 and 5.6%, an excess of 70% for the patients with nervous illness. The excess occurred entirely among white patients, and the premature birth rates were 10.3 and 3.9% for white patients with a history of nervousness and without nervousness. For the white patients under 30 years of age the excess was statistically significant, but it was not significant for the combined white and Negro patients.

The premature birth rate among first and second births showed nearly the same differences as for women under 30 years of age. The rate was 70% higher for the nervous patients (10.8 vs. 6.3%), but the difference is not statistically significant. For white patients only, the premature birth rate for women with a history of nervousness was 12.5% compared with 4.6% for all other white women having their first or second baby, and the difference is significant (P < 0.01).

The small number of Negro patients with nervousness, only 22, does not permit any reliable evaluation of this group separately. Only one premature birth occurred compared with two expected on the basis of the rate for all Negro patients.

Although the expected delivery date is very unreliable as a basis for estimating prematurity, it is of interest to examine the time of delivery for these prenatal patients. The distribution of patients with and without nervous history is shown in Table VIII according to the estimated weeks of gestation at delivery. Among the patients with nervousness, 17% were delivered more than two weeks early compared with 11% for the patients without nervous history. For white patients only, the respective percentages were 17 and 9%. The difference is of borderline significance (P = 0.04–0.05) for the white patients. Among Negroes, delivery more than two weeks early was about equally frequent for patients with and without nervous history, 18 and 17%. Thus, for the white population, but not for the Negro patients, by both standards, premature births were much more frequent among the patients with nervous illness.

Delivery more than two weeks *after* the expected date also occurred more frequently among white patients with history of nervous illness than among other white patients; but among Negro patients there were few late deliveries and no difference was associated with nervousness. Late deliveries among white patients were 14 and 8% respectively for those with and those without nervous illness.

The high rate for premature deliveries by gestation period among white patients with nervous illness is found only for

TABLE VIII

Weeks of Gestation at Delivery for Patients Classified by History of
Nervous Illness and by Age and Color

Age Group and History of Nervousness	Number of Patients	Per Cent of Patients Delivered at Specified Weeks of Gestation			
		Total	< 38 weeks	38–41 weeks	42 weeks +
All Patients					
Total, all ages					
No nervousness	1,476	100.0	11.3	81.9	6.8
Nervousness	94	100.0	17.0	72.3	10.6
Under 30 years					
No nervousness	1,146	100.0	10.6	82.3[a]	7.2
Nervousness	74	100.0	18.9[a]	71.6	9.5
30 years or older					
No nervousness	330	100.0	13.9	80.6	5.5
Nervousness	20	100.0	10.0	75.0	15.0
White Patients					
Total, all ages					
No nervousness	1,091	100.0	9.4	82.9[b]	7.7
Nervousness	72	100.0	16.7[a]	69.4	13.9
Under 30 years					
No nervousness	850	100.0	8.4	83.5[b]	8.1
Nervousness	58	100.0	19.0[b]	69.0	12.1
30 years or older					
No nervousness	241	100.0	13.3	80.5	6.2
Nervousness	14	100.0	7.1	71.4	21.4[a]
Negro Patients					
Total, all ages					
No nervousness	385	100.0	16.6	79.2	4.2
Nervousness	22	100.0	18.2	81.8	0

[a] Significantly higher, P = 0.01–0.05.
[b] Significantly higher, P = < 0.01.

the group under 30 years of age, and this finding is the same
as for prematurity by birth weight. The excess in frequency of
delivery more than two weeks after due date was concentrated
in the age group 30 years and older.

The estimated weeks of gestation at delivery and the hours of labor for patients classified by parity are shown in Table IX for the patients with and those without a history of nervousness.

Among the nulliparae with nervousness, the percentage of patients delivered more than two weeks before expected due date was about twice as high as for the other patients, and the percentage having a short labor also was higher; but the differences were not statistically significant. Delivery two weeks or more late and labor lasting more than 24 hours occurred with about equal frequency among the nulliparae in the two groups.

Among the multiparae, the patients with nervousness differed significantly from other patients both in time of delivery and in hours of labor. For women having their second baby (Para 1) a significantly higher percentage of deliveries were late, and a significantly higher percentage had long labor in the group with history of nervousness. There was no difference in the percentages of patients delivered before 38 weeks of gestation, although it has been shown that Para 1 patients with nervousness had a significantly higher rate for babies premature by weight. Only the babies premature by weight were premature by gestation in the group with nervousness, but in the group without nervousness about one-third of the babies with an estimated gestation period of less than 38 weeks weighed 5.5 pounds or less. The number of Para 1 women in the nervous group is small (26), but their record seems to indicate a relatively high rate of premature babies and a high rate for delayed labor and long labor. Among women having their third baby, or higher number, those with history of nervousness had no significant excess of early or late delivery and no excess in frequency of labor lasting more than 24 hours. However, there were significantly fewer short labors of less than six hours for those with nervousness, 17% as against 44% with short labor among the women without nervousness.

At delivery, Caesarean section was the method of delivery for a larger percentage of patients with a history of nervousness than of the other patients. This was true only for white patients.

TABLE IX. Weeks of Gestation at Delivery and Hours of Labor for Patients Classified by History of Nervous Illness and by Color and Parity

Parity and History of Nervousness	Weeks of Gestation			Hours of Labor		
	Total No. of patients	Per cent of total delivered at		Total No.[a] of patients	Per cent of total in labor	
		Less than 38 wks	42 wks or more		Less than 6.5 hrs	24.5 hrs or more
All Patients						
Para 0						
No nervousness	682	9.8	8.7	632	11.1	19.4
Nervousness	30	20.0	10.0	30	20.0	20.0
Para 1						
No nervousness	489	12.7	5.3	462	38.8	2.4
Nervousness	35	11.4	14.3[b]	31	35.5	16.1[c]
Para 2 or more						
No nervousness	305	12.5	4.9	288	44.8[b]	4.5
Nervousness	29	20.7	6.9	23	17.4	4.3
White Patients						
Para 0						
No nervousness	506	7.9	9.5	473	9.1	19.2
Nervousness	22	18.2	13.6	22	13.6	22.7
Para 1						
No nervousness	364	11.3	6.0	348	36.7	2.9
Nervousness	26	11.5	19.2[b]	23	39.1	21.7[c]
Para 2 or more						
No nervousness	221	10.0	6.3	208	44.2[b]	4.3
Nervousness	24	20.8	8.3	18	16.7	5.6

[a] Excludes patients delivered by Caesarean section (55 white patients of which 8 had a history of nervousness, and 24 Negro patients of which 1 had nervousness); also excludes 25 patients with unknown length of labor.
[b] Significantly higher, P = 0.01–0.05.
[c] Significantly higher, P < 0.001.

Caesarean section was done for 8 of the 72 white patients with nervousness, or 11%, compared with 4.3% of the other white patients. All of the eight patients were multiparae, and 7 of them had had a previous section. The rate for previous Caesarean section for the 50 multiparae in the nervous group was 14% compared with 2.4% for white multiparae with no history of nervousness. The higher rate of Caesarean section at delivery of these patients with history of nervousness reflects, therefore, the high frequency of section for previous deliveries.

For all Negro patients, the rate for Caesarean section was 5.9%, and only one of the 22 patients with a history of nervousness (4.5%) was delivered by Caesarean section. She was a multipara with no previous section.

Conclusion

The pregnancy histories for this small group of prenatal patients who reported a previous nervous breakdown or nervous illness have indicated a relatively high frequency of a number of conditions that may be considered as signs of a poor physiological response to the demands of pregnancy.

Nausea and vomiting that persisted into the latter half of pregnancy was the only prenatal complication that occurred at a significantly higher rate for both white and Negro patients of all ages. At younger ages (under 25 years), more of the patients with nervousness had experienced early nausea and vomiting which had been classified as severe. Other prenatal complications, such as toxemia, edema, excessive gain in weight, and elevated blood pressure, were noted no more frequently for patients with a history of nervousness than for other patients.

For white patients, there is evidence of less favorable delivery for a larger percentage of those with history of nervousness.

Among the multiparae, the frequency of Caesarean section was higher, and more of them had very long labor of over 24 hours duration for second births, and fewer had the short labor characteristic of other patients having a third or fourth baby. Among the primiparae, a higher percentage of the white patients with nervousness were delivered more than two weeks before the estimated due date. At ages under 30 years, women with nervousness had an excess of births at less than 38 weeks of gestation, and at older ages they had an excess of births at 42 weeks or later.

The premature birth rate on the basis of birth weight of 5.5 pounds or less was much higher among first and second births to white patients with a history of nervousness than to those without. Since prematurity is an important problem to public health, the possible association between emotional status and premature birth is of special interest.

This group of prenatal patients with nervous illness is too small and the illnesses reported are too ill-defined and heterogeneous to afford more than suggestive evidence of an interrelation between nervous disorders and the various problems of pregnancy that have been discussed. Positive findings are mostly limited to very small subgroups, such as younger patients or specific para, and some significant differences would be expected by chance alone. However, the results of this study do indicate that more careful and planned investigations along these lines would be desirable.

REFERENCE

1. Wiehl, Dorothy G., and Winslow T. Tompkins. Maternal nutrition studies at Philadelphia Lying-In Hospital. I. Method of study and description of sample. In *Promotion of Maternal and Newborn Health*. Proc. the 1954 Ann. Conf. Milbank Memorial Fund, 1955.

DISCUSSION

DR. MORTON KRAMER: There is increasing evidence that prematurity and associated complications of pregnancy, labor, and delivery which influence infant loss are correlated with increased risk of such neuropsychiatric disorders of childhood as cerebral palsy, epilepsy, mental deficiency, and behavior disorders (1, 2). Thus, learning more about the physical and mental health of childbearing women both prior to and during pregnancy is an essential step in acquiring knowledge that may be used to control and prevent such complications.

Studies by Lemkau *et al.* (3), Pasamanick (4), and Collins *et al.* (5) show that adult women experience a higher prevalence and incidence of psychoneuroses and nonpsychotic mental illnesses than do males. Further, although males have higher first admission rates to mental hospitals than do females, the females have quite a high first admission rate during the age span 15–45 years, the reproductive years of life. Thus, since an attack of a mental disorder during the reproductive years is not an uncommon event in females, it would seem quite important to find out what effect a history of mental disorder in a pregnant woman may have on the course and the outcome of pregnancy. It would also seem important to investigate what effect a pregnancy may have on precipitating an attack of mental disorder both in women who have never been mentally ill as well as in women who may have had a history of such illness and recovered at some prior date.

The authors of this paper have attempted to investigate these problems through an analysis of the records of 1,570 prenatal patients who registered at the clinic of the Philadelphia Lying-In Hospital and were delivered in the ward service between 1947 and 1953. In addition to the regular physical histories obtained by the examining M.D., a clerk was assigned to ask each patient "if she had ever had a nervous breakdown." If the answer was "yes," the clerk recorded the approximate date of occurrence and whatever information the patient volunteered concerning the characteristics of the breakdown and precipitating event. No attempt was made to follow up these reports by a professionally trained person nor was any attempt made to screen out "yes" answers that were not primarily nervous disorders. Comparisons were then made between the women who reported a history of nervousness and those who reported no such history with respect to outcome of previous pregnancies, complications, and outcome of current pregnancy controlling for such factors as age, parity, and color.

I presume that Miss Wiehl and her associates would agree with me if I were to classify this carefully done statistical study as a pilot study, the results of which might be used to improve the design of subsequent studies in this area and to suggest ways of improving methods of collecting data for obtaining more clear-cut answers to the questions under investigation.

The basic problem to be solved in studies such as this is the development of a method for detecting those pregnant women who have ever experienced a nervous breakdown. This involves a definition of what constitutes a "nervous breakdown" or a history of nervousness and the development of an instrument that permits the gathering of data that may serve as an appropriate basis for separating the females involved into those who have had the condition and those who have not. I have no way of determining how well the question asked by the clerk screened out the women with a positive history and how many such women it missed. That is, we have no information on the proportion of false positives in the "yes" group and false negatives in the "no" group. Nor is it possible to tell how seriously ill most of the women were (except for a few who reported history of shock treatment, chorea, paralysis, hospitalization for nervousness). The authors emphasize that the women with a positive history were very heterogeneous with respect to type of illness, severity, duration, and probability of complete recovery.

Gardiner and Yerushalmy (6) have shown that mothers who have had prior reproductive losses are a group particularly susceptible to subsequent stillbirths and neonatal deaths. It would seem to me that a mother who has had a reproductive casualty has undergone a particularly stressful experience and may well have experienced some emotional damage. In some instances this may have resulted in excessive "nervousness" and may have affected her attitude toward subsequent pregnancies so that she might approach each such experience with more fear and worry about the outcome than mothers who have never experienced such loss. It would be useful if the authors were to reanalyze the data of Table IV to determine whether multiparas with one or more casualties were more likely to report histories of nervousness than multiparas who had never experienced such casualties. It would also be useful to compare the "nervous" history of these two groups with that of the primiparas.

Some preliminary analyses of the data in Table IV suggest that mothers who have experienced a perinatal loss report a much higher rate of "nervousness" than other groups. If the results were to come out in the expected direction, then more confidence might be placed on the adequacy of the questionnaire that was used for screening out the "nervous" women.

I would like also to say something about the generalizability of the results of a study of this kind. Let us assume for a moment that the questionnaire method for detecting previous nervous illness is beyond reproach. The women in this study consist of white women primarily of Italian stock and urban Negroes. Women in each of these groups undoubtedly have their own attitudes toward pregnancy and the stress and strain as well as joy that may be associated with this event. Patterns of living and husband-wife relationships differ as well as attitudes of husband toward the role of women both as a bearer of children and as a member of the family. It would seem important, therefore, to investigate the relationship of these attitudes to the occurrence of nervousness in these groups of women and to extend these observations to other ethnic and socio-economic groups.

To summarize, the effect of previous history of mental and nervous disorders on course and outcome of pregnancy is an important area of research. However, before the results of this study can be fully evaluated, more information is needed on the effectiveness of the screening device used for detecting women with such history. It would be important to compare the results of the questionnaire method in which a clerk asked a patient whether she ever had a nervous breakdown with what might be obtained from a careful psychiatric interview and examination.

Studies of this kind should be extended to a variety of socio-economic and cultural groups and should be supplemented by studies of the attitudes of women in these groups as well as of their husbands toward pregnancy and what relationship these attitudes may have to the occurrence of mental disorder.

REFERENCES

1. Lilienfeld, A. M., B. Pasamanick, and M. Rogers. Relationship between pregnancy experience and the development of certain neuropsychiatric disorders in childhood. *Am. J. Public Health, 45,* 637–43 (1955).

2. Douglas, J. W. B., and C. Mogford. Health of premature children from birth to four years. *Brit. Med. J., 1,* 748 (1953).
3. Lemkau, Paul, C. Tietze, and M. Cooper. Complaint of nervousness and the psychoneuroses. *Am. J. Orthopsychiat., 12,* 214–23 (1942).
4. Pasamanick, B., D. W. Roberts, P. V. Lemkau, and D. W. Krueger. A survey of mental disease in an urban population. I. Prevalence by age, sex, and severity of impairment. *Am. J. Public Health, 47,* 923–29 (1957).
5. Collins, S. D., R. Phillips, and D. S. Oliver. Disabling illness from specific causes among males and females of various ages. *Public Health Repts. (U.S.), 66,* 1649–71 (1951).
6. Gardiner, F. M., and J. Yerushalmy. Familial susceptibility to still births and neonatal deaths. *Am. J. Hyg., 30,* 11–31 (1939).

COUNTER DISCUSSION

MISS D. G. WIEHL: Dr. Kramer has made many good suggestions for studying the interrelation between nervous illness and catastrophes of pregnancy and for investigating factors that may affect the occurrence of such illness among pregnant women. I think we agree that these are problems which are important to study. I certainly agree that results from this analysis of the Philadelphia data provide only suggestive evidence which requires more careful investigation.

I might say that the question on history of nervous breakdown grew out of an interest in studying the relation of nervous illness to complications of pregnancy, but it was not possible to arrange for follow-up interviews by professionally trained personnel.

Epidemiological Aspects of Prognosis in Mental Illness[1]

JOSEPH ZUBIN, E. I. BURDOCK, SAMUEL SUTTON,
AND FRANCES CHEEK

Biometrics Research, New York State Department
of Mental Hygiene and Columbia University, New York

The juxtaposition of such an individual-centered term as prognosis with such a group-centered term as epidemiological requires, to say the least, some explanation. This is especially true when these two strange bedfellows are found together in the bedstead of mental illness. Epidemiological investigations in the mental disorders are in a very early stage of development, and prognoses in mental illness are very hazardous. Any attempt at providing an epidemiological model for prognosis may therefore be premature.

Until recently, epidemiologists of mental illness were chiefly concerned with etiology. Such factors as socio-economic status, employment, mobility, type of residential neighborhood, national origins, paranatal influences, early development, home environment, parental attitudes, and familial incidence were examined for their etiological import. But their significance for outcome of illness has not been stressed in the past. Recent experience in the care of the mentally ill in England and elsewhere has placed a new emphasis on the importance of epidemiological factors for outcome. If we adopt a psychogenic model for mental disorders,

[1] This investigation was supported in part by Research Grant M586 (C3) from the National Institute of Mental Health of the National Institutes of Health, Public Health Service.

the type of environment to which a patient is returned is the most important factor in his rehabilitation. In terms of a biogenic model, the environment is critical because the advent of new stresses may be fatal to recovery. Even those who deny that we can cure mental illness admit that a more favorable environment will permit patients to remain in the community who otherwise would require hospitalization. In fact, the attitude of the patient and of the community toward mental illness is such a potent factor in outcome that it is reminiscent of a story about two members of parliament in a legendary country in which the attitude toward mental illness is reported to be so benign that the population has accepted hospitalization for mental illness on the same terms as hospitalization for physical illness. One M.P. in the heat of debate, told his opponent, "What you say doesn't make sense. You must be crazy!" Whereupon his interlocutor pulled a document from his breast pocket and pointing to it said, "Here is a certificate from Hospital X declaring me sane. Can you match it?"

In this paper we shall limit ourselves to the contribution of epidemiology to prediction of outcome of mental illness. It is quite fitting for this paper to be read at Kraepelin's centennial since it was he who introduced prognosis and follow-up studies into psychiatry. While his attempt to base diagnosis on *outcome* alone may be open to question, his heroic tour de force did much to establish order where chaos reigned. While keeping his eye on eventual outcome, he was able to disentangle the nondeteriorating from the deteriorating psychoses, and in the latter he was able to distinguish the course of organic deterioration from that of functional deterioration. Such accomplishments loom large when compared with the confusion which preceded Kraepelin, and which might recur if we discarded his system completely. The importance of prognosis, which Kraepelin urgently insisted on, remains undiminished today. The chief aim of this paper is to introduce greater objectivity in the prognostic approach.

Most clinical prognoses are purely impressionistic and their overall accuracy is generally so low that it is not surprising to find many clinicians utilizing the prognostic category of "guarded" in self defense. Nevertheless, the clinical prognoses are in reality true predictions whereas the epidemiologic studies, being actuarial in nature, are usually not prognostic but hysterognostic, i.e., based on a retrospective evaluation of the past after the outcome of illness is already known. The relative merits of actuarial and clinical prognoses have recently been examined by Meehl (10) and by others (11). A careful review of this controversy leads perforce to the conclusion that whenever objective criteria for the evaluation of outcome are available, it is to be expected that the retrospectively validated studies of actuarians should prove superior to the clinical judgments, since the latter do not have the benefit of formalized regression equations and crystalized, mathematically formulated previous experience. However, when the criteria for evaluating outcome are not specified nor even definitely known, as is the case in mental illness at the present time, it is impossible to decide which method is superior.

But why is prognosis so difficult? First of all, it is difficult because prophesy is always difficult. Any attempt to predict runs up against the possibility that the conditions which characterized a previous observation are not duplicated in the future observations. But aside from the intrinsic difficulty of predicting, the field of mental illness presents us with a situation in which there is a lack of objective criteria for gaging improvement, nor is there any agreement on those criteria which have been provided. These criteria range from ability to withstand pressure of external events, capacity to tolerate uncertainty, deprivation, and frustration . . . to freedom from symptoms, . . . adjustment and pleasure in social and sexual life (15). It is clear that such criteria cannot constitute the objective framework required for scientific evaluation. A third difficulty stems from the fact that the disease entities themselves are ill defined and do not present us with homogeneous categories of individuals. A fourth difficulty is the total absence of knowledge regarding the natural history of the illness and the absence of valid information regarding follow-up of discharged cases. A fifth source of difficulty is the failure on the part of the examiner to take into consideration the stage of the illness at which the prognosis is being made and his failure to indicate for what period of time in the future his prognosis is to come true. In the studies in this field immediate outcome after therapy bears little or no relationship to the eventual outcome on five year follow-up. A sixth source of difficulty is the potential role of the specific therapy or of the therapist as a possible factor in influencing outcome. What one therapist can apparently accomplish, another one sometimes finds it difficult to carry out. A seventh and final difficulty stems from the fact that the prognosticator very often fails to accept certain inherent deficiencies as residual effects of the disease in the same way that the physician in physical illness takes into consideration the residual effects produced by chronic physical illness even after its amelioration. Since mental illness is a chronic state, it is quite unlikely that the patient will return to his premorbid level as if no disease had occurred. The fact that the patient has aged during his hospital stay and the possible role that the degree of community and family acceptance plays in his final rehabilitation are important factors that need to be considered in any prognosis. The role of the community and the family should loom high in any consideration of epidemiologic factors in prognosis.

But why is prognosis so important today? Before the advent of specific therapies, prognosis was not so important because treatment was not specific, and selection of patients for type of care available did not depend on any prognostic features since there was one universal method of treating all mental patients, namely, custodial care. With the advent of the new therapies it becomes necessary to determine for each patient what particular therapy he is most likely to benefit from. As a matter of fact neglect of prognosis has brought about the unsavory result that all therapies, no matter whether they be of the psychotherapeutic variety or the somatic variety tend to produce results on five-year follow-up which are no better than those characterizing patients receiving nonspecific therapy or even no treatment at all. Thus, although on immediate outcome there is a definite advantage for specific therapies, when an accounting of the five-year follow-up takes place, the temporary advantages, good as they are and important as they are, disappear, and there is no permanent advantage left for any of the therapies (12).

The paradox of superior immediate outcome in the face of insignificant gains in the long run requires an explanation. Three hypotheses are offered. First, the "specific" treatments are not specific to the illness. They merely serve to hasten the improvement in those who would eventually improve anyhow and bring about temporary improvement in the other cases, followed eventually by relapse. Secondly, the therapies may be effective as the short run prognoses would indicate, but in the long run outcome may be altered either by "spontaneous" recurrence of the illness, which has been temporarily ameliorated by the therapy, or by recurrence of the illness as a result of social factors, e.g., stresses on the individual from a "sick" family environment. A third possibility is that the specific therapies are truly specific for certain types of patients only and not for all patients. If we could by some means determine the therapy of choice for each patient and administer to him only the preferred therapy, the improvement rates in specific therapies for both immediate and final outcome would then rise and stay above the rates obtained under nonspecific therapy. In the first case, maintenance of medication would be the answer and in the second, removal from a destructive environment, or social work or milieu therapy with the family. The third possibility leads to the need for prognosis. It is evident then that in the short run evaluation of therapy, differential types and degrees of pathology must be taken into account, and in the long run, additionally, quality of home environment must be considered. The tremendous cost of mental disease and the need not only for concentrating on those who get well under treatment but for identifying those who do not get well under current therapies, leads to the conclusion that prognosis is the method of choice. Moreover, in designing experiments for the evaluation of a new therapy, it is important to have some idea of the prognosis for each individual under nonspecific therapy, for only then can control groups be established which would be equivalent in expected final outcome. Only with such equivalent groups can a reliable decision be reached as to the efficacy of a particular therapy.

Specific Problems in Epidemiological Prognosis

There are at least three types of prognostic indicators in mental illness: the psychiatric or clinical prognoses, the psychological test prognoses, and the sociological or social work prognoses. Each of these sources has a time-honored history, and until recently there were very few attempts at evaluating the vast literature which is available in each of these areas. More recently, Dr. Charles Windle (13), a former staff member of our department, undertook a survey of psychological test prognosis in psychopathology. After examining some five hundred articles he found one hundred and eighty-three suitable for analysis with regard to the relationship between psychological test performance and outcome. The remaining 300-odd articles, although they dealt with prognosis, did not give sufficient information to enable Dr. Windle to draw any conclusions from their data. Even the 183 articles that were included failed to give pertinent information in many instances so that the analysis has to be regarded as only tentative. He concludes that although there is no dearth of prognostic studies attempting to relate psychological test performance to eventual outcome, many of the individual studies fail to demonstrate empirical justification for the conclusions drawn. Furthermore, comparisons among studies reveal little agreement among findings. Consequently all that we have left after this survey are a few plausible hunches but no verified conclusions. With the possible exception of these few hunches that may eventually be found valid, it appears that previous research on prognosis with psychological tests can tell us only that it is not possible to discover reliable prognostic criteria without controlling variables to a much greater extent than has been customary.

The very minimal criteria that need to be provided in a study in order that it may be helpful in demonstrating the prognostic power of psychological tests are: (*a*) The conditions of the research must be specified. This means that the patient population must be described in all pertinent detail, the conditions of therapy must be stipulated, and objective criteria of outcome must be presented. (*b*) The experiment must deal with relatively homogeneous populations and conditions. If such investigation were done, we could eventually build up a composite picture, an accomplishment much less likely to result from studies in which these variables are uncontrolled. (*c*) Findings should be reported in terms amenable to statistical evaluation. (*d*) Findings must be subjected to cross validation. Since most prognostic studies are really hysterognostic, that is retrospective in nature, it is quite likely that many of the studies reported in the literature have capitalized on chance variations which are only pseudo-significant. Only a cross validation of these findings can help separate the wheat from the chaff. As Cochran and Cox (3) have shown clearly, studies in which differences are picked out after the completion of the investigation simply because they are so large, often lead to erroneous conclusions. The experimenter may think he is making a t-test on the 5% level when he is actually testing at the 13% level or the 40% level, etc. When investigators in this field recognize a need for minimal experimental and evaluative procedures they may hope to discover what, if any, prognostic power psychological tests may have.

A similar investigation of the prognostic value of background characteristics has been launched recently with the help of a grant from the Milbank Memorial Fund. Some 800 English and foreign articles were found bearing upon this problem, and these have been analyzed item by item to determine the relevance of each characteristic for outcome. Here again it was found that the vast majority of these studies failed to give sufficient information about the nature of the patient and about the nature of the therapy and about many of the other pertinent factors, so that the results must be regarded as only tentative. Despite these shortcomings, however, the rather large number of studies permitted the emergence of certain consistencies in the findings. The prognostic indicators were divided into categories grouped under the rubrics of premorbid factors and course of illness. The studies in each category which indicated good or poor prognosis for hospitalized schizophrenics were tabulated. The categories were as follows: (1) Socio-economic characteristics, (2) personality traits, (3) physical characteristics, genetic factors, (4) disease history, (5) feelings and emotions, and (6) thought processes.

The results are shown in Table I.

The items leading to good or poor prognosis can be integrated under such well-known concepts as Langfeldt's (8) nuclear vs. schizophreniform psychoses or process vs. reactive psychoses; but it is too early to test either one of these hypotheses with the data at hand.

It might be interesting to inquire whether each of these indicators possesses the same prognostic power for nonspecific therapy or custodial care as it does for some of the specific therapies. It was found that in the vast majority of instances the patient who possessed characteristics prognostic of good outcome or of poor outcome under nonspecific therapy, achieved similar good or poor outcome regardless of the specific therapy applied. For a small proportion of the items, some 10%, the specific therapy showed an advantage while for another 10%, the specific therapy showed a disadvantage, that is, patients who would have improved under nonspecific therapy failed to do so under the specific therapy in question. In 82% of the items, the direction of prognosis is unchanged from that expected in nonspecific therapy, regardless of the type of therapy employed. This would seem to indicate that in the vast majority of instances the specific therapies do not make any great difference. We are now engaged in investigating the background information of some 200 patients with all the alleged prognostic items included. When these data are collected, it may be possible to make pattern analyses of the constellations of prognostic indicators that may be more helpful in the evaluation of outcome than single items taken one at a time.

On the sociological level, quality of home environment also bears investigation as a prognostic factor in the outcome of schizophrenia. In the summer of 1956 a pilot study supported by the Department of Mental Hygiene was undertaken to investigate the relation of home environment to prognosis. The investigation originated as a result of an observation made in a psychological prognostic study conducted under a grant from the National Institute of Mental Health. In the latter study it was noted that several patients with a "poor" psychological test prognosis had a "good" outcome, being out of the hospital one year following admission, while several others with a "good" prognosis had a "poor" outcome. It was further noted that those who failed despite good prognosis came from rather "good" homes while those who succeeded despite a poor prognosis came from rather "poor" homes. An investigation was therefore made during the summer of 1955 [3] of the social backgrounds of all the patients in the prognostic project with the aid of records of preconvalescent and convalescent home evaluations by hospital social workers. The results indicated that the ratings of the home for readiness to receive the patient, as evidenced by interest, warmth, insight, and financial security, were inversely associated with patient outcome defined as *in* or *out* of the hospital at the end of one year after admission. In other words,

[3] Supported by a grant from the Columbia University Social Science Research Council.

TABLE I

Prognostic Value of Background Factors for Outcome of Schizophrenia

Prognostic Indicators	Number of Studies Showing Positive Prognosis	Number of Studies Showing Negative Prognosis
Premorbid Factors		
Socio-economic characteristics		
Married status	4	0
Clerical or skilled occupation	1	0
Good deportment in school	0	3
Limited education (females only)	1	0
Possessing an immediate family		
(females only)	1	0
Personality traits		
Obsessive	1	0
Cyclothymic vs. schizothymic	13	0
Good premorbid adjustment	8	0
High intelligence	2	1
Good social adjustment (friends,		
heterosexual relations—dates)	4	0
Religious	1	0
Physical characteristics, genetic factors		
Body type		
Athletic	8	0
Pyknic	12	1
Family history of schizophrenia	0	2
Male sex	2	4
Course of Illness		
Disease history		
Age at admission:		
Early	2	3
Specifically between 20 and 40	4	1
Previous episodes	3	1
Immobility during first two years		
of illness	0	2
Sudden onset	20	0
Brief duration of symptoms	17	0
Psychogenic precipitating factors	10	0
Diagnosis		
Catatonic	9	0
Paranoid	0	6
Hebephrenic	1	6
Symptomatology		
Atypical	3	0
Somatic	1	0

TABLE I (*continued*)

Prognostic Value of Background Factors for Outcome of Schizophrenia

Prognostic Indicators	Number of Studies Showing Positive Prognosis	Number of Studies Showing Negative Prognosis
Course of Illness (continued)		
Feelings and emotions		
Anxious	6	0
Manic depressive (i.e., depression, elation, agitation, restlessness, impulsiveness)	15	0
Dull affect (apathy)	0	7
Inappropriate affect	1	7
Hostility	0	2
Externally directed aggression	2	2
Hypochondriasis	1	2
Thought processes		
Delusions:		
Intrapunitive	1	0
Changing	3	0
Of reference, of influence, persecutory, bizarre, of depersonalization, somatic	1	19
Hallucinations	2	9
Confusion, perplexity, cloudiness	9	1
Flight of ideas	2	0
Disorientations of time, place, person	7	4

patients remaining in the hospital at the end of one year following admission tended to come from better homes than those who were *out* of the hospital. In an attempt to explain this finding analyses were made of the social and psychopathological characteristics of each patient in his premorbid and morbid state. Items were assigned positive or negative values on the basis of their prognostic value as reported in the literature survey, and an index of psychopathology was constructed. It was found that the patients who were out of the hospital tended to be those whose psychopathology was less malignant and that they also tended to come from homes which were rated as "poor." On the other hand, the patients who were *in* the hospital tended to have more severe psychopathology and also tended to come from homes generally rated as "good."

This pilot study utilized for its evaluation of home environment the unstructured preconvalescent studies of hospital social workers. Further refinement of what was meant by "good," "fair," or "poor" environment and more careful collection of systematic data on the problem were found necessary. A group of seven social work students at the New York School of Social Work (2) undertook this task, working with 31 of the original 51 families included in the pilot study with whom it was possible to arrange interviews. They developed a set of criteria for a "good" home which included emotional factors such as warmth, freedom to change, consistency, preservation of integrated family living without undue pressure as the result of the needs of the patient, and physical environment of the home. The criterion of outcome used was changed to number of admissions to Brooklyn State Hospital or other mental hospitals since 1953.

When the home evaluations were compared with outcome it was found that outcome in both "good" and "poor" homes was worse than outcome in "fair" homes. Moreover, the pattern of frequency and duration of rehospitalization revealed that in the "good" homes there were shorter and more frequent hospitalizations, in the "fair" homes less frequent hospitalizations, whether long or short, and in the "poor" homes there were primarily short and very frequent hospitalizations. Degree of pathology was not taken into consideration in this study, but it was hypothesized that poor outcome in the "poor" homes might reflect the environmental factor.

The small size of the sample precluded more refined statistical analysis, and it was decided to test the interrelationships of degree of pathology, defined by an index based on case history items, home environment, as evaluated by a skilled social worker in a systematically structured interview with the family and convalescent adjustment, with evaluation by a skilled social worker in a structured interview with family and patient, for the entire sample of 230 schizophrenic patients collected since 1953 at Brooklyn State Hospital. This study is now in progress.

One of the baffling problems involved in the evaluation of outcome of illness is the selection of the criterion of outcome. For the most part, the studies reported in the literature have dealt with rather vague undefinable concepts such as "improved" or "in and out of the hospital." In an attempt to develop a more basic measure of the outcome of therapy, the stability of the patient during his posthospitalization period has been investigated. The proportion of time following release from the hospital which the patient spent in the community is computed, and this becomes an index of the stability of outcome. Some patients leave the hospital never to return and they, of course, have 100% ratings. Some patients return to the hospital several times in the course of the follow-up period for longer or shorter stays, and the proportion of time spent out of the hospital is recorded as the index of stability of outcome. We have found this index to be superior to the "in and out of the hospital" index and to ratings on improvement. In a related investigation we found that immobility during the two years following first admission is one of the better prognostic indicators of eventual outcome. By analyzing the number of months of hospitalization during the two years following first admission of a patient and dividing the number of months spent in the hospital by the number of moves made into the hospital, including the first admission as the first move, an index is obtained which may range all the way from 1 to 24. This index, designated the immobility index (4), relates very highly to outcome on 5-year, 10-year, and 15-year follow-up. Several studies, including those of Kramer *et al.* (6), have demonstrated that the first two years following hospitalization are crucial years and that most of the patients who stay in the hospital longer than this period are chronic incurable cases. The proportion of patients released during the first two years has varied considerably over the last thirty or forty years, but the proportion of patients who have been in the hospital two years or longer who were released has remained steady over the years.

That is why we consider the immobility index based on the first two years as a very stable index of the characteristics of the patient.

Another criterion of outcome is level of adjustment of the patient in his social roles in the family or community. A study of level of adjustment as a criterion is presently in progress. In this study, a social worker interviews patient and family at specified intervals after release from the hospital and uses a standardized interview schedule in which information is obtained regarding quality and quantity of interaction by the patient in his roles in the family, work, social, and community areas. An attempt will be made to assign weights to the items of the scale in order to derive an index of convalescent adjustment. Inasmuch as the "in hospital" status may have a variety of meanings, because of difficulties of placement, etc., another criterion now being studied is behavior while in the hospital. Behavior scales have been developed for ward attendants containing 150 statements about observable "bits" of behavior. The items are so constructed as to minimize ambiguity of meaning.

At present in a study under way at Brooklyn State Hospital, patients admitted during a 3-month period were rated on admission and rated again on the same scale 6 months after admission or just prior to release if release came before 6 months. The amount of information conveyed by each item will be determined and an index of hospital adjustment will be computed.

Perhaps the most important problem facing the biometrician in this area is that of integrating the variety of measures obtained from psychological tests, psychiatric evaluation, prognostic indicators, and evaluations of family and social environment. Instead of the conventional methods used in the past, new ones must be found employing techniques suitable for the analysis of the single individual as well as for the group. Two such techniques have been utilized: agreement score technique (14), and distance function (9).

The agreement score technique consists of dividing the distribution of test scores for each test at its median and considering scores above the median as plus and those below the median as minus. The number of agreements (either double plus or minuses) between each pair of patients is then computed to constitute the agreement scores. There are several methods by which these agreement scores can be further analyzed to obtain a fractionation of the sample. If a patient agrees more closely with his own group than with any of the other groups, he is regarded as well placed in his own group. If he agrees more closely with some other group, he is regarded as belonging to that group, even though his admission status is different. In this way, the number of patients in each type of admission status who showed highest agreement with their own group, or highest agreement with any of the other groups, was determined. The agreement scores correctly locate 65.8% of the patients. In other words, of the patients whose agreement scores would place them in the "First Admission" category, 51.2% were actually so classified clinically. Similarly, of the patients whose agreement scores would place them in the "Chronic" category, 81.6% were actually so classified clinically, and for the total group 65.8% are correctly classified. Conversely, of those patients clinically classified as First Admission, 80.8% are so identified by their agreement scores, while 60.8% of the patients whose clinical classification was Chronic, were so designated by their agreement scores. The overall concordance is thus 64.6%.

Mahalanobis' distance score was also computed for these data. This measure gives the distance between pairs of individuals positioned by their test scores in a hyperspace of suitable dimensionality. The smaller the distance between any pair of individuals, the greater the similarity between them.

With the distance score as a basis of classification, 50.0% of the First Admissions are classified as clinical First Admissions, 82.5% of the Chronics are classified clinically as Chronics. On the other hand, taking clinical status as the criterion, 78.6% of the First Admissions and 57.9% of the Chronics are classified correctly.

Apparently both the distance and the likemindedness scores have a tendency to misclassify Chronics as First Admissions. Both methods also show a higher degree of concordance between clinical status and agreement score for the First Admissions than for the Chronics.

In view of the variety of approaches we have presented to the problem of prognosis, it might be well to summarize the different efforts. The factors that have prognostic value can be classified into three groups: (*a*) individual factors, including both psychological test results and psychiatric evaluation; (*b*) intra-individual factors; (*c*) social or cultural factors. With regard to the first group, the individual factors, we have described elsewhere (1) a schema for classifying individual behavior in terms of physiological, sensory, perceptual, psychomotor, and conceptual response tendencies. This classification has been of value for differentiating the mentally ill from the mentally well and for predicting outcome.

In connection with this attempt the following quotation is of more than passing interest:

As soon as our methodology has sufficiently proved itself through experience with healthy individuals, it would be possible to approach the actual ultimate goal of these efforts, the investigation of sick personality, especially of the inborn pathological disposition. In an investigation of many individuals we will always find some who deviate profoundly from the behavior of the vast majority in one or another aspect. If this deviation appears to be damaging to the mental life, and if it reaches a certain degree—which admittedly can only be arbitrarily determined—then we tend to regard it as an illness. Experience teaches us that persons with pathological traits of this kind are, on the whole, in greater danger of a general mental disturbance than those personalities (natures) whose characteristics are in the middle range. We therefore have first of all to investigate whether it is possible by means of psychological tests to determine individual deviations, which cannot be recognized by ordinary observation. If that succeeds, we would be in the position, through the quantitative determinations at our disposal, to establish the borderline between health and disease much more precisely and more validly than has been possible so far (7).

This was written in 1894 by a man named Emil Kraepelin.

There are other individual factors based on psychiatric evaluation such as type of onset, precipitating events, course of illness, duration of hospitalization, symptomatology, which are included in the prognostic index based on the survey of the literature.

The intra-individual methods involve biochemical analysis of molecular structures. The role of genetics has recently been spotlighted in the significant pronouncement that "there is no crooked thought without a crooked molecule behind it."

The cultural and social factors involve those characteristics that deal with development, environment, and the general social organization that goes under the name of culture. We have tried to point out that in the social-cultural area there is a host of factors involving both the patient's feelings and attitudes toward his fellows and those of his fellows toward him, a matrix in which specific factors can be defined and their patterning and grouping into syndromes arranged so as to predict outcome of mental illness.

The implications of these methods for the institutional agencies which society has developed for dealing with the mentally ill are of considerable interest. A deeper understanding of the variables that lie behind the illness can go far toward influencing our legal approaches to the problem of insanity, our approaches to the problem of hospitalization, and lastly, our attempts both at educating the general population for preventive purposes and for dealing with the rehabilitated mentally ill.

A striking example of the importance of community attitude toward treatment of mental illness is afforded by the town of Gheel in Belgium. While the story of Gheel is well known, I would like to quote some recent impressions from Alan Gregg (5):

But nothing shows so clearly the power of the layman's attitude toward psychiatric disease as does a visit to the town of Gheel in Belgium. There even today some 2,600 insane are billeted by the state in the families of the citizens of Gheel because of a religious vow, or at least a wonderfully tenacious tradition, in force since the thirteenth century that the citizens of Gheel would always extend this expression of human sympathy and kindliness to the insane. Today on the condition of providing a separate room for the patient, a laborer or tradesman or farmer of Gheel can have an insane person as a member of his family, paid for by the state. The low incidence of crimes of violence by or against the patients in Gheel amazes most visitors. The impression I received on a visit there drew additional flavor when I learned that scarcely any native of that town but had been tended as a child by one or another of the insane of Gheel.

Gregg concludes that apparently mental disorders are more sensitive to atmosphere, sympathy, tolerance, and quiet tenacity and faith than any other branch of health and healing.

If we adopt the psychogenic model for mental illness, epidemiological factors become an important tool in rehabilitation. If we adapt the biologic model, the epidemiological factors become important in relieving or preventing stresses that may aggravate the improved patient. If we conclude that the present treatment of mental illness is purely on an ameliorative basis, epidemiological factors become the chief source of the maintenance of the patient in the community. Thus, whichever way the die falls, epidemiological factors loom large in the welfare of the patient.

The achievements of epidemiology in warding off the effect of epidemic physical disease have been notable. But these achievements have hardly touched mental disease. In fact, if anything, the increase in survival and freedom from infectious disease has probably aggravated the problem of mental disorders. It is high time that the epidemiological approach be extended to our field to see what good it can achieve.

REFERENCES

1. Burdock, E. I., S. Sutton, and J. Zubin. Personality and psychopathology. *J. Abnorm. Social Psychol., 56,* 18–30 (1958).
2. Ceraso, Joanne, Phyllis M. Fields, Shirley Harris, H. L. Morris, Dale Sealy, Pearl Singerman, and Joyce B. Wien. An exploratory study of the homes to which 51 schizophrenic patients were dis-

charged from Brooklyn State Hospital to determine the relationship between the quality of the home and patient adjustment. Unpublished master's dissertation, N. Y. School of Social Work, Columbia University, 1955.

3. Cochran, W. G., and Gertrude M. Cox. *Experimental Designs,* 2nd edition. Wiley, John & Sons, New York, 1957.
4. Crandell, A., J. Zubin, F. A. Mettler, and N. Kugelmass. "Mobility" in chronic schizophrenia with special regard to psychosurgery. *Psychiat. Quart., 30,* 96–113 (1956).
5. Gregg, A. Psychiatry in the general hospital. In *Theory and Treatment of the Psychoses.* Washington University, St. Louis, Mo., 1956. Pages 1–13.
6. Kramer, M., H. Goldstein, R. H. Israel, and N. A. Johnson. A historical study of disposition of first admissions to a state mental hospital. *Public Health Monogr. No. 32,* 1955.
7. Kraepelin, E. Der psychologische Versuch in der Psychiatrie. *Psychol. Arb., 1,* 77 (1896).
8. Langfeldt, G. *The Prognosis in Schizophrenia and the Factors Influencing the Course of the Disease.* Levin and Munksgaard, Copenhagen, 1937.
9. Mahalanobis, P. C. On the generalized distance in statistics. *Proc. Natl. Inst. Sci. (India), 49,* 452–82 (1936).
10. Meehl, P. E. *Clinical vs. Statistical Prediction.* University of Minnesota Press, Minneapolis, Minn., 1954.
11. Sanford, N., C. C. McArthur, J. Zubin, L. G. Humphreys, and P. E. Meehl. Panel discussion: "Clinical vs. actuarial prediction." In R. E. Berdie (Chairman) *Invitational Conference on Testing Problems.* Educational Testing Service, Princeton, N. J., 1955.
12. Staudt, Virginia, and J. Zubin. A biometric evaluation of the somatotherapies in schizophrenia. *Psychol. Bull., 56,* 171–96 (1957).
13. Windle, C. Psychological tests in psychopathological prognosis. *Psychol. Bull., 49,* 452–82 (1952).
14. Zubin, J. A technique for measuring like-mindedness. *J. Abnorm. Social Psychol., 38,* 508–16 (1938).
15. Zubin, J. Evaluation of therapeutic outcome in mental disorders. *J. Nervous Mental Disease, 117,* 95–111 (1953).

DISCUSSION

DR. ISIDOR CHEIN: This paper is an admirable and lucid exposition of the major payoff question in the field of mental disease. As I get the question, it runs something like this: What clinical syndromes at which stages of their development and in what kinds of patients respond under what conditions in what short and long range ways to which measures administered by whom?

The question may be compared to a complicated maze, each "what," "which," and "whom" representing a many-alternatived choice point, with the alternatives at each choice point being obscured by a heavy curtain of fog. The choices we must make are among the variables that may be taken into account, the factors with which we might work. There are many correct pathways through this maze, each leading to its appropriate reward, a definitive and precise prediction ratio. The problem is not merely to get to one or more reward boxes, but, in each case, to get to that reward box which is appropriate to the starting point. In other words, the correct alternative at any choice point depends not merely on where we stand at any given moment, but on how we got there and which particular reward box we are heading for.

Consider the various choice points:

1. *What Clinical Syndromes.* Even assuming no errors of diagnosis and further assuming that all the things assigned to one nosological category belong together more closely than they belong with elements of other nosological categories, it is still almost certain that quite different things are being put into any given category. There is, therefore, no reason to assume that the elements of a given category are homogeneously subject to the same fate. Moreover, the distribution of fates is subject to the vagaries of chance in determining the relative distributions of the different types of elements in any given category at any given time in any given clinical population. It follows that we cannot afford to take current diagnostic categories at face value, but must multiply distinctions far beyond the point that would make sense in the current era of clinical practice. The problem is what distinctions to make. Needless to say, before the search is ended, the categories will be shuffled and reshuffled to make for the optimum alignments between diagnoses and treatments.

2. *At Which Stages of Their Development.* At the present moment we hardly have any more reliable guides than the arbitrary measure of the duration of the disturbance and the degree of discouragement we have already experienced in trying to treat it. Again the problem before us is to place our bets on what are likely to be the distinctions with the maximum payoffs.

3. *In What Kinds of Patients.* Here we have some guidance from the demographic and other variables that have turned out to be

significant in epidemiological studies of the distributions of various
disturbances and in studies of short range effects of various treatments.
Alas, as a measure of how much we have learned, these turn out to
be the very variables, for the most part, that I learned to recite by rote
in my first psychology class, almost thirty years ago, variables that
need to be controlled in any experiment—age, sex, race, religious and
cultural background, socio-economic status, rural-urban residence,
education, intelligence, and initial level of the criterion variables.
Most of us have learned in the face of practical limitations to honor
them in the breach rather than in the observance. To these we may
add, in our special case, such variables as ward behavior and willingness to respond to therapeutic efforts.

However we behave at each of the preceding choice points, the
cross classifications define the ultimate stratification cells—"ulstriths,"
as Toops calls them—for the elements of which we want to prognosticate. The more homogeneous our ulstriths, the greater may our
confidence be that we have something sensible to prognosticate about.
The less homogeneous they are, the more we have to rely on the
gods of chance that they are not heterogeneous in such ways as to
make them unprognosticable.

4. *Under What Conditions.* What we need here is a theory of the
environment and of organism-environment interactions that will
direct our attention to the aspects that are relevant to our prog-
nostications. Studies by my associates and myself, for example, indicate that whereas familial environmental deprivations play a role
in the etiologies of both juvenile delinquency and juvenile drug
addiction, the kinds of deprivation involved are quite different in
the two conditions, and that those addicts who are delinquents
independently of their addiction have been deprived in both respects.
Or, to take another instance: In an unpublished doctoral thesis,
Robert Lane showed that while hypothesized schizophrenogenic
family relationships did indeed discriminate between middle class
schizophrenic patients and controls, they were equally characteristic
for middle and lower class patients. They were also characteristic
to the same degree for the lower class controls. One way of interpreting this finding is to assume that schizophrenogenic environmental
stresses may take different forms in the middle and lower classes. The
presumption is that we have a much better theory of the schizophrenogenic middle class environment than of the parallel lower
class environment.

What is true of etiology is presumably also true of prognosis. The
time is long since past (if there ever was such a time) when we

could afford to look upon the environment, as did the researchers on the heredity-environment problem, as though it were a unidimensional variate. But this means that we have to make relevant distinctions in the environments to which our patients return.

The way of a prophet may be hard, but it is much harder if he has to prophesy without regard to the events that intervene between his prophecy and his target date. This task is easiest if his prophecies are simply conditional—in the form, "If the intervening events are so-and-so, then the outcome will be thus-and-so, but if they are such-and-such, then the outcome will be thus-and-such."

I am afraid that time will not permit me to review the remaining "what," "which," and "whom." I should like instead to refer to one difficulty that Dr. Zubin and his associates may have underestimated to some extent. This is the fact that whichever gods constructed our maze, they built into it some complicated servomechanisms as a result of which the various choice points do not operate autonomously, i.e., what we do at one determines to some extent what we will do at another.

Dr. Zubin *et al.* provide us with a nice case in point, especially when I give a slightly different reading to one of their reported findings. According to them, patients coming from better homes tend to have more severe psychopathology and greater likelihood of being in the hospital one year following admission than patients from poorer homes. I assume that this does not mean that better homes produce more severe psychopathology, but rather that better homes can more readily than poorer homes carry their less severely disturbed individuals without requiring hospitalization. Curiously, Zubin and his associates do not draw the inference that it makes little sense to evaluate outcome in terms of hospitalization after a given period or in terms of number or time of hospitalizations during a given period without taking into account the differential probabilities of hospitalization for a given degree of disturbance. I take it, however, that we have here an interaction between a kind of patient variable (kind of home background) and the significance of an outcome variable (hospitalization).

Other possible interactions of our choice points are also readily indicated. Hollingshead and Redlich have reported that lower class hospital patients are not as likely as middle class patients to receive psychotherapy—an at least three-way interaction involving kind of patient, kind of treatment, and kind of therapist. Similarly, one may suspect that at least part of the social class differences in relative frequency of neuroses and psychoses found by Hollingshead and

Redlich may be accounted for by a differential readiness to diagnose a particular condition in these different kinds of patient. That this may actually happen has been neatly demonstrated experimentally in another unpublished dissertation by William Haase. Identical Rorschach records were not identically evaluated when presented with social histories indicative of lower class origin and when presented with social histories indicative of middle class origin. The lower class received less favorable trait ratings, more severe diagnostic ratings, and less favorable prognoses.

The point of calling attention to these interactions is that, if we are not alert to them, we may find ourselves with all kinds of artifacts in our data, including the most dangerous artifact of them all, the self-fulfilling prophecy.

One additional point: In our concern with successful prediction, we may overlook a major root source of knowledge on which we may base better prediction formulas—intensive study of the cases in which predictions fail and the reasons for the failure.

DR. MORTON KRAMER: I would urge Dr. Zubin to look more carefully at the statement he made about epidemiological studies, prospective and retroactive type studies. I think I can point to many studies which have taken the epidemiological approach to evaluate what happened to particular individuals with particular disease entities on a prospective basis; that is, they had to be followed to find out what happened to these individuals.

For example, the recent evaluation of polio vaccine was not a retroactive type study. Nor were studies done of tuberculous individuals to find out something about mortality of individuals who were patients with particular degrees of illness. Nor have the studies on effects of fluoride for correction of dental caries been done on a retroactive basis. They were designed to use the Kingston population to find out fully what happened to different individuals subject to different kinds of stresses. I am sure in the mental health field and also all other areas of chronic illness, you can find similar studies.

DR. PAUL HOCH: I might say something about Dr. Kramer's discussion. I think to add confusion to confusion, Dr. Kramer was speaking about experimental studies, although prospective studies may be epidemiologic.

DR. J. ZUBIN: Dr. Chein's disagreement with me reminds me of a story I heard not long ago. The scene is a country cottage with a long front porch. At one end sit two proverbial spinsters. At the other end, sit two traveling salesmen. They haven't yet met. Suddenly, a hen goes running by with a rooster in hot pursuit. Just as the rooster is about to catch up with the hen, he espies a piece of bread in the road, so he puts the brakes on and turns toward the bread. The poor hen, not knowing the chase is over, continues out into the road and gets run over by a truck.

The response of the two groups of observers to this tragic scene is as follows: The spinsters: "You see, she'd rather be dead!" The salesmen: "Boy, I hope I never get that hungry!"

Now, it all depends upon the point of view from which you are viewing the scene, and I dare say there are many things that we see in our program which may not be apparent to others. I don't see, however, any real basic differences between our points of view.

For example, take the question of homogeneity. Certainly, one patient who is classified as dementia praecox, or schizophrenic, is not the same as another one classified as such, and that is why we introduced the concept of likemindedness. We wanted to see whether we could get natural groupings in our data so as to reduce the heterogeneity. If Dr. Chein knows of a better method, I certainly would want to buy it.

The whole study arose from an attempt to find out why it was that certain people who we predicted should get well did not get well, and did not go home; while others we predicted would not get well did go home.

We were very close to the individual in our investigation, and I think we agree that epidemiological studies not supported by individual investigations of each case, certainly will get you nowhere.

Now, in the long run, our real goal is not to make predictions. We like them to come true when we do make them, but that is not our real goal; that is our assumed goal. Our real goal is to understand schizophrenia and to control it eventually. I don't know of any better way than to try to predict and then to go back and see whether we made any mistakes in our predictions. We learn from our mistakes, of course, by picking up the very cases for whom we failed to predict and by finding out what happened to divert them from the course which we thought they would take. That is perhaps the only excuse we have for engaging in this activity. Simply to play the game of prophet and prognosticator, would not really justify our efforts.

As for Dr. Kramer's question with regard to the prospective and retrospective studies, I think he will agree with me that in the field of mental health we don't know of any such studies. It is in the other areas perhaps where we have had such studies.

Housing Environment and Mental Health[1]

DANIEL M. WILNER AND ROSABELLE PRICE WALKLEY

School of Hygiene and Public Health,
The Johns Hopkins University, Baltimore, Maryland

For several years we have been interested in the specific influence that housing environment has upon certain factors related to the concept of mental health, namely, personal and family adjustment and particular aspects of physical health. Many investigators have been interested in these relationships in years past, and a certain amount of data bearing on the subject has been accumulated.

The purpose of this paper is to discuss two methods of collecting information regarding the relationship between housing and mental health. The first method, which is a good deal more common than the second, consists of an investigation of a given population at a single point in time. The second method consists of multiple investigations of the same population over an extended period of time. Thus, the distinction is between the single-point-in-time and the longitudinal study.

Our primary focus will be on the relative soundness, efficiency, and definitiveness of conclusions that may be drawn from the two methods as applied to the study of housing and health. We shall also point to some important procedural differences. In both cases, we shall draw upon our own experience in connection

[1] This is Department of Biostatistics Paper No. 318.

This investigation is being supported by a research grant from the National Institutes of Health, Public Health Service, U.S. Department of Health, Education, and Welfare.

with a study of 1,000 families in the city of Baltimore, Maryland.

We will be less concerned with the obviously very important matters of content, inasmuch as the measures of health and adjustment are identical in both methods of procedure in the examples we will be using for illustration. Very briefly, we are obtaining three kinds of information relevant to the mental health and adjustments of families in our study. First, we are inquiring in detail about the physical health of family members; here we are interested in acute and chronic conditions and symptoms that affect everyone in the household, and we hope, in part, to be able to sort out conditions and symptoms that are customarily considered psychosomatic in origin. A second kind of data relevant to mental health comes from information on a number of matters related to family life, life in the neighborhood and in the community, and certain personal attitudes and feeling states. A third kind of information comes from official records of hospitals, courts, social agencies, and schools. Except, of course, for the official records, our informant for the family on all matters is the female head of the household. It is from these three clusters of variables that we hope at the end of the study to obtain some estimate of the mental health of our families. The data we will be reporting presently derive from the second category, that is, the attitude and feeling state information collected in the adjustment interview. Our medical data are now in process of being analyzed; the court, school, and hospital data are only now being collected.

Although we have been making quite extensive measures of the quality of the housing environment of our families, we will confine ourselves at present to a crude index of housing quality. This index consists of the unweighted deficiencies arising from nine components, for example, the presence or absence of ordinary facilities like a toilet or hot running water, the sharing of facilities like kitchen or bathroom, vermin infestation, the extent of sleep-crowding, and a general measure of dilapidation.

We shall not describe at present precisely how we selected our 1,000 families. It will suffice to say that all were in the low-income bracket, and all were applicants for public housing. At the time the presently reported data were collected, none had been awarded an apartment. Thus, all the families "needed" housing. Yet, among them, some were in relatively better housing circumstances than others. We found families at every point on the housing quality index just described.

The Single-Point-in-Time Study

Let us turn now to a discussion of the first of the two kinds of methods for collecting information on the relationship between housing and health, namely, the single-point-in-time study. For the purpose of illustrating this type of study, we sampled from among our 1,000 families two groups, those with zero housing quality deficiencies and those with deficiency scores of 6 or more, and we will contrast these two groups on each variable to be discussed. Lest you find the comparison of extremes disturbing, let us say that there were no mansions or split levels among the "relatively well housed" in our sample, but rather dwelling units in which rudimentary facilities were present, were not shared with other families or individuals, and in which there was relatively little crowding. Many of these same zero deficiency dwelling units would undoubtedly be given a low score on an absolute index of housing quality.

We will now present several groups of variables beginning with those most directly related to the housing situation and ending with a series of psychological scales we have devised for our own purposes titled "mood," "nervousness," "potency: efficacy of self-help," etc. It should be remembered that the respondent answering the questions is the woman of the house.

Table I shows the answer to several questions regarding the respondent's liking for her apartment, the neighborhood, and the people in it. To illustrate the relationship which housing quality bears to these attitudes, 42% of the well-housed com-

pared with 7% of the poorly housed liked the apartment "a lot."
On the other hand, only 4% of the well housed, but 35% of the
badly housed liked the apartment "not at all." The direction of
the differences is the same for the questions concerning the
neighborhood and the people in it: the well housed tended to
like them more than did the poorly housed.

TABLE I

Housing Quality and Point of View toward Apartment, Neighborhood,
and People Who Live in Neighborhood

(*a*) In general, how do you like your apartment—would you say you like it:

	Housing Quality Deficiencies	
	Zero	*6 or more*
	(*Good housing*)	(*Bad housing*)
_____ A lot	42%	7%
_____ Quite a bit	32	15
_____ Only a little	22	41
_____ Not at all	4	35
No answer	—	2
(Number of respondents)	(50)	(60)

(*b*) In general, would you say this neighborhood is:

	Housing Quality Deficiencies	
	Zero	*6 or more*
_____ Very good as a place to live	60%	25%
_____ Fairly good	38	44
_____ Not so good	—	13
_____ Not good at all	2	18
(Number of respondents)	(50)	(60)

(*c*) In general, how well do you like the people who live around here—would you say you like them:

	Housing Quality Deficiencies	
	Zero	*6 or more*
_____ A lot	38%	27%
_____ Quite a bit	42	33
_____ Only a little	12	38
Don't know	8	2
(Number of respondents)	(50)	(60)

Table II tells something of the inhibitions to sociality that are seemingly related to quality of housing. The questions were:

Sometimes people don't invite their friends to their home as often as they would like, because they feel they don't *have enough space to entertain* them. Have you ever felt this way about your present apartment?

Sometimes people don't invite other people into their home because they feel their home doesn't *look quite nice enough*. Have you ever felt this way about your present apartment?

Only 24% and 18% of the well-housed answered "yes" to each of the two questions respectively, compared with 68 and 60% of the badly housed.

TABLE II

Housing Quality and Attitudes toward Inviting People into House because of Space and Appearance of House

(*a*) Sometimes people don't invite their friends to their home as often as they would like because they feel they don't *have enough space to entertain them*. Have you ever felt this way about your present apartment?

	Housing Quality Deficiencies	
	Zero	6 or more
Yes	24%	68%
No	76	32
(Number of respondents)	(50)	(60)

(*b*) Sometimes people don't invite other people into their home because they feel their home doesn't *look quite nice enough*. Have you ever felt this way about your present apartment?

	Housing Quality Deficiencies	
	Zero	6 or more
Yes	18%	60%
No	82	38
No answer	—	2
(Number of respondents)	(50)	(60)

Table III shows how the two groups of families differed in the extent to which the respondent reported that the family members sat down to a meal together. The well housed were considerably *more* likely than the badly housed to eat together "always," 65% compared with 35%, and *less* likely than the badly housed to eat together "only some of the time," 11% compared with 27%. Very few families in either group "never" ate together.

TABLE III

Housing Quality and Family Practice of Eating Together

How often does *everyone* in your family who lives in this apartment sit down to the evening meal together? Would you say:

	Housing Quality Deficiencies	
	Zero	6 or more
_____ Always	65%	35%
_____ Most of the time	22	35
_____ Only some of the time	11	27
_____ Never	2	3
(Number of respondents)	(45)[a]	(55)[a]

[a] The difference between the number of respondents appearing here and in Tables I and II is due to the fact that this question did not apply to a few families as a consequence of their family composition, for example, a family consisting only of the mother and one or two very young children.

Table IV gives the distribution of answers to another question on housing:

Sometimes a person wants to be by herself somewhere in the apartment without being bothered by other family members. How easy would it be for you to do this if you wanted to?

Sixty-seven per cent of the well housed compared with 16% of the poorly housed found this "very easy," while only 4% of the well housed compared to 49% of the poorly housed found it "very hard."

TABLE IV

Housing Quality and Opportunity for Privacy

Sometimes a person wants to be by herself somewhere in the apartment without being bothered by other family members. How easy would it be for you to do this if you wanted to? Would you say:

	Housing Quality Deficiencies	
	Zero	6 or more
___ Very easy	67%	16%
___ Fairly easy	27	22
___ Fairly hard	2	13
___ Very hard	4	49
(Number of respondents)	(45)[a]	(55)[a]

[a] The difference between the number of respondents appearing here and in Tables I and II is due to the fact that this question did not apply to a few families as a consequence of their family composition, for example, a family consisting only of the mother and one or two very young children.

In Table V we have the answers to questions regarding the self-perceived social mobility of the two groups of families. The questions were:

Compared to, say, five years ago, do you feel you are:

___ Better off in life now than you were then,
___ About the same now as then, or
___ Worse off in life now than you were then?"

Which of these groups of people would you say you belong to:

___ People who are going up in the world,
___ People who are not really going up or down,
___ People who have gone somewhat down in the world?"

On the first item, that relating to improved status, the proportion of the well housed reporting that they were better off now was almost twice that of the poorly housed (72% compared with 38%). The differences are smaller, but in the same direction, for the answers to the second item, that on group ascendency.

TABLE V

Housing Quality and Perceived Social Mobility

(*a*) Compared to say, five years ago, do you feel you are:

	Housing Quality Deficiencies	
	Zero	6 or more
_____ Better off in life now than you were then	72%	38%
_____ About the same now as then	20	30
_____ Worse off in life now than you were then	8	32
(Number of respondents)	(50)	(60)

(*b*) Which of these groups of people would you say you belong to:

	Housing Quality Deficiencies	
	Zero	6 or more
_____ People who are going up in the world	76%	62%
_____ People who are not really going up or going down	20	22
_____ People who have gone somewhat down in the world	4	14
No answer	—	2
(Number of respondents)	(50)	(60)

Table VI shows the distribution of responses to five "psychological state" scales assembled especially for this study.[2] The title of the scale and a characteristic item from each follows:

Scale 1. *Potency: Efficacy of self-help. Item:*

When you come right down to it, there's nothing you can do to make things really better for yourself.

Scale 2. *Morale: Optimism-pessimism. Item:*

If things seem to be going well for a while, there's usually some trouble right around the corner.

---

[2] These are Guttman-type, unidimensional scales, which were constructed and tested on an independent group immediately prior to the assembling of the data now being discussed. The scales met the criterion of 95% reproducibility.

Scale 3. *Morale: Satisfaction with status quo. Item:*

I'm really very happy about the way I've been getting along lately.

Scale 4. *Nervousness. Item:*

Are you often so nervous or upset that you can't go on with what you are doing?

Scale 5. *Mood. Item:*

Are you sometimes so blue that you feel there's no use going on?

TABLE VI

Housing Quality and Certain Indicators of Psychological State

Scale 1. *Potency: Efficacy of self-help[a]*

No. of Items[b]	Housing Quality Deficiencies	
	Zero	6 or more
5 (most committed to efficacy of self-help)	34 ⎱64%	8 ⎱26%
4	30 ⎰	18 ⎰
3	10 ⎱28%	29 ⎱51
2	18 ⎰	22 ⎰
1	8 ⎱	20 ⎱
0 (least committed to efficacy of self-help)	— ⎰ 8	3 ⎰23
(Number of respondents)	(50)	(60)

Scale 2. *Morale: Optimism-pessimism*

	Zero	6 or more
4 (most optimistic)	34 ⎱64%	5 ⎱25%
3	30 ⎰	20 ⎰
2	22 } 22	35 } 35
1	4 ⎱14	30 ⎱40
0 (least optimistic)	10 ⎰	10 ⎰
(Number of respondents)	(50)	(60)

Scale 3. *Morale: Satisfaction with status quo*

	Zero	6 or more
4 (most satisfied)	62 ⎱76%	39 ⎱51%
3	14 ⎰	12 ⎰
2	12 } 12	18 } 18
1	8 ⎱12	13 ⎱31
0 (least satisfied)	4 ⎰	18 ⎰
(Number of respondents)	(50)	(60)

TABLE VI (*continued*)

Scale 4. *Nervousness*

5 (least nervous)	10 }72%	7 }47%
4	62	40
3	18 }24	23 }36
2	6	13
1	4 }4	12 }17
0 (most nervous)	—	5
(Number of respondents)	(50)	(60)

Scale 5. *Mood*

No. of Items[b]	Housing Quality Deficiencies	
	Zero	6 or more
4 (least moody)	22 }60%	8 }36%
3	38	28
2	22 }22	34 }34
1	10 }18	25 }30
0 (most moody)	8	5
(Number of respondents)	(50)	(60)

[a] For the items composing each scale, see Appendix.

[b] Items responded to in the direction indicating for: Scale 1, belief in efficacy of self-help; Scale 2, optimism; Scale 3, satisfaction with status quo; Scale 4, freedom from nervousness; Scale 5, freedom from moodiness.

For each item on each scale there is a direction of response related to the title of the scale. Thus, for the prototype item of the potency scale, *agreement* with the item is taken to signify *lack* of perceived potency; disagreement, the presence of perceived potency. As can be seen from the answers to the potency items, the well housed were considerably more likely than the poorly housed (64% compared with 26% for the top two categories) to take the more potent positions on the scale. The well housed were also less likely (8% compared with 23% for the bottom two categories) to take the less potent positions. Similar, consistent, large differences were found on the other scales as well: the well housed were more likely than the poorly housed to be optimistic and to believe that things were going well (Scales 2 and 3); the poorly housed indicated more nervousness (Scale 4) and more moodiness (Scale 5).

These are all the substantive data that we will present at this time. The items offered (with the exception of the scales of "psychological state") may appear as a haphazard assemblage of issues related to housing. Actually, we have not yet tabulated the responses to all the questions we asked in the course of our interviews. Those given here represent only a small portion of the matters covered. The entire group of questions were designed to test point by point a systematic theory we have been developing regarding the role played by slum housing—*everything else being held constant*—in physical health, personal and family adjustment. Time does not permit a full description of the entire theory in detail. It may suffice to mention that our thinking has led us to view the slum dwelling as offering a series of inhibitions and restraints upon: (*a*) the development of wholesome personal and family interrelationships, characterized, for example, by the warmth and compatibility existing among family members, and by the extent to which the family takes part in common activities in a compatible manner; (*b*) the development of sociality and neighborliness as characterized by extent and nature of interaction with the families nearby as well as outlook and point of view toward neighbors as persons; (*c*) the development of good citizenship in the general community, as characterized by participation in community activities as well as attitude and point of view toward the larger community. Finally, we have considered slum housing from the point of view of personal psychological development, as providing inhibitions and restraints upon realistic aspirations for self and family, upon morale, and upon appropriate solutions of, and points of view toward, life's problems.

The data just presented, as they derive from this theory, suggest at first glance solid confirmation for many of our speculations. The poorly housed (and their housing is very poor indeed) certainly tended more to dislike their neighborhood and their neighbors (although the neighborhoods were, by and large, the same as those of the well housed); the poorly housed did less inviting-in for housing-connected reasons; the poorly housed families tended less toward so common and characteristic a family enterprise as eating together in the evening; they tended more to view their status position and ascent in a more pessimistic light; the poorly housed respondent found it harder to be alone if she wanted to; and the "psychological state" scales suggest that she was moodier, more pessimistic, and edgier.

But are the differences we have found actually derivable from differences in the quality of the dwelling units occupied by our two groups? Remember that it is housing quality and nothing else, for the moment, the extent of whose effects we are interested in gaging. Unfortunately (for our hypotheses) we cannot be sure that it is housing quality that causes the differences. The crucial issue hinges around a phrase we used earlier, "everything else being held constant." Perhaps it isn't housing at all; perhaps the differences are attributable to differences in educational level of the two groups of families or the length of residence in the city—factors that may be highly correlated with housing.

Let us attempt to explore these possibilities further now. Both groups of families appear similar on a number of characteristics. Both groups have shown similar social "knowhow" in applying for public housing. They are both homogeneous as to ethnic background and stock. The total family income range is very similar, the median for both groups being in the $2000–$2500 bracket; 70% in both groups have lived in the city 15 years or longer; education is similar, the median level attained in both groups being junior high school.

But, note these differences: the poorly housed are more likely than the well housed (*a*) to be on welfare (30% compared with 14%); (*b*) to keep house rather than work (79% compared with 42%);[3] (*c*) to be younger (40% are 25 years of age or younger, compared with 20% of the well housed); and, finally, (*d*) to have more children (70% of the poorly housed have 3 or more children, compared with 30% among the well housed). The latter figures are especially noteworthy. Although the two groups have similar distributions on total family income, the fact that the

[3] Only 12% of the poorly housed women held full-time jobs, compared with 42% of the well-housed women.

median number of children is higher in the poorly housed group means that the effective income *per person* in that group is lower; thus, the same money must be stretched to cover more persons.

These data would lead us to believe that perhaps factors other than housing, per se, might account for the attitudinal and "psychological state" differences we have observed, or in any event that there is probably interaction between housing, income, etc. However, one may ask what difference it makes whether our dependent variables have been shown related to poor housing, or to low income, or to low level of education, or to any of the numerous indicators that have been used to define social class and position in life. Isn't it enough to know that all these factors seem to be playing some role, perhaps in concert, acting as a complex? We would agree that for many theoretical and socially practical purposes it would suffice.

Thus, we see a distinct advance arising from the large body of single-visit and cross-sectional studies of the past thirty years that have described the relationship between indicators of social class and many kinds of physical, behavioral, and social pathologies. The list of pathologies so related is long, beginning with the early studies (prompted by the thinking of Park and Burgess) of Shaw and McKay on crime and delinquency (5, 6). Other examples are alcoholism, broken homes, and divorce (Beverly Hills notwithstanding), syphilis, tuberculosis, and childhood communicable diseases. New entries are being made as time goes by: reading disability has recently entered the lists, as has the incidence of narcotics use among teen-agers, as well as the incidence of mental illness. [Studies involving the social characteristics of the mentally ill and some valuable summaries of the literature have been assembled in a volume edited by Rose (4).]

This class of studies has, to say the least, done the service of pointing to the social class locus of many of the pressing problems of society today, documenting systematically what society itself is reluctant to believe. Thus, in one phase of a recent study of teen-age narcotics use conducted by Chein and his colleagues, it was found that, in Manhattan, 85% of heroin use among young people takes place in 16% of the census tracts of the borough (2). To know the social characteristics of these users and their neighborhoods is already the first step in the building of a theory accounting for juvenile drug use.

However, single-point-in-time studies often run into serious difficulties of interpretation when interest is focused on one or only a few of the variables which as part of the larger complex of social class have been found related to personal and social pathology. Cloudiness of interpretation is sometimes overcome by careful and painstaking secondary analysis by using the techniques of partial correlation. But often, such approaches are of little use, inasmuch as the elements of social class indices are generally highly correlated with one another.

Interest in housing, in particular, as a factor in physical, behavioral, and social ills arises from some of the very studies of relationships to social class that we have been talking about. Many studies have shown the direct connection between housing and, say, physical health (1) or juvenile antisocial behavior (6). In others, the factor of housing has been incorporated in indices of social class. In many instances, housing shows an almost unequivocal *inverse* relationship with social ills, the latter rising as the quality of housing deteriorates. In other studies, particularly those of mental health and illness, the direction of relationship depends on the particular condition being investigated. Thus, the psychoses have been found to be related to housing quality (as a component of a social class index) in the manner just indicated; the neuroses, however, increase with improved housing quality.

The Longitudinal Study

The second method of collecting information which we wish to discuss is the longitudinal study. The controlled longitudinal study seems to hold the promise of answering many of the vexing problems of interpretation that beset the single-point-in-time study. It was with this hope in mind that, in 1952, members of the American Public Health Association and the National Association of Housing and Redevelopment officials organized a Joint Committee on the Hygiene of Housing. The memberships of both organizations, by the way, are committed to programs of improving housing quality even in advance of unimpeachable evidence that housing and housing alone has ameliorating effects. By 1954, the Joint Committee had interested the National Institutes of Health in providing funds for a controlled longitudinal study of some of the physical and social effects of housing.

The research mandate was to explore two general content areas, the area of physical health and sickness, broadly defined, and the area with which this paper is concerned, personal and social adjustment and mental health. The latter area, as we have mentioned previously, was to be concerned primarily with family life, neighborhood and community attitudes and affiliation, and the feeling states and attitudes of the respondents. Information on all these matters was to be obtained by means of home interviews. Additional adjustment and mental health information was to be collected from hospitals, schools, and social agencies.

The general study plan was to locate a population that was known to be moving from "bad" to "good" housing. This was to constitute the "test" group. Measurements were to be made on this group prior to the move, and were to continue for a three-year period afterwards. In order to evaluate the effects of housing in any changes that took place, a control group was planned which would be matched carefully with the test group on many relevant characteristics, and which would also undergo "before and after" measurements.[3]

The research design was put into effect through the cooperation of a local housing authority in the following way. A test group of 400 families was selected from among 800, all of whom were to move from the slum to a new housing project. Initial measurements were made on this group before the move.

[3] The details of the background of the study and certain of its features appear in an earlier paper (7).

As the test families were being chosen, a control group of approximately 600 families was selected, matched as closely as possible to the test families. This study of both groups is now well under way. To date, the rehoused families have lived in the project approximately one year on the average. A good deal of "after" data on both adjustment and physical health has already been accumulated from repeated interviews with the families of both groups, and much of it is being processed at present. There will be a total of thirteen "after" measures through interviews conducted once every ten weeks.

It is the results of this longitudinal data that we would like to be able to contrast with the single-point-in-time data presented earlier—*the latter data incidentally were derived from the "before" measures of the full-scale study.*[4] However, our longitudinal data are as yet too incomplete to make such a comparison possible. Instead we wish to point out some apparent advantages to be gained from the longitudinal study that has a controlled before and after design, and at the same time, we wish to discuss, with illustrations from our own work, some of the grave difficulties that attend carrying out such a study, and some of the elements that seem necessary to make it feasible.

One of the distinct advantages of a controlled longitudinal study arises from the fact that if the two groups who are to undergo differential housing experience are very similar at the beginning of the study, and if the character of the housing they occupy is the only difference between them *during* the period of the study, then any differences between them at the conclusion of the study can logically be attributed to housing. Furthermore, a sounder base for more refined analysis is possible. Thus, for example, it may be suspected that families at different income levels are not equally affected by differences in housing. It may

[4] The "zero" and the "6 or more" housing quality deficiency groups contained both test and control families in about equal proportions. Since the direction of the findings was seen to be the same, the data for the test and control groups were combined.

be that when we contrast the well-housed and the poorly housed among families of low income, the effect of housing is quite large; on the other hand, the effects of housing at higher income levels may be negligible. In any event, in the controlled longitudinal study, we have the possibility of pulling housing out of the circular chain that confounds interpretation of single-point-in-time studies. On logical grounds, when one is interested in the precise effects of a single variable, the controlled long-term study is superior to the single-point-in-time study.

The difficulties of the longitudinal study begin to arise when one attempts to ensure the basic assumptions of such a study; for example, the assumption of initial comparability of the two groups under examination. Another difficulty arises from the problem of attrition from both test and control samples, either as outright loss through refusal to continue cooperation, or as "losses" of another kind in which, for example, families originally in the control group finally move into a housing project during the course of the study. A third difficulty arises from staff and field practices that are intrinsic to long-time studies, such as maintaining uniformity of interviewing procedures over time and at any one time ensuring identity of procedure with both test and control groups. As we proceed, we shall show our attempts to overcome these difficulties.

Initial Comparability of Test and Control Groups

In order to draw the least equivocal conclusions from the controlled longitudinal study, the two groups under examination must be well matched at the outset. Unless this is the case, differences in the dependent variable, such as mental health, may at the end of the study be attributable in greater or lesser degree to differences in background, etc., that existed when the samples were originally selected. This is obviously the case when one considers the actual mental health of families in our two groups at the outset, for if the test families were healthier than the control families, it would be no surprise in line with the hypotheses to see them different at the end of the study. The argument applies with equal force to factors expected to be *related* to mental health, for example, certain background characteristics, which, by the way, are often the only descriptions available regarding the families when they are selected.

Sometimes, minor mismatching, if it involves few variables, may be acceptable in lieu of perfect matching, with the view to correcting for the inequity at the time of analysis of the data. On the other hand, if mismatching is gross on some variables, it may be very difficult to apply statistically sound corrections.

Efforts to obtain well-matched groups at the outset of a study may have one consequence that in some respects vitiates the generalizability of the general theory under test. Thus, it may turn out that the only well-matched groups available are very small in number or may have such unusual characteristics that they represent a special group of persons or families to whom the general theory applies in only a limited way.

We will illustrate some of these problems from our own study. As mentioned earlier, the test group of 400 families was selected from a total of 800 successful applicants for a public housing project. It was understood by all that for reasons of policy the housing authority was to choose the successful applicants according to its usual procedures; the study staff was to have no hand in the selection of the families who moved in. However, out of the 800 families we were free to choose any 400 we wished for the test group. The *particular* 400 test families we chose depended in good measure on the characteristics of the potential *control* families who would serve as their matches and who, for various reasons, were also to come from the housing authority files. There were two considerations arising from the nature of the pool of potential control families available to us: the size of a given stratum in the pool and the likelihood of the particular stratum remaining in the slum for the duration of the study. These considerations led us, for example, to tend to avoid choosing as *test* families those with certain characteristics of age and number of children, because that category of families was in short supply in the *control* pool. Similarly, we tended to avoid an excess number of small-sized families because from information at hand, the probabilities were high that these families would be rehoused during the course of the study. Thus, even the test families chosen were to some extent determined by the desire to match the groups well.

The initial matching was done by using the pair-by-pair method on the basis of systematic information about both test and control families found in the housing authority's application files. After both groups had been assembled and the initial interview accomplished, we reviewed the goodness of matching and used, this time, the up-to-date information on the initial matching variables that was obtained in the "before" interviews. In addition, we now included in our criteria for goodness of match certain other relevant background, health, and attitude factors. From this new information, some 44% of our initially satisfactory matches now proved to be unsatisfactory. We were able to reduce this number to less than 10% because of a fact that we considered an expensive nuisance at the time it took place, namely, because of the way in which we were given lists of applicants by the housing authority, we had interviewed an excess of 700 potential control families. It was from this group that we found replacements for our originally unsatisfactory matches.

The final outcome is that we are now satisfied that we began our study with two well-matched groups of families. But, here is the price we paid. Our groups contain no *white* families, relatively few Negro *veteran* families, and thus we have probably a somewhat unrepresentative sample of typical housing applicants. We were willing to pay this price, since the range of family types and of personal characteristics of individuals remaining in our groups is still sufficiently great to permit the drawing of comprehensive generalizations from our findings. It may be that in other studies, the price paid for satisfactory matching places too great a constriction on the range of the desired characteristics.

Attrition of Members from Samples

Almost all sample surveys suffer losses from initially defined samples. The usual figure in a single-visit study is 6 to 10% loss from outright refusal to continue in the study, non-locates, and from respondents not at home. In analyzing the data, the usual procedure is, regrettably, to ignore losses, the assumption effectively being that they divide themselves on all issues as do the bulk of the sample remaining in the study. Often, ignoring the possible deviation of losses from the general trend does little damage to the data; sometimes, however, the damage to interpretation is sizable.

In the controlled longitudinal study, permanent losses may cripple a study before its announced termination date. If the usual 6 to 10% loss occurred during each series of home visits, three afterwaves of interviewing might result in an 18 to 30% loss. Permanent losses of this magnitude would make sound conclusions from the study almost impossible to draw, especially if there is reason to believe that the attrition is biased in some way.

We are finding that the intactness of a sample over time is a direct function of the efforts made to obtain the interview. In our study we have kept permanent losses to little more than 1% per wave of interviewing. This is accomplished in three ways. First, we have abandoned the traditional limit of three or four visits before giving up. Half the families on any wave give the interview at the first call. But 10% of the families require five or more visits before the respondent is found home or is ready to talk to the interviewer. Secondly, we make considerable effort to trace our families when they move. During a wave of interviewing, half of one person's time is devoted to phone tracing, in addition to considerable field tracing activity. Thirdly, every respondent who refuses is visited as a last resort by the directors of the study. Many apparently firm refusals are restored to active status after some explanation and persuasion by the senior study personnel.

Another type of "loss" peculiar to our study has a different character altogether. Since our control families are applicants for public housing, some are eventually awarded apartments in one or another of the city's housing projects. We are continuing to interview these control families even though they no longer live in the slum. In general, this improvement in housing for a portion of our control group can mean only a lessening of the difference in housing quality between the initially constituted test and control groups and may make it harder for us to detect dependent variable differences. We are reluctant to drop them altogether since there may be some bias in who makes the move. We will, by the way, attempt to capitalize on this group in a special analysis, since it will represent families on whom we have *several* "before" measures prior to an improvement in housing. In any event, the losses in this category have been about 5% in the nine months after the original test and control samples were constituted.

Staff and Field Procedures

Every sample survey, whether of the single-visit or the longitudinal variety, must face the problem of interviewer variability in performance and the resulting effect on the nature and quality of the responses brought back from the field. The problem is akin to the issue of the reliability of diagnoses and judgments in the clinic and hospital. It is an established fact in survey interviewing that interviewers will vary in response rate in connection with certain kinds of questions.

In many single-visit surveys this problem is neglected and such neglect may distort the findings. Thus, in the data presented earlier in this paper, a number of interviewers were involved, and response rates almost certainly differed among them. In any one wave of the controlled longitudinal study, the problem is similar to that in the single-visit study. An added complication arises from the fact of repeated visits where we are faced not only with ordinary between-interviewer variability but also with between-*wave* variability, and possibly, most dangerous of all, between-*group* variability. All three kinds of variability may have influence on the data and in general can be corrected for only partly at the time of analysis through adjusting group percentages by weighting the response tendencies of the interviewer.

In our own study we are using a series of procedures of assignment and quality control which appear to be useful in curbing the variabilities we have been talking about. For example, within a wave, we are giving each interviewer a proper allocation of assignments in the test and control groups. This is accomplished primarily through the requirement that each interviewer be assigned the twins of a matched pair of families. The between-wave and between-group variability is curbed through the efforts of a team of field supervisors whose business it is to keep track of interview quality. The elements of the quality control system are, first, the observation of each interviewer at least once each week during a wave: the supervisor accompanies the interviewer into the home, observes manner and technique, records along with the interviewer, and later comments on the interview and instructs the interviewer. Secondly, a sample of one out of every two interview records is reviewed the week they are received, and errors and inconsistencies are communicated to the interviewer. Thirdly, a quarter of the sample is postenumerated each wave with a brief version of the questionnaire, in order to verify the facts reported in the original interview.

Summary and Conclusion

The problems of matching, of attrition, and of field procedures just discussed are, in addition to other problems not discussed, the price one must pay for the expected sounder conclusions to be reached from a controlled longitudinal study. It is clear from what we have said that to some extent many of the problems, like attrition and within-wave quality control, also exist in the single-visit study. But the problems of matching and rematching, of certain categories of losses from the sample, and of wave-by-wave quality control are inherent strictly to the longitudinal study.

We would like in conclusion to mention two other kinds of difference between the single-visit study and the longitudinal methods of collecting data. The first has to do with the relative financial costs of the two kinds of studies. We estimate that the financial outlay necessary to do the long-term study, with the elements seemingly needed to do it in a sound manner, is five to seven times greater than the outlay for a hypothetical single-visit study that in general covers the same ground. The point is that in the longitudinal study proper implementation of the design requires enormous outlay in personnel and funds.

The second difference between the two kinds of methods arises from their differential impact on the researchers themselves, a matter that rarely receives attention. Investigators like ourselves with experience primarily in single-visit studies find the longitudinal study by far the "busiest" research they have undertaken. The clue to the situation has, of course, to do with the relative place of the field work in the entire scheme. The total time span of most of the simpler studies may be divided without great error into the ratio: 3:3:4, that is three-tenths of the study time for preparation, three-tenths for field work, and four-tenths for analysis and preliminary reports, respectively. In our study, the ratios look more like 2:6:2, two-tenths for preparation, six-tenths for field work, and two-tenths for the final stages. Things are further complicated by the fact that because of the divers elements in the study, preparation of materials for different phases runs concurrently with the field work. Finally, in the conduct of a longitudinal study, the researcher feels the absence of psychological *closure* usually to be found much earlier in the conduct of single-visit studies. In many studies, the basic findings are understood and the hypotheses are confirmed or not within a year from the onset of the field work. In our study, we are even now after two and one-half years of activity without major findings, and with none in sight for perhaps another year.

As a consequence, to paraphrase some of the variables of our own study, an individual on the study staff sometimes wishes he could be alone by himself away from the hurly-burly of every-day activities; more often than he likes, he misses taking the evening meal at home; he often is not satisfied with the status quo; he is sometimes moody and nervous. Yet withal, optimism seems to prevail. And as for potency, that is, the point of view toward what self-help can accomplish, it probably keeps us going throughout the conduct of what appears to be an impossible task. There are times when it would appear that we are driven mainly by an insatiable curiosity about the question that, having gone this far, can the study really be done at all? After two and one-half years it would appear that it can.

Acknowledgment

We are indebted to numerous consultants in varied fields who shared their experience and knowledge with us. Special recognition is due Alan S. Meyer, College of the City of New York, Eunice Cooper, New York University, and Nehemiah Jordan, National Institutes of Health, who made numerous valuable contributions in the early stages of the study.

REFERENCES

1. Britton, R. H., J. E. Brown, and I. Altman. Certain characteristics of urban housing and their relation to illness and accidents: Summary of findings of the National Health Survey. *Milbank Mem. Fund Quart. 18,* 91–113 (1940).
2. Chein, I., and E. Rosenfeld. Juvenile heroin users in New York City. *Law and Contemporary Problems, 22,* 52–68 (1957).
3. Park, R. E., and E. W. Burgess. *The City.* University of Chicago Press, Chicago, Ill., 1925.
4. Rose, A. M., Editor. *Mental Health and Mental Disorder, A Sociological Approach.* W. W. Norton, New York, 1955.
5. Shaw, C. R., and H. D. McKay. *Juvenile Delinquency and Urban Areas.* University of Chicago Press, Chicago, Ill., 1942.

6. Shaw, C. R., F. Zorbaugh, H. D. McKay, and L. S. Cottrell. *Delinquency Areas.* University of Chicago Press, Chicago, Ill., 1929.
7. Wilner, D. M., Rosabelle Price Walkley, and M. Tayback. How does the quality of housing affect health and family adjustment? *Am. J. Public Health, 46,* 736–44 (1956).

APPENDIX

Presented below are the individual items constituting each of the Guttman-type scales presented in Table VI. A plus sign (+) in a column shows the response that is in the direction indicating probable "better psychological state."

Scale 1. *Potency: Efficacy of self-help*

	True	Not True[a]
a. When you come right down to it, there's nothing you can do to make things really better for yourself.		+
b. It's all right to try to improve yourself, but things being the way they are don't count on being able to accomplish too much.		+
c. Things will get better only if you actually get out and do something to make them better.	+	
d. No matter how hard you try, there's not much you can do to make a real change for the better.		+
e. You can work and work and in the end you're back about where you started.		+

Scale 2. *Morale: Optimism-pessimism*

a. It's hardly fair to bring a child into the world the way things look for the future.		+

[a] A "don't know" or "can't decide" alternative was also provided for each item in all scales.

	True	Not True
b. There's no reason to believe that things are going to be a great deal better in future.		+
c. If things seem to be going well for a while, there's usually some trouble right around the corner.		+
d. It's better not to look on the bright side of things because you will only be disappointed in the end.		+

Scale 3. *Morale: Satisfaction with status quo*

	True	Not True
a. I'm really very happy about the way I've been getting along lately.	+	
b. Everything seems to go wrong for me nowadays.		+
c. I'm generally satisfied with the way things are going for me.	+	
d. Life is treating me pretty bad right now.		+

Scale 4. *Nervousness*

	Yes	No
a. Are you one of those persons who never gets nervous?	+	
b. Are you often so nervous or upset that you can't go on with what you are doing?		+
c. Do you generally take things calmly without getting upset?	+	
d. Do you often feel that you are about to go to pieces?		+
e. Are you a nervous person?		+

Scale 5. *Mood*

	Yes	No
a. Can you say that you hardly ever feel blue?	+	
b. Are you sometimes so blue that you feel there's no use going on?		+
c. Do little things often make you feel blue?		+

	Yes	*No*
d. Are there times when you are so blue that you want to cry?		+

DISCUSSION

DR. SIMON DINITZ: This paper is obviously one of the first in what undoubtedly will be a long series of research reports. Consequently the substantive data appear, as the authors themselves indicate, to be a somewhat "haphazard assemblage of issues related to housing." Inasmuch then as this paper is chiefly concerned with methodological issues rather than substantive data, this discussion will chiefly focus on some of these methodological and theoretical issues concerning mental health and housing as presented by the authors.

Before going into these matters, however, a word or two of clarification on the data presented might be in order. The authors compare, within a group of poorly housed families, those living in extremely deficient dwellings with those living under somewhat less serious housing handicaps and find, as expected, that the families living in the relatively better dwellings are apparently more neighborly, do more entertaining, have more privacy, are more ritualistic in their meal taking and less pessimistic—all this, of course, according to the responses of the housewives interviewed. It should be stressed, as the authors themselves are aware, that the more poorly housed respondents were more frequently in the home all day and had a larger number of children. These two variables alone could without resort to almost any housing criteria at all no doubt account for much of the variation between the two groups.

One other comment on these data. The authors are essentially dealing with the problem of relative deprivation. They find that more of the relatively better housed families are satisfied, indeed most satisfied, with their present status. Yet they pay no particular attention to one of the greatest discrepancies between the two groups, namely, that 72% of these zero deficiency housing families stated that they are better off now than they were five years ago as compared with only 38% of the less well-housed families. Perhaps part, at least, of this improved status includes being better housed today than previously. Although no evidence is offered on this point, it is certainly conceivable that the present housing of the zero deficiency families may represent a considerable improvement over their previous situations and that consequently their generally "healthier" attitudes may reflect this improvement rather than their current housing per se.

On the theoretical side, one would be hard put to disagree with the authors' contention that research on housing and its relation to social-psychological and health variables is necessary and useful. We would question, of course, whether the "slum ethos" and the disorganization of the slum area or the slum dwelling as such imposes the greater restraints on, to quote, "the development of wholesome personal and family relationships characterized, for example, by the warmth and compatibility existing among family members and by the extent to which the family takes part in common activites in a compatible manner."

I should like to digress only momentarily here to point out that the goal of improved housing which is obviously implicit in this research need not be justified on the grounds of research findings. The major argument for better housing, no less than for school integration, is and should be a moral and humanitarian one and only secondarily one based on the results and findings of research—however conclusive these may be.

This paper is mostly concerned, as has already been noted, with a methodological question concerning the relative merits and limitations of a well-conceived one-shot survey, as the authors term it, versus an equally well thought out longitudinal, matched sample, experimentally designed investigation. Drs. Wilner and Walkley rightly suggest and amply illustrate that the results of a single survey on housing and its significance on physical, psychological and social ills are difficult to interpret since, as all would no doubt agree, there are too many pertinent, intervening, and extraneous variables involved. Consequently, the authors are to be commended for attempting, though somewhat reluctantly, to use an experimental design as a basis for minimizing the shortcomings of the one-shot survey and also as a means of comparing the results of the two types of designs.

Despite its virtues, the authors found this experimental design to entail the usual difficulties. Among these were the adequate selection and matching of test and control families over which, in this study, they had only partial control. These difficulties also included the attrition of sample members, the enormous expenditure of manpower on successive waves of interviewing, the relocation in equally favorable dwellings of some of the control group families, and so on.

Any one even passingly familiar with the nature of the survey method can appreciate the trials and tribulations involved in an effort of this magnitude. Changes in staff composition, staff discontent, minor revolutions on the part of sample respondents and the myriad of additional problems which beset the researchers are all a part of almost any type of research endeavor on human behavior. They assume even larger proportions in a longitudinal study of this type.

The question which their public no less than the authors, who are obviously nearing the end of the trail on this project, now want answered is "Was it worth it?" Though the authors are modest and somewhat dubious, the answer is obviously in the affirmative, even if the results and gains achieved by this experimental design over the one-shot survey are negative.

Unlike much of the present research in the social sciences, the authors of this methodologically sophisticated comparison of two methods of investigation were not so completely concerned with methodological purity and innovation that the real issues and problems under study were neglected in the process. Nonetheless, even in this investigation, the emphasis on complete methodological precision is perhaps too great for the problem at hand. Note, for example, that the definition of mental health used in this study is at best vague and certainly that the typical lower class housewife of my own interviewing experience knows very little about the symptomatology of many physical ills to say nothing of psychosomatic symptoms. Note finally that the authors, for the sake of the design *alone,* eventually ended up with an *all Negro* sample and thereby in effect precluded any general conclusions about the relationship of housing and mental health.

Quite apart from this study, it may be that the social sciences need a new or different rationale of research fully as much as continually refined methodological virtuosity. Present techniques, whether of experimental, ex post facto, one-shot, or longitudinal design, and no matter how cleverly conceived, are all based on the one crucial assumption that the researcher is able, either statistically or otherwise, to exercise control over his variables. It is our belief that behavioral research will not reach complete maturity as long as the investigator is unable even to state, let alone control, all the necessary and sufficient variables in the social phenomenon being studied.

While quite optimistic about our ability to achieve eventually this type of control, it is suggested that for the present we also consider other approaches and rationale, such as that of analytical induction and closure theory, as a means of investigating crucial social phenomena. In the meantime, I, for one, shall be extremely interested in reading the research papers stemming from the investigation reported here.

DR. E. M. GRUENBERG: I should like to ask two questions concerning the methods that were used. Was the fact of being chosen from many for the housing development by the Housing Authority regarded as a possible cause of some effect in morale and mental health; likewise, of course, the effect of being turned down and living in a neighborhood in which one's neighbors are moving into housing developments?

My second question has to do with the ordering of the questions in the interview. As I went through these it struck me that if at the beginning many questions are given that imply that the quality of housing is very important, and in which the respondent is asked to acknowledge these facts for virtues of housing, this might have a carry-over effect in questions regarding one's morale and self attitude. I wondered if these problems were considered.

DR. D. M. WILNER: Regarding the impact on morale of being or not being successful applicants, I can say that this issue is not a factor in the data presented today inasmuch as it was taken from the initial interviews with our families, conducted prior to the time that any of them moved, and in fact prior to the Housing Authority's notifying them that an apartment was available.

In the longitudinal study, this point has perhaps more force, although several factors work to mitigate the effects on our control group of "not being chosen." For one thing, at least half of our control sample had applied for public housing two or more years prior to the full occupancy of the housing project under study and had thus weathered many disappointments prior to the "disappointment" of being passed over again. Secondly, prior to the opening of the project, both test and control groups lived in a vast geographic area spread over many square miles, and occupied by perhaps 150,000 persons. Thus the probability was small that unsuccessful applicants knew personally families who were moving into the project. An additional point is that the process of occupying the project was gradual and took almost a year. In summary, it seems unlikely to us that the disappointment at being unsuccessful in the face of neighbors' success could in itself have been a powerful force detrimental to morale and mental health.

A general word may be in order about the selection of families for the test and control groups and about the possibilities of intrinsic differences between the groups because of Housing Authority procedures in awarding apartments. The study staff of course had no hand in the selection of families who moved into the project. Once chosen, however, we went to great pains to select controls from among remaining applicants in the Housing Authority's files who were carefully matched with the test families.

It is true that despite our matching there might have been some bias between the two groups introduced by criteria employed at the Housing Authority in choosing successful families. Three factors which I will describe only briefly helped, it seems to us, to mitigate this possibility. The first factor is that successful awards of apartments were made according to many strata of applicants, so that within a final stratum the choice usually came down to a chance selection from among families each equally in need of housing. The second factor was that we chose some of our controls from among families who were only temporarily ineligible because some essential piece of information was missing or out of date (e.g., the new address was absent), and who were therefore not considered in awarding apartments. The third factor had to do with the fact that, in a number of cases, an apartment awarded to an otherwise successful family was rejected because the family was unable to move at the time of award for a variety of factors, none intrinsically related to the dependent variables.

With regard to the ordering of the questions, it should be noted that the order of presentation of data in our paper did not correspond to the order of items in the questionnaire. The questionnaire itself, in the initial version, contained some 140 or 150 questions which were well mixed; the housing issues were not necessarily first in order of asking.

Now, I would like to address myself, in summary, to some of Dr. Dinitz' comments.

Dr. Dinitz is mistaken if he assumes that the reason for the interest of members of the senior study staff in this study is the justification for providing improved housing. As citizens we happen to agree that if improved housing is to be recommended at all, it should be done on grounds other than research findings, perhaps, as Dr. Dinitz suggests, on "moral and humanitarian" grounds.

I think, however, that Dr. Dinitz' comments in this connection arise from a further assumption that "improved" housing necessarily brings with it "improvements" in physical and mental health, and that this study is merely a methodological exercise in confirming what has already been concluded from rationalistic analysis of the situation. My own motives in undertaking direction of this study are twofold. First of all, I have general interest in the effects—whether good, bad or indifferent—of environmental factors on behavior and emotional life. A second interest derives from frank suspicion of the notion that improved housing in urban United States in the second half of the twentieth century necessarily has "good" effects. My own "analytic inductions," to use Dr. Dinitz' term, have left me unsure, and I am interested in finding out whether this notion is true or false, or partly true and partly false. It is possible that Dr. Dinitz may have been misled by the relatively formal and positive manner in which we have stated hypotheses and expectancies.

As a matter of fact, preliminary analysis of before and after data of the longitudinal study suggests some interesting possibilities that good housing, as constituted by the housing development under study, may not only *not* bring differences in the "expected" direction on a great many issues, but also in fact may give rise to some contrary differences. Thus, preliminary examination of illness rates suggests the real possibility that upper respiratory infections and the infectious diseases of childhood may find greatest opportunity for spread in the "good" housing of our study, and that this is likely to prevail mostly among families with many small children. A possible reason is the fact that our "good" housing consists of apartments in 11-story buildings that have 10 families to a story, with a corresponding very high density of persons per square foot of ground area. Many settings in the housing project, for example the elevator and even the play area on each floor, may be conducive to aerial transmission of disease in a way not characteristic of the 2- and 3-story slum dwellings from which the families came.

In other words, it is not at all clear that the effects of housing are all "really" already known and merely need final confirmation. Much is not known, and, I suspect, knowledge will be further explicated only by longitudinal studies like this one, which, it is to be hoped, can help serious investigators to cut through the circularity arising out of cross-sectional studies. It seems to us that inductive analyses at some point or other need the hardest kind of empirical test.

On the matter of generalizability of our findings, it is true that since our sample consists of low-income, non-white, families, our findings will be of most direct application to this group. It would surprise me if certain generalizations applying to other groups of human beings will not also be possible.

Treated and Untreated Mental Disorder in the Metropolis

LEO SROLE AND THOMAS LANGNER

Department of Psychiatry,
Cornell University Medical School, New York City

This paper was prepared by the authors in 1956 and by 1959 they felt that it was "conceptually obsolete." They therefore requested that it be withdrawn from the volume. The final reformulated version appears as a section of a chapter in the monograph *Midtown Manhattan: The Mental Health Story,* by Leo Srole, Thomas Langner, and Thomas A. C. Rennie, to be published by McGraw-Hill in 1960.

The discussion of the paper by Dr. Srole and Dr. Langner, as presented at the meeting, is included here without the counter discussion.

DISCUSSION

DR. REMA LAPOUSE: I cannot help being impressed with the high frequency of severe psychopathology which the authors reveal. In what may well be an undercount due to the omission of some age ranges and certain possible high risk groups in the population, the authors disclose that 400, or 24% of persons in their sample of 1,660, were classified as having extreme, marked, or serious mental pathology indicated by degree of symptom formation and difficulty of social functioning.

If we apply these rates in a crude way to the New York City population, we come out with some two million persons who are severely disturbed, and presumably require treatment. Of these, according to the data presented by Drs. Srole and Langner, 1½ million will not have had any psychiatric care whatsoever.

The mental health and public health problem thus posed by the findings of the Cornell group is of such magnitude that I cannot imagine an administrative or therapeutic system, no matter how ideally devised, which could possibly tackle, much less solve it.

If the problem is indeed as great as suggested, then we must now find ways and means somehow of meeting it. I do not deny the possibility that some two million people in New York City suffer from mental disorder of a pretty advanced degree, but I do suggest that the implications and consequences of such a finding are so shaking to the very foundation of our social structure that very careful analysis must be made to ascertain if it is really so.

It might be well to start, first of all, with a comparison of the findings of this study with those of others. By using as a baseline the figures of this study, a prevalence rate was found of 240 cases per thousand population in the more severely disturbed categories.

Roth and Luton, using techniques similar to the Stirling County group to survey mental disorder in Williamson County, Tennessee, reported in 1935 a rate of 69 per thousand in all categories of mental and personality disorder.

The 1936 survey of the Eastern Health District of Baltimore, by Lemkau, Tietze, and Cooper, reviewed the rosters of social agencies and disclosed a prevalence rate of 61 per thousand for all categories.

The Selective Service rejectee rate for psychiatric disorders was reported by Dr. Srole as approximately 110 per thousand. Figures that I found stated this rate to be about 55 per thousand on the overall count, although this represented a wide range of practices varying with the psychiatrist, the region, and the progress of the war.

A recent investigation of chronic illness in Baltimore by Pasamanick, Roberts, Lemkau, and Krueger revealed a rate of less than 100 per thousand, excluding the American Psychiatric Association diagnostic categories of "other mental, psychoneurotic and personality disorders."

Another chronic disease study completed last year by Trussell, Elinson, and Levin in Hunterdon County, New Jersey, reported a prevalence rate for major and minor mental disorders of 180 per thousand.

The Stirling County study claimed 370 per thousand as a "firm core" of psychiatric cases requiring treatment.

This wide range of prevalence rates of mental disorder found by various investigators focuses the need for an exploration of the reasons for these differences. It is obvious, for one thing, that the methodological approaches vary. Certainly, a survey of the rosters of social agencies will yield a smaller number of psychiatrically ill persons than the direct examination of a population or a representative sample thereof. In turn, examination by a psychiatrically sophisticated investigator will be more likely to uncover psychopathology than examination by a naive observer.

The differences cannot be explained, however, solely on these grounds. One of the nagging and as yet unresolved questions in the epidemiological study of mental disease is the one mentioned by Dr. Srole, and that is what criteria should be established for the inclusion or exclusion of a person as a psychiatric case.

Lacking a universally accepted definition of a case, comparable prevalence studies cannot be done. I recall, for example, that Dr. Christopher Tietze pointed out that in 1933 certain social agencies in Baltimore reported a large number of cases diagnosed as neurosis, personality disorder, psychopathic personality, and so on and so forth, because at that time a person who could not hold a job was considered a deviate. In the next few years the concepts changed, and an unemployed person was merely a victim of circumstances. With the change in concept of what was a case, these same social agencies in 1936 reported far fewer diagnoses of character and behavior deviations. What, then, can be the conclusions drawn about prevalence rates for mental disorders from these two studies carried out by the same observers, using essentially the same method and differing only in the separation of three years?

There is, regretfully, no reliable laboratory test for diagnosing mental disorder. In some schools of psychiatric thinking, diagnosis is even considered a rather stuffy and old-fashioned practice, the preference being for classification by psychodynamic factors. Diagnosis varies, to some extent, with the times and the fashions. Lacking in many instances a consensus agreement on specific criteria, diagnosis is often at the mercy of the interpreter's bias in accordance with his personal beliefs and the school of psychiatric thought to which he adheres.

The definition of a case is contingent upon the elaboration of specific distinguishing criteria, particularly in the marginal disorders, where much of the confusion lies. If a psychiatrist conceives of human behavior as having a narrow range of normality, his considered diagnosis of psychopathology will include many cases which another psychiatrist with a broader concept of normality would exclude.

It becomes, therefore, very important to reflect on the basic thinking that went into the design of the Midtown study. One of the people associated with the Cornell group stated his point of view as follows: "A case is a person, because every person is involved in a continuous process of adaptation to a stressful environment." The foundation for this definition is the theoretical formulation that psychiatric disorder falls into the continuum which Gordon calls, "the biological gradient of disease." The idea developed in Gordon's concept is that disease quantitatively varies from "a minimal departure from an established norm, termed health, to severe manifestations commonly resulting in death." Implicit in this concept is the understanding that in each instance it deals with a single disease entity.

In some epidemiological studies pertaining to mental disorder, there is the tacit or expressed assumption that all psychiatric deviations constitute a single entity, ranging in severity from minor maladjustments to psychoses. Witness the statement of a member of the Cornell group: "Any human being in a process of adaptation has only a certain number of psychological and physiological defenses or devices he can employ. . . . There is no essential difference in the psychotic and his psychological devices or defenses from the less psychotic, from the neurotic, from the so-called normal. . . . We can see the entire gamut of psychiatric illness played out with the same kinds of psychological and physiological mechanisms that everybody —normal, semi-normal, half-sick, seriously sick, and so on and so forth—uses in the continuum of adaptation."

This unitary theory of psychiatric disorder, comparable perhaps to Benjamin Rush's assumption 150 years ago that all disease has one cause, is unwarranted at the present level of knowledge when etiology still evades discovery. The present day situation does not yet vary too much from that of Pinel's time, when organic and non-organic psychoses were lumped together because they manifested the same symptoms and, no doubt, the same psychological mechanisms. With the continuum viewpoint, one could not have distinguished the specific etiological agents of such diseases as pellagra or general paresis. It must be emphasized, therefore, that mere similarity of mechanisms of response to disease processes does not argue either for their continuity or their identity, for the human organism has only a limited number of psychological and physiological mechanisms at its command. Inflammation occurs, for example, in response to infection, trauma, or neoplasm, but then one would hardly propose to identify these as the same disease process or to suggest a common etiology.

I would like to ask Dr. Srole what specific criteria were used in this study to delimit a case. If these criteria were based on the previously stated definition, that "a case is a person," then one could reasonably expect such a finding as was reported in a previous paper of this group, that somewhere around two-thirds of their sample population suffered from mental disorder.

I would also like to know on what basis the decisions were made to classify patients into the categories of extreme, serious, marked, moderate, and mild. It would be helpful if Dr. Srole were able to clarify these points since without this information, the prevalence rates found by his group could not be adequately evaluated.

To proceed to another point, I note that the interviewers obtained data on "the dimensions of mental disturbance" which, Dr. Srole indicated, included "a wide range of signs of tension, anxiety, inadequacy, phobias, depression, schizoid-like withdrawal, paranoid-like suspiciousness, compulsive-like rigidity, psychopathy-like immaturity, etc."

In this paper I see no mention of the method whereby the interviewers determined the presence or absence of such signs, and I am not at all sure what "paranoid-like suspiciousness, schizoid-like withdrawal, compulsive-like rigidity, psychopathy-like immaturity" mean. Why "like"? I should think that it would be difficult enough to determine the presence of suspiciousness, withdrawal, rigidity and immaturity, without the additional problem of deciding whether or not they are "paranoid-like, compulsive-like," and so on and so forth.

Lacking description, I do not have clues as to the nature of the newly derived personality questions which were used in the interviews nor how these were validated.

If, however, interpretations by interviewers were used in any way to determine the presence or absence of symptoms, one might wonder if these persons were really qualified to make such judgments. The interviewers were asked in addition to note their own observations and impressions of the respondent. Both the interview material and the interviewer's impressions were subsequently submitted to the psychiatrist who made the final evaluation, presumably on the basis of both kinds of information.

I need not point out to this audience that interviewer bias arises from too much scope for subjective interpretation, and that such bias may contribute an important source of error to the basic data. Precautions against this type of bias would be especially necessary, I might speculate, when more or less psychiatrically oriented professional persons, such as social workers, psychologists, sociologists, and anthropologists, are employed as interviewers. The source of error I am suggesting here is the possibility of overinterpretation which, like an inclusive definition of a case, results in overcounting.

In conclusion, I am sure that all of us look forward to the publication of the two monographs from the Cornell group which will cast light on all these questions by providing more precise information on the criteria and methods used.

DR. J. ZUBIN: I think we have been treated to a most unusual discussion, first, of the problems involved in determining prevalence rates in mental illness, and secondly, by the discussant on the nature of the possible interpretation of such attempts. I should like to turn the thing around, if I may, just because I think that we have stressed so much the problems that arises from an attempt at evaluating mental disease, and say, what about mental health?

Has the time arrived that we may go out to the community and, instead of inquiring how much mental disease there is, inquire how much psychopathology the normal person is entitled to? What I am suggesting is making a sort of Kinsey-like investigation of the number of accidents that the normal person experiences in the course of a month or so, the number of depressive moods, the number of blue funk conditions he is entitled to, and try to evaluate, not what we ordinarily call mental disease, but the kinds of things that a person may expect in his life and yet retain his normal balance.

Put it this way. How many accidents can a person have and yet not really call himself accident prone? How many deviations can a person experience and yet be well within his normal capacity to continue functioning, holding his job, taking care of his family, and so on and so forth?

When we get that question answered, even on a small sample, we may be able to have a better understanding of this borderline between health and disease.

DR. ABRAHAM LILIENFELD: Just following up Dr. Lapouse's comments, I would like to ask Dr. Srole whether or not he looked at the differences attained by the various interviewers. That is, if you look at each interviewer, what was the prevalence rate of his cases, or what have you individually by each of the interviewers? How variable were the interviewers in determining this?

In addition, I was wondering whether or not they incorporated into their study a re-interview of the sample of the individuals in order to see how variable the individuals are in responding to the interviewers.

It seems to me that in studies of this sort it is necessary to look at these sources of variation. I say this because we are carrying out a study of a similar nature in Buffalo on a sample survey of the population. We reinterviewed a sample of the respondents in a period of two or three months. So far—and this is just a preliminary analysis—looking at a few of the items which we have analyzed, we have found on only about 66% of the questions agreement between the two interviewers.

Now, actually, this is understating the case. In our particular instance, the information on these items was not obtained by interview; the questionnaire was given to the respondent, and the respondent filled this out himself because we were very much concerned about the variability of interviewers in obtaining information of this sort. Even though the person filled the items out himself, even though the person checked these various categories, we have so far in this preliminary analysis obtained a fair amount of discrepancy in what the person himself states his feelings were.

Dr. P. V. Lemkau: I would like to comment on one point that has to do with the identification of what the patient says troubles him and a conception that this is disease. The problem relates somewhat to the whole question of the inclusion of social health as a criterion of health generally. This is a relatively new concept as to whether the way one lives, environment in the sense of psychiatric living, is necessarily directly correlated with the presence and absence of disease.

The question is closely related to that that Dr. Lapouse raised in the concept of the continuum of psychiatric disease, from the very severe to the well, as opposed to the concept of a series of diseases, some of which may be severe, such as schizophrenia or senile degeneration; some of which may be relatively mild, as an occasional anxiety attack. But the idea that these two extremes are points on a continuum from one to the other, rather than the manifestation of more or less specific disease entities, is the problem that I would like to raise. In association with it is the problem of whether social health can be defined also as mental health, and whether social discomfort is the same thing as psychiatric disease.

One other question I would like to ask is this. It seems to me on the basis of the words I heard—and I make this very clear—any contact with psychiatrists, nerve specialists, or psychologists was pre-

sumed to be a treatment contact. I happen to know that a great
many of these contacts are merely diagnostic contacts and have no
relationship to treatment whatever, nor even ambition to be treatment interviews. I would like to ask Dr. Srole whether a distinction
was made between treatment and other kinds of contacts with
the specialist.

A Survey of Mental Disease in an Urban Population: Prevalence by Race and Income

BENJAMIN PASAMANICK,[1] DEAN W. ROBERTS,[2]
PAUL W. LEMKAU,[3] AND DEAN B. KRUEGER,[4]

The Commission on Chronic Illness, an independent agency founded jointly by the American Hospital Association, the American Medical Association, the American Public Health Association, and the American Public Welfare Association, financed by a series of grants from the National Institutes of Health and the Commonwealth Fund, has completed a study of the prevalence of chronic illness and needs for care in an urban area begun in 1952. The objectives of the investigation started in Baltimore were, broadly, to determine the prevalence of diagnosed and asymptomatic chronic disease and resulting disability, and its variations by socio-economic distribution, to estimate rehabilitation potentials, to evaluate multiple screening methods, and to develop new methods of studying the chronic disease problem.

The study was planned and carried out in four phases, of which only the first two are of relevance to this report and will be described briefly.

Step 1. A household canvass was carried out in the classical

[1] Columbus Psychiatric Institute and Hospital, and Ohio State University College of Medicine, Columbus, Ohio.
[2] The National Society for Crippled Children and Adults, Chicago, Illinois.
[3] New York City Community Mental Health Board, New York.
[4] School of Public Health, Columbia University, New York.

morbidity survey method by trained lay interviewers under the direction of the United States Bureau of the Census on approximately four thousand households, including about twelve thousand people representing a random sample of the population of Baltimore. Persons in medical institutions for long-term care, including mental hospitals, were not sampled. The sampling procedures, interview methods, preparation, and findings will be described in detail in future reports of the Commission.[5] At this time it is sufficient to state that the sample surveyed was a probability sample of the city's population in terms of age, race and sex characteristics, and that interviews were completed in 97.7% of the addresses selected for sampling.

Step 2. This consisted of the "clinical evaluation" of a subsample. About 10% of the basic survey group of twelve thousand were chosen as the sample for this step. They were stratified in the following manner so that the bulk of the intensive evaluation would be devoted to persons with substantially disabling health conditions as determined by the household interview data: (1) 100% of the persons reporting maximum disability; (2) 100% of those reporting diabetes, CNS disease and neoplasm, 40% of those reporting heart disease, 25% reporting arthritis and rheumatism, 7% of those reporting all other diseases; (3) approximately 6% of the remainder reporting no disease or only short term or nondisabling conditions.

Of this stratified subsample, 731 individuals were examined at the Evaluation Clinic, 33 were examined at home, and an additional 45 whose current medical data were secured from physicians in hospitals in sufficient degrees of completeness were included to make a total of 809 and a response rate of 62.6%. The report presented here will be limited to the data on mental illness gathered from step 2 of the Chronic Disease Commission survey. Details of subsampling, field work, evaluation, staff, and findings will be found in later reports of the Commission.

[5] *Chronic Illness in a Large City,* Vol. 4 of *Chronic Illness in the United States,* Commonwealth Fund and the Harvard University Press, 1957.

Briefly, the evaluation of the persons in this step was carried out at the Johns Hopkins Hospital by a panel of physicians specializing in internal medicine or pediatrics who were either full-time fellows in their respective departments or physicians in private practice with hospital staff appointments. These physicians performed the physical examinations and ordered any consultations, including psychiatric, or special diagnostic tests needed to clarify the medical status of the patient. A number of additional routine procedures were carried out, in all requiring some three to four hours for the complete clinic evaluation. For each evaluee, the examining physician completed a record in which significant chronic conditions were analyzed in terms of severity, history, disabling effects, treatment and care required, and prognosis. Each record was reviewed by the rehabilitation counselor to identify those who had any potential for rehabilitation, and a home visit was made by a counselor on these cases. Half of each of group 1 and group 2 described above were randomly selected, and in those who showed significant health disability thorough home investigation was made by either a public health nurse, social worker, or rehabilitation counselor, depending on the greatest apparent need. The records of all these cases so investigated were reviewed by the Commission staff and the home investigators to establish or confirm all the existing noted conditions.

After thorough perusal of the case material, the impressions, and the diagnoses, every record which contained any material which might pertain to some factor associated with the possibility of mental illness was turned over to the psychiatrist for his "clinical evaluation." Approximately one quarter of the step 2 subsample cases were so reviewed. On the basis of the material contained in these records diagnosis of mental disorders was made using the definitions contained in the 1952 Diagnostic and Statistical Manual of the American Psychiatric Association.

Diagnoses were not allowed to stand unless the data recorded in the medical records supported the diagnosis. This resulted in one-third of the patients (32%) for whom the examining physician recorded a psychiatric diagnosis having the diagnosis deleted on review by the psychiatrist. Change from one diagnosis to another was not accounted as a deletion. It is possible that some psychiatric diagnoses made by the examining internist were deleted merely because all the information available to the internist was not recorded and therefore was not available to the reviewing psychiatrist.

Examining internists recorded "impressions" but not diagnosis of psychiatric disease for 24 patients. For ten of these patients the reviewing psychiatrist considered the record and the data as supporting a diagnosis of psychiatric disease. Four additional diagnoses of psychiatric disease were made by the reviewing psychiatrist through changing a single diagnosis made by the examining internist into two psychiatric diagnoses, or by making a diagnosis in cases selected by the medical editing staff as probably involving psychiatric disease. In general, the effect of the review by the psychiatrist was to reduce substantially the figures on prevalence of psychiatric disease.

In addition, it must be noted that the findings to be presented represent prevalence as of the date of clinical evaluation, rather than the "lifetime" prevalence which some studies have reported. Some diagnoses were deleted because it was felt that there was no psychiatric illness present at the time of examination, although this had probably been present sometime in the past and might be again in the future. Along with diagnostic ratings, the psychiatrist made judgments of severity based on the degree of psychiatric impairment scaled in the Diagnostic and Statistical Manual of:

(*a*) No impairment where there were no medical reasons for changing employment or life situation.

(*b*) *Minimal* indicating incapacity of perceptible degree but not to exceed 10%.

(*c*) *Mild impairment* in social and occupational adjustment of 20% to 30% disability.

(*d*) *Moderate,* indicating serious interference with a patient's ability to carry on premorbid social and vocational adjustment and having a 30% to 50% disability rating.

(*e*) *Severe,* indicating that for practical purposes the patient could not function at his premorbid social and vocational levels and had over 50% disability.

Findings

The findings to be discussed in this preliminary report will be limited to the distribution of psychoses, psychoneuroses, and psychophysiologic autonomic and visceral disorders in our total sample of examined patients by race and economic status.

They do not include the category of "other mental, psychoneurotic, and personality disorders," which will be included in the general Commission report. This category which includes a number of childhood behavior disorders, mild mental defect, alcoholism, and other minor personality or behavior difficulties and has an adjusted rate of 15.2 per thousand is excluded from this report because the judgments of both the examining physicians and psychiatrists are probably not very reliable. This is particularly true in most of the judgments of mental deficiency and psychopathic personality. In a number of cases where it seemed apparent to the psychiatrist that the behavior or personality disorder, such as alcoholism, was symptomatic of a psychoneurosis or of another psychiatric disorder, the diagnosis was so changed. On the whole this was infrequent, and the category of "other mental psychoneurotic and personality disorders" usually containing vague or equivocal psychiatric illness, social maladjustment, and behavior patterns unacceptable to middle class diagnosticians was poorly recorded or judged in this survey as in most other similar studies. It was therefore thought best to confine this paper to those conditions generally considered as obvious mental illness.

The step 2 clinical evaluation sample was selected in such a fashion that adjustment of the data for differences in sampling

proportions of the various groups and for differences in the proportions participating could be done through the application of
weights. This permitted expression of the findings of the clinical
evaluation in terms of the approximately twelve thousand persons surveyed in step 1, who in turn were found to be very
similar to the total population of the city in terms of age and
color. After proper weighting, our 809 evaluees were found to
be distributed almost identically by age, color, and sex with
the household survey sample. To the extent then that their distribution by these characteristics was significantly related to mental health, this sample is representative of the mental health of
the noninstitutionalized population of the city of Baltimore.

Before we enter upon a discussion of our findings of mental
disorder by race and economic status, we thought that it might
be of some value to review briefly our findings of total prevalence
and distribution by sex and age as well as severity which we
have reported previously.

Table I presenting total prevalence and prevalence by sex of

TABLE I

Prevalence of Mental Disorder as a Rate per 1,000 Persons Evaluated
by Diagnosis and Sex

Diagnosis	Number of Cases Unweighted	Rate Based on Weighted Number of Cases		
		Both sexes	Males	Females
Psychoses	17	4.3	6.0	2.7
Psychoneuroses	51	52.6	35.6	68.0
Psychophysiologic, auto- nomic, and visceral disorders	18	36.5	18.9	52.4
Total	86	93.4	60.5	123.1

the clinical entities under consideration indicates that after conservative estimation approximately 10% of a noninstitutional

urban population are at one moment in time mentally ill. There is approximately twelve times as much psychoneurosis as psychosis while psychophysiologic autonomic and visceral disorders are two-thirds as common as the neuroses. Male psychoses appear to be twice as frequent as those in women, but, because of the small numbers involved, probably is not statistically significant. On the other hand, females have more psychoneuroses and psychophysiologic autonomic and visceral disorders.

Table II containing the mental disorders classified by severity

TABLE II

Mental Disorders Classified by Severity of Impairment
as Defined by American Psychiatric Association

Diagnosis	Number of Cases Unweignted	Percentage Distribution by Severity of Impairment Based on Weighted Number of Cases					
		Total	None	Minimal	Mild	Moderate	Severe
Psychoses	17	100.0	—	3.6	6.5	22.7	67.2
Psychoneuroses	50[a]	100.0	20.5	47.8	22.8	6.0	2.8
Psychophysiologic autonomic and visceral disorders	18	100.0	23.2	34.1	35.3	1.8	5.5

[a] Excludes one case with unknown severity.

of impairment indicates, as might be expected, that the psychoses were generally classified as being moderate to severe, while the psychoneuroses and psychophysiologic, autonomic, and visceral disorders had either no significant impairment or ranged up to and including mild impairment with below 30% disability.

In Table III we present the prevalence of these types of mental disorder by age group. Psychoses rise precipitously with increasing age. With no cases under 15, only 0.4 per thousand in the age group 15 to 34, increasing 14-fold in the group 35 to 64, which in turn is multiplied by 5 in the group 65 and over. In contrast, the psychoneuroses are almost uniformly distributed in

TABLE III

Prevalence of Mental Disorder as a Rate per 1,000
Persons Evaluated in Each Age Group

		Rate Based on Weighted Number of Cases				
Diagnosis	Number of Cases Unweighted	All ages	Under 15	15–34	35–64	65 and over
Psychoses	17	4.3	—	0.4	5.8	27.8
Psychoneuroses	51	52.6	8.3	68.8	69.2	70.8
Psychophysiologic, autonomic, and visceral disorders	18	36.5	—	78.7	38.6	—
Total	86	93.4	8.3	147.9	113.6	98.6

the age groups over 15, but are less than 0.1% under 15. The psychophysiologic disorders exhibit an entirely different pattern of distribution with no cases reported under 15 or over 65, but with more cases in the 15 to 34 group than in the 35 to 64.

Table IV offers our findings in respect to a distribution of mental illness by color. The designation non-white refers almost

TABLE IV

Prevalence of Mental Disorder as a Rate per 1,000 Persons Evaluated
by Diagnosis and Color

		Rate Based on Weighted Number of Cases		
Diagnosis	Number of Cases Unweighted	Total white and non-white	White	Non-white
Psychoses	17	4.3	5.8	0.3
Psychoneuroses	51	52.6	62.2	27.5
Psychophysiologic, autonomic and visceral disorders	18	36.5	43.7	17.7
Total	86	93.4	111.7	45.5

wholly to Negroes, and in our discussion these terms will be used interchangeably. It is apparent that in the three groups of clinical entities included in this report, whites have by far more mental illness recorded than non-whites. Approximately nineteen times as much psychosis, twice as much psychoneurosis, and almost three times as many autonomic and visceral disorders of psychophysiologic origin.

In Table V, we present the distribution of mental disorder by

TABLE V

Prevalence of Mental Disorder as a Rate per 1,000
Persons Evaluated by Diagnosis and Income

Diagnosis	Number of Cases Unweighted	Rate Based on Weighted Number of Cases				
		All incomes[a]	Under $2,000	$2000–$3,999	$4,000–$5,999	$6,000 and over
Psychoses	17	4.3	4.1	8.7	1.5	0.8
Psychoneuroses	51	52.6	80.1	55.4	13.4	62.5
Psychophysiologic, autonomic, and visceral disorders	18	36.5	—	18.2	47.2	72.5
Total	86	93.4	84.2	82.3	62.1	135.8

[a] Includes income not stated.

economic status as indicated by household income. In the group of psychoses, except for the lowest income category (under $2,000 a year) the prevalence of psychoses falls as income increases. In the neurotic group prevalence is highest in the lowest income category and falls progressively only to rise again in the highest economic group of yearly income $6,000 and over. In the psychophysiologic, autonomic, and visceral disorders, prevalence increases directly with income.

Discussion

Before entering upon a discussion of the implications of these findings some comment on the limitations of the investigation other than the somewhat small numbers involved seems to be in order. Except for one characteristic, Baltimore differs very little from other urban centers, or indeed the rest of the country, in respect to age distribution and family income. However, it does differ markedly in having a higher proportion of non-whites, 26.7% as contrasted to 13.2% in all cities over 100,000 population in 1950. As was demonstrated, this characteristic tends to lower prevalence rates in our survey.

As was indicated before, the "response rates" for the clinical evaluation was 62.6%. Unexpectedly, there was no significant difference in the response rate according to degree of disability and even absence of disability. There were, however, significant differences by age, color and sex, the rates being higher for children and lower for the aged, higher for the non-whites and slightly higher for males. With a non-response rate of 37.4%, the question of bias must be considered carefully. With the data from the household survey for both respondents and non-respondents, it becomes possible to evaluate to some degree the bias due to non-response. Chronic conditions were reported during interviews at a slightly lower rate for the 809 individuals clinically evaluated (after weighting) than for the total survey sample. Our conclusion is that the amount of bias for all chronic disease due to non-response is probably quite small, and that the interview data available do not establish with certainty the direction of bias, though it seems likely to be in the direction of a little more disease among the persons clinically evaluated than among the total survey sample.

What can be said of the bias introduced by the method of having the original diagnostic impression made by a non-psychiatrist and supplemented by information from other sources? Very little, but impressions can be offered on this score. Since a fairly sizable group of physicians was employed in the clinical evaluations, it might be expected that considerable variation in psychiatric judgment and evaluation existed. These were largely well-trained and sophisticated young individuals alert to the psychiatric implications of illness. The impression is that the total direction of bias may be slightly toward overdiagnosis of mental disorder. There is some support for this in the finding that there was no significant impairment in over one-fifth of the cases of psychoneurosis and psychophysiologic disorders, while an additional two-fifths had only minimal impairment. On the other hand, the psychiatrist reviewing these cases and eliminating approximately one-third where a diagnostic impression of mental disorder was made, because of lack of recorded supporting evidence or differing opinion, probably deleted a number of cases which on closer scrutiny and examination might have been included as mental disorders. The reliability of judgments of physicians and psychiatrist was not tested.

The total bias and direction is quite difficult to estimate. It may very well be that there is some tendency toward underreporting. However, this is not judged to be very great, and in any event nothing like the reports of approximately two-thirds of the population being mentally ill, as indicated in two recent surveys is approached. Our findings that approximately one-tenth of an urban population have one or more of the relatively well-defined mental disorders is sufficiently alarming and one obviously calling for serious and prompt consideration.

What explanations or hypotheses can be offered for some of the differences in the racial and economic distributions of mental disorder found in the Baltimore survey? How can we account for the much lower prevalence of mental illness among the Negro evaluees? First, as far the psychoses are concerned, since we are apparently dealing largely with psychoses of old age in a non-institutionalized population, Negroes whose life expectancy is under 60 years would not be expected to contribute significantly to the population of psychotics. In addition, because of their social and economic circumstances they probably would not be as able to care for psychotic individuals at home as might those in easier circumstances. This is supported by the higher first admission rates to mental hospitals for Negroes. As for the difference in prevalence of psychoneuroses, how much of this may be attributable to the fact that the examiners were white, middle or upper class individuals with all that implies concerning cultural, class, and caste biases in interviewing and evaluation. Is this one of the reasons why the prevalence of "other mental psychoneurotic and personality disorders" was higher amongst the non-white? The latter would at least account for part of the difference. It is obviously not accountable for on the basis of economic status since in both the psychoses and the psychoneuroses the lower economic status groups had higher prevalence rates. Are these possible biases also operative in the group of psychophysiologic autonomic and visceral disorders where again the non-whites have a much lower rate? It is interesting to note that when we look at the rates of a number of disorders such as asthma, obesity, and hypertension without heart disease, which have been said to have psychogenic components, that the rates for non-whites are the same or even slightly higher than that for the white sample. Is the white examiner more likely to seek and therefore find psychologic components in members of his own race than in that of another?

The distribution of diagnostic categories by income offers a number of possible hypotheses by way of explanation. The prevalence of four psychoses per thousand in the category under $2,000 as contrasted to the next higher category with nine per thousand is probably attributable to the fact that the lowest income group contains most of the Negroes, and since they had a much lower rate than that of whites in the noninstitutionalized population, this finding could have been predicted. However, it appears that on the whole lowered economic status is associated with more psychoses. How much of this is cause and how much effect we cannot state from our data. It is quite likely that both mechanisms are operative here. A certain number have probably been forced into the lower economic status because of psychosis, and it is also probable that because of a number of factors associated with low income a sizable group of elderly individuals have been forced into this psychotic group. However, because of the small numbers involved too much emphasis cannot be placed upon the differences found.

Our findings relative to the prevalence of psychoneuroses in different income groups is rather interesting. Despite the fact that Negroes had a low rate of psychoneuroses reported, the highest rate of psychoneuroses recorded was in the lowest 70% of the population with incomes under $4,000. The rate falls in the $4,000 to $6,000 group, which makes up 17% of the population, and then rises again in the over $6,000 a year income group, which includes 11% of the Baltimore population. This is in contrast to a number of other surveys which found psychoneuroses rising with income. Hypotheses of etiology might best be discussed in relation to specific psychoneurotic diagnoses. However, on the face it would appear that stress is greatest in the lowest and highest social economic strata, in the former due to deprivation and the frustrations consequent to deprivation and in the latter possibly due to various social and cultural inconsistencies and stress consequent to attempt to maintain status.

As in the case of the psychoses, it is unfortunate that we were unable to report more cases of autonomic and visceral disorders so that the reliability of our findings would be greater, but contrary to the findings in psychoses, there appears to be a definite trend toward increase in the prevalence of these disorders with increasing income. Is this a reflection of increased chronic tension and stress with income, or is it possibly another indication of bias in the examiners who might tend to find more psychogenicity in individuals of their own class? Were it not for the increase in psychoneuroses in the highest economic stratum, it might have been said that whereas psychoneuroses are unacceptable in our culture, autonomic and visceral disorders are permissible. One might even tortuously evolve the hypothesis that in these days of psychiatric sophistication in the well to do, it is fashionable for the rich to be neurotic, unacceptable to the middle class, but frequent in the lower class because of lack of sophistication and increased stress.

Undoubtedly many other explanations could be offered as acceptable as the above, or even more so, but these were advanced merely as examples of the large number of hypotheses which immediately offer themselves for testing. It is some indication of the dearth of our knowledge in this area and the long way still to be traveled toward the knowledge of etiology of mental disorders.

Summary

The Chronic Disease Commission's survey of mental disorder in Baltimore found that approximately one-tenth of a non-institutionalized population exhibited obvious mental illness. Whites were recorded as having much more disorder than non-whites. In the psychoses this may be due to the lower life expectancy of Negroes, but in psychoneuroses and autonomic and visceral disorders it may possibly be due to bias on the part of the examiners. Psychoses were more prevalent in the lower income groups; however, autonomic and visceral disorders of psychogenic origin increased with income. The psychoneuroses were most common in the lowest and highest income groups. Some hypotheses are offered for these differences.

DISCUSSION

DR. OSKAR DIETHELM: It is a happy coincidence that this group honors the memory of Emil Kraepelin. It is happy for me because it will permit me to illustrate some points from the work of Kraepelin. I might add that I have been very remote from Kraepelin and only in recent years, through historical evaluation, have I been able to appreciate some of his contributions. Among the contributions of great value are his diagnostic classifications which have withstood the test of time. Kraepelin showed very early an interest (from a rather philosophic point of view) in the broader aspects of mental health and diagnosis in general.

He, being trained in experimental psychology before he went into medicine and psychiatry, applied his training, for his time very unusual training, to clinical psychiatry. He pointed out that it is very important that we have a definition of clinical psychiatry. In his time that referred primarily to what he called psychosis. We have to keep that in mind. But the same formulation of diagnosis, which he gave when he defined psychoses, and its limitations would apply today when we discuss psychiatric illness.

Kraepelin stressed that we have to have facts and that we have to be able to put the facts together into something which is called a diagnosis. If we cannot do that, then we have to realize that we do not have sufficient facts and should designate it as such.

He showed his practical interest in the whole problem of mental health in a little paper, which I happened to read as an assistant resident, which dealt with the topic of women who moved from one location to another and developed depressive reactions. He touched on fundamental aspects of what we call now social psychiatry, mental health, and social environment.

When he talked of psychiatric illnesses he stressed that we have to be careful not to take physical signs as an indication of poor mental health. In his studies two-thirds of one group did not show any signs of definite psychiatric illness.

He pointed out that the same has to apply to the study of alcoholism. We should have definitions which are based on maladjustments of alcoholism and not on the amount which is drunk by various people, or the influence it has on the physical condition of the person.

Those are definite aspects to consider.

I was therefore very pleased to see that in this paper the authors use "psychophysiological disorders" instead of "psychological" and that they point up the physiologic function. We cannot consider such conditions just psychiatric disorders. Otherwise, we would include many conditions in psychiatric disorders, including all kinds of hypertensions and rheumatic disorders which have a psychologic component but don't make for a psychiatric condition.

Kraepelin probably would have wondered whether it is correct to oppose mental health to mental illness, or mental pathology, any more than he would oppose physical health to physical illness. In mental health especially it is highly questionable whether we can oppose it to mental illness.

The term "mental morbidity" has to be closely questioned. Does it really mean morbidity in the sense that it is usually used? Do we not use the term with a different concept? That is something Kraepelin also pointed out: Using the same term to refer to two different concepts is not acceptable.

It is Kraepelin who brought an experimental basis to psychopathology versus a merely descriptive basis. We say he is descriptive. He was descriptive in the sense of a scientist who is able to describe facts, but he did not mean to say that one ought to stay on the level of mere description. In his basic concept of psychopathology, based on experimental psychology of his own group and groups like Titchener and others, he proposed broader and better defined concepts.

If we look at present at the developments in pathology in general, there has been considerable change. Many in the field of pathology no longer accept merely a quantitative evaluation of etiologic factors. Many bring in the problem of adaptability and adjustment, just as the authors did in this paper, making it very complicated and forcing us to define what we mean.

We are in a new field of formulation of pathology and psychopathology. We have not found the answer, but we have the right to go ahead.

Kraepelin was the first one, as far as I know, who introduced an interdisciplinary approach, showing his scientific attitude by placing representatives of various disciplines on the same level. Psychiatrists who talk of interdisciplinary approach stress that the psychiatrist is in charge of this approach. Kraepelin, in developing the Research Institute in Munich, did not have this attitude. Sometimes it was the chemist, sometimes the histologist, and sometimes the clinical psychiatrist who was in charge.

I think that we psychiatrists should be modest and see where our place is when we work with other disciplines, including physicians, surgeons, sociologists, and chemists.

Dr. P. V. Lemkau: In the research which Dr. Pasamanick just reported, the interdisciplinary tended to mix medical specialists rather than specialists in different fields. I remember as we sat in the group that made the final adjustments for the counting of these cases, how rare it was that I had sat down with experts in other specialties to work over a person's problems.

While we preach interdisciplinary research and interdisciplinary operation, as psychiatrists we very frequently do not include among the disciplines the specialists in other fields of medicine such as the dropping of the pediatrician, who originally was part of the child guidance clinic term.

DR. J. A. CLAUSEN: I was particularly struck by the fact that of the 17 persons who were designated as probably psychotic the great bulk were apparently in the age over 65. I don't know what the rate for the population under 65 would be, but from the table I would guess, or, just guessing at the distributions, it probably was not much over 1 per thousand in that under 65 group.

In any event, it seems to me apparent that it is much lower than suggested by those people who objected to my statement that schizophrenia was a relatively rare phenomenon because the schizophrenics would be just one component of this category. I got to wondering whether in the roughly one-third of the population that did not come in one would not expect to find a rather high proportion of the schizophrenias.

In the family study that we are doing, I know wives will frequently make medical appointments for their husbands well in advance of the period of hospitalization, and they are quite exasperated at the fact that the husband will not go to see the doctor after the wife has made the appointment. The husbands may even occasionally make appointments themselves and then fail to keep these appointments.

I would think then that the schizophrenic would be a person less likely to cooperate, to come in for an examination. I wonder whether this might not rather markedly alter the picture.

DR. J. ZUBIN: I am interested in the Negro question, of why there are so few Negroes recorded in this sampling. In addition to the hypothesis that Dr. Pasamanick has suggested, I should like to ask whether it is possible that it may be explained on this basis.

Some years ago we were interested in the distribution of mental deficiency. We noted some kind of a gradient for Negro mental defectives as compared to the mental defectives in the population. It was in an institution, that is, those in an institution.

It looked as if the gradient is such that as you go farther North, there is an increase in the ratio of Negro defectives institutionalized to whites; as you get farther and farther away from the South, where the number of Negroes in population gets smaller, the hospital institutional rate gets larger. Maybe Maryland is in that particular lower area where they do not hospitalize or institutionalize, which may mean they, not feeling that certain conditions which whites consider to be severe are really severe, fail to report it.

DR. E. M. GRUENBERG: I would like to amplify Dr. Zubin's remarks by asking a similar kind of question which I think is highly relevant to all surveying for personality disorders and psychological functioning. I would like to ask something about the characteristics of the population that was doing the examining of the sample as contrasted to the characteristics of the example, or of the sample. I should like to know, for example, what proportion of the doctors who examined the patients were Negro.

DR. P. V. LEMKAU: None.

DR. GRUENBERG: I would like to know what proportion of the enumerators who enumerated the population was Negro. And I would like to know whether the investigators feel that in the last twenty years Johns Hopkins has changed sufficiently so that a white doctor ordinarily achieves any rapport with the Negro he is examining.

MR. ALBERT DEUTSCH: If I may make a footnote to Dr. Zubin's question? Some years ago I had the occasion to write a paper on the census of the insane in 1840 and its use in pro-slavery propaganda. In this paper I traced how the census of 1840, which showed the first census of the insane, showed that there was ten times more reported insanity among the free Negroes of the North as among the slave Negroes of the South. To make it short, it was discovered by Dr. Jarvis that the census takers, for instance, had taken a whole population of the insane asylum, which was about 242, and marked them all down as Negroes, whereas there were only three Negroes in the institution.

Another very significant point was that they had institutional provisions for Negroes in the North while in the South there was almost no institutional provision whatever. That was a significant reason for the greater institutionalization of Negroes in the North than in the South.

DR. B. PASAMANICK: I would like to thank the discussants for their discussion and questions and try to answer some of them.

To Dr. Diethelm I would like to say I hope we used the concept of disease in the classical manner and as I hope Dr. Diethelm uses it. I think that to be sure of what we are speaking about we have to think of psychiatric disease as we think of all diseases and not differently. I think we add confusion to confusion if we do not define at least one parameter.

Dr. Clausen, I think that our rates in the younger age groups of psychoses, although I don't recall them, are probably closer to 5 per thousand rather than 1 per thousand, and are probably similar to those in institutions. I think we could probably just double the number to arrive at some estimate of the total prevalence.

His second point is very well taken. I can only agree with it.

To Dr. Zubin, as far as hospitalization of mental defectives are concerned, as we go North I think we find more urbanization of the Negro and consequently less ability to care for a defective individual at home. This is particularly true in the lowest socio-economic groups, so that I think we would find more institutionalization as we go North, in all psychiatric disorders. This may account for lower rates in the noninstitutionalized.

As Mr. Deutsch pointed out, there are probably worse and less facilities in the South for the care of defectives. As for his second point—it is similar to the one made by Dr. Zubin and I agree wholly.

I can only agree completely with what Dr. Gruenberg said. We said almost the same thing, but he emphasized the point that the bias in middle class and upper class wholly white examiners was probably a very important point in the difference in rates between whites and non-whites.

None of the physicians was a Negro.

For the enumerators, some were Negro, but I cannot recall the number. These were employed by the Bureau of the Census. As you know, there isn't very much discrimination there—particularly since the pay is rather low.

A Survey Technique for Estimating the Prevalence of Psychoneurotic and Related Types of Disorders in Communities[1]

ALLISTER MILES MACMILLAN

Cornell University, Ithaca, New York

It may be appropriate to present a brief overview of the Stirling County Study, as a background, before amplifying one particular aspect of it, the experimenting with a psychological screening test, which has been one of the writer's main research responsi-

[1] This paper comes from the Stirling County Study which is being conducted by Cornell University in collaboration with the Department of Public Health of the Province of Nova Scotia and with the cooperation of Acadia and Dalhousie Universities. Invaluable help has also been provided by the Faculté des Sciences Sociales, Université Laval. Within Cornell, the Stirling County Study is attached administratively to the Social Science Research Center and is sponsored by the Department of Sociology and Anthropology and the Department of Psychiatry of the New York Hospital and Cornell Medical College. Financial support is provided by the Carnegie Corporation of New York, by the Department of National Health and Welfare of Canada, by the Department of Public Health of the Province of Nova Scotia, and by the Milbank Memorial Fund.
The staff of the project at the time this paper was written consisted of the following: Alexander H. Leighton, Director; Allister M. Macmillan, Deputy Directory; Charles C. Hughes, Social Science Coordinator; Christopher Haffner, Chief of the Psychiatric Clinic; Bruce Dohrenwend, Social Analyst; Bernard Hebert, Clinical Psychologist; Dorothea C. Leighton, Research Psychiatrist; and Ruth O. Kent, Administrative Secretary. Grateful acknowledgment is made to Oskar Diethelm, John S. Harding, and Robin M. Williams, Jr., for manuscript review.

bilities. The central aim of the Stirling study is to explore the relationship between psychiatric disorder and environment in order to evaluate the proposition that social and cultural factors have causal effects (1). In other words, it is desired to see if telling differences can be detected in the distributions of persons with and without psychiatric symptoms in different parts of the socio-cultural environment.

Stirling is the code name for a predominantly rural county in one of the Atlantic provinces of Canada. It has a population of about 20,000 with approximately equal proportions of English and French-Acadians, living side by side since the days of the American Revolution. This rural maritime region is dotted with a few small towns and several villages, and the balance of the population is thinly scattered in hamlets over an area about 40 miles along the ocean but with the settlement pattern penetrating only about 8 miles inland from the sea. Beyond this hinterland stretch miles of rough unsettled forest lands. There is a total of 97 place-names in the county. Principal occupations include lumbering, farming, and fishing as well as the usual supply services.

Pilot studies were done during 1948 and 1949, and the present project began in 1950. The research staff, representing a variety of disciplines, was recruited about equally from Canada and the United States, and financial support has come from both countries. Most of the field work was completed in six years, and in mid-1956 the staff began a program of final analysis, integration, and writing of reports which are planned as a four-volume series to be completed in 1959–60.

Briefly, our approach was twofold: on the one hand, utilizing a number of methods in describing the varying socio-cultural environments of the population and, on the other, in assessing the distribution of psychiatric symptoms in the same population— in each case, represented by probability sampling. Our social science research included field operations designed to examine different communities in terms of their social organization-disorganization by a number of methods including participant observation, key informant interviewing, sociological surveys, and analysis of existing records, in order to collect data on such aspects as: poverty-affluence; secularization; acculturation; disasters; rapid social change; migration; physical health; leadership; associations; communication; crime and delinquency; broken homes, and hostility. For an outline of the frame of reference of the study see Leighton (2).

Since it was impossible to give adequate field work coverage of all 97 place-named communities in the county, and since it was important to do more intensive studies in depth than provided by some of our methods with probability sampling, we selected eight communities, after considerable field work, for the more intensive community studies. The selections were based upon relative degrees of organization-disorganization, and we called them "focus areas."

Two focus areas were well or highly organized, while at the opposite pole were four disorganized areas (3). The other two were selected as falling in between the extremes and were called mixed or intermediate in organization. It will be against the social patterns of the extreme communities that we will compare the symptom distribution data to evaluate the relationship between symptoms and socio-cultural context.

The study of symptom distribution in Stirling was shared by two research teams using different methods—the psychiatric unit and the screening-test unit. The latter will be discussed later. One of our first steps was to sponsor the establishment of a psychiatric clinic in the county town of 3,000. Here we received the cooperation of the local medical association as well as the federal and provincial departments of health and welfare. Besides its regular service function the clinic group has been carrying out a number of research activities including intensive case studies of psychodynamics, in several cases of members of the one family group over several generations. It has also experimented with preventive psychiatry in the community.

A panel of psychiatrists has been evaluating cross-section samples of community adults in terms of "ill" and "well" together with number and kinds of symptom patterns, instead of attempting diagnosis per se. The material used in these psychiatric evaluations includes structured health interviews, hospital records, and solicited comments by local physicians and others in the community about the respondent. [Preliminary results of a portion of these evaluations may be seen in Leighton (4).] Also, a pilot study is being completed on the administration of a battery of psychological tests to community adults evaluated as ill and well, and to clinic patients, to assess the personality differences between these categories of individuals.

Though the major emphasis has been on the study of adults, we have undertaken supplementary and complementary work on children. This includes the operation of demonstration nursery schools in both English and Acadian communities, intelligence testing in the communities using both group and individual tests, a child-rearing practice survey in selected focus areas of the county, and a special study of school children in the county town. The last included standardized test data on both personal and social adjustment as well as a health questionnaire. Perhaps this will suffice to provide an outline of our work. Now, let us proceed to a description of the screening unit's attempt to devise and standardize a psychological test for assessing the rough proportions of the ill and well in our rural communities.

We felt the need for such a test to complement and supplement the assessments of our panel of psychiatrists in their evaluations. In short, it was to be a symptom-finding device, and possibly to give a gross indication of illness and wellness—but not in any sense a diagnostic instrument.

It would not be appropriate to take the time in this meeting to review the history of screening tests—suffice it to say that after an extensive review of the literature and consultations with investigators who were active in the field of screening, we found no test that had been standardized on small town and rural adults nor, for that matter, any other test which appeared readily adaptable to our rural research situation. Further, it appeared that those tests available most closely related to our actual field possibilities were some developed and used in the armed forces. Since these, for the most part, had been standardized on young males, and under rather special circumstances, it became evident that it would be necessary for us to build a test for our own situation.

We would need to adapt our test for both young and old subjects, applicable to both sexes, and standardize it on the type of population under investigation. The standardization, however, should be done outside the Stirling County research area but on a similar rural population. It seemed clear, also, that instead of a "personality measurement" our aim should be in obtaining an instrument which would provide a rough measure of neurotic and related symptoms among rural community adults; that is, to detect those adults whose responses to questions about their health approximated those of patients with psychiatric diagnoses, and which differed, on the other hand, from the general responses of controls drawn at random from communities. It did not seem at all feasible, at our current level of knowledge, to attempt any elaborate analysis of personality factors or a precise psychiatric diagnosis appraisal. The general conclusions, at this stage, agreed closely with those expressed later by Mackinnon (5).

With these considerations and others in mind, a two-county area, with socio-cultural characteristics similar to those of Stirling County was selected as the locale for the standardization operation. Also, permission was obtained to administer our test to patients at the nearest psychiatric hospitals and out-patient clinic. These research settings provided a community group to screen and a criterion ill group whose illnesses had been diagnosed.

Field Procedures

In selecting and arranging the test and its mode of administration, certain known health attitudes and "sets" prevalent in the community population were taken into account. For example, the people were for the most part unfamiliar with social research and questionnaires; they were reticent in discussing personal matters with strangers; they were unaccustomed to doing "paper work." It thus seemed advisable that the test should contain no offensive items (e.g., "Do you believe in God?"); that it should be administered confidentially; that the interviewer should do the writing, and the respondent should not have to concentrate upon answering questions for more than about 20 minutes. Further, we gave our operation a name which we felt would adequately and frankly express our aims in terms acceptable and meaningful to the group to be screened—the Health Opinion Survey (hereafter called the HOS).

The test was built up of items from a number of sources. About 20% were questions from the Army's Neuropsychiatric Screening Adjunct (6) with additional questions reported to be useful neurotic discriminators by Eysenk (7), Rimoldi (8), and a few other investigators. Local general practitioners were consulted by the author in order to establish criteria as to the suitability of the various items that seemed most pertinent. As finally constituted, the test schedule comprised a total of 75 health-oriented queries, the majority being of the psychophysiological-complaint type and the balance dealing with social relationships. In most cases the respondent was required to select one of three possible answers like the "often-sometimes-never" alternatives of the Army NSA. The more familiar and easily answered sociological questions, such as marital status, religion, and occupation came first, followed by some very general questions about health, in order to reassure the respondent and provide some orientation before reaching the main section, the screening items.

Eight interviewers, selected from students at Acadia and

Dalhousie universities, received three weeks of special training session, by the author. Six of them interviewed in the two-county area and two at the psychiatric hospitals. The hospitals afforded facilities for conducting the interviews in private. To ensure similar privacy in the community interviewing, without the necessity of bringing respondents to a central place, house trailers were rented and the interiors were arranged for the purpose (see Fig. 1). In the community situation, a slight *quid pro quo* as well as a reinforcement of the medical atmosphere was pro-

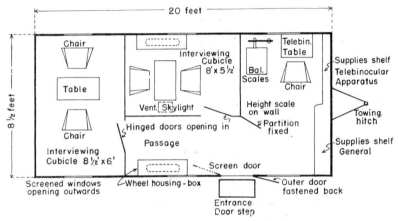

FIGURE 1.   Interviewing trailer showing plywood partitions and equipment layout.

vided by measuring height and weight and by testing the respondent's eyesight with a telebinocular before completing the questionnaire.

County agricultural agents were consulted for their opinions concerning socio-economic grouping of the rural community residents, and their advice led to the identification of subgroups differentiated as "Good farm," "Average farm," "Poor farm," "Day labor" and "Urban" (small town, actually). By random cluster sampling methods 559 white adults aged 20 to 59 years were selected from these subgroups and interviewed. At the same time, 210 hospitalized or out-patient subjects were interviewed in the hospital setting. The diagnoses carried the usual range, and 78 adult psychoneurotics were selected as our "ill" criterion group. The entire interviewing operation occupied three months.

Standardization—Discriminant Function Analysis of Good-Farm and Psychoneurotic Groups

The needs of the on-going research program in Stirling County forced a rapid analysis, in at least a preliminary form, to see if the screening test was sufficiently useful to be given a trial as a case-finding instrument. For this reason, initial efforts were limited to comparing the 78 clearly defined neurotics with the county subgroups.[2] Findings reported in this paper will be similarly restricted.

Trials at Guttman scaling of the data failed to indicate a "quasi" scale related to personality disturbances such as had been found in the United States Army research with the NSA items (6). Therefore it became necessary to devise a special form of item analysis aimed at constructing a composite health score or index.

Chi-square comparisons between the county residents as a whole and the hospital neurotics revealed that 40 of the 75 HOS items discriminated between the two groups at the 1% level of significance. However, technical limitations of the statistical method we were to use forced us to reduce this number for computing scoring weights. In addition, there was some variability in responses to certain of the test items among the different socio-economic subgroups (Good-farm, Poor-farm, etc.) which we considered important to examine. Therefore chi square comparisons were made between the hospital neurotics on the one hand and each subgroup separately on the other. By this means, the 40 significant items were reduced to 20 that, for every sub-

[2] It may be of interest to note that in a later analysis we found the Character Disorder group had answered the HOS items very similarly to the Neurotics.

group, maintained the discrimination at a 1% level of significance. These 20 items are considered "universals" (10).

In carrying out the interviewing program a strong impression developed that the subgroup which the agricultural agent had named "Good Farm" was made up mainly of healthy, well-adjusted, asymptomatic individuals. The impression was corroborated by the findings in the preliminary analysis that not only the 20 universals but an additional 16 HOS test items distinguished this group from the hospital neurotics at a 1% level of significance. Since the Good Farm group provided the greatest contrast with the hospital neurotics, the data from it were used in a special form of discriminant function analysis to determine the optimal scoring weights to give each of the 20 universal items so that the distribution of scores of the Good Farm group would be maximally distinguished from that of the hospital neurotics.[3] The weights found by this analytic procedure were then applied to the scoring of the 20 universal items in all the protocols in such a fashion as to give a higher score to the nonsymptom responses and a lower score to the neurotic-like answers. Table I shows the rounded weights obtained by the computation. It can be seen that the scoring system is adjusted to provide a higher score to the "well-type" responses and the smaller scores to responses that indicate some "health trouble." For instance, a person who answered "Often" to all the 20 HOS items given here would obtain a Health Score of zero.

Figure 2 compares the distributions of the Good Farm and the diagnosed neurotics (Pn) and indicates some degree of overlap between the community and the diagnosed groups, but this is a minimum, as we should expect from our statistical manipulation of the data. Figure 3, on the other hand, shows how the same scoring system distributes the rest of the two-county community population (N 419) in relation to the diagnosed neurotics.

---

[3] This special discriminant function formula was devised by the late Garnet E. McCreary, formerly the Stirling County Study statistician, who supervised the computations of the discriminant function analysis.

TABLE I

Selected HOS Items with Computed Weights (Rounded)
Arranged to Provide a Health Score

	Responses and Weights		
HOS Items	Never	Sometimes	Often
1. Do you have loss of appetite?	25	(½ Never weight)	0
2. How often are you bothered by having an upset stomach?	16	(½ Never weight)	0
3. Has any ill health affected the amount of work you do?	13	(½ Never weight)	0
4. Have you ever felt you were going to have a nervous breakdown?	12	(½ Never weight)	0
5. Are you ever troubled by your hands sweating so they feel damp and clammy? (Items 6–15 obtained derived weights from 6.0 to 0.4)	10	(½ Never weight)	0
16. Are you ever bothered by nervousness?	−2	(½ Never weight)	0
17. Have you ever been bothered by shortness of breath when you were not exercising or working hard?	−4	(½ Never weight)	0
18. Do you tend to feel tired in the morning?	−5	(½ Never weight)	0
19. For the most part, do you feel healthy enough to carry out the things you would like to do?	−7	(½ Never weight)	0
20. Have you ever been troubled by "cold sweats"?	−11	(½ Never weight)	0

At a cutting point of 59–60 in the score scale, we see that 25% of this community sample have responded like 92% of the diagnosed group. A major problem at this stage of such analysis is in establishing a cutting point which will serve as an optimal dividing line between neurotic and well, with the fewest false negatives on one side and false positives on the other. This is essentially the problem of validating the test.

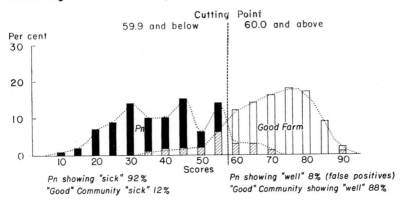

FIGURE 2. Distributions of Good Farm and diagnosed neurotics.

Validation of the HOS

By Interviewer Observations

Two possible explanations come to mind for the appearance of county residents on the neurotic side of the cutting point: (*a*) that the test does not adequately distinguish between neurotic and non-neurotic, and (*b*) (much more probable) that there are

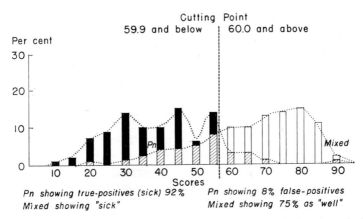

FIGURE 3. Distribution of rest of community population in relation to the diagnosed neurotics.

people in the county with neurotic symptoms even though they have not been so diagnosed. During the testing program in the county, the interviewers were instructed to keep separate notes on behavior and remarks of respondents which seemed significant. These were, of course, not utilized in scoring the questions but were assessed independently later. Most of the interviewers' comments turned out to be either describing overt behavior or complaints of the respondents such as are commonly found among clinically recognized neurotics (11, 12), for example, restlessness, irritability and aggression, complaints of fatigue, tremors, and excessive perspiration.

After the distributions of HOS scores had been worked out at Cornell, the interviews of county residents whose scores fell on the neurotic side of the 59–60 cutting point were examined to see if there were interviewer comments or notations of significant symptoms or complaints. It was found that of those subjects scoring in the 50's, 46% had some such indication; of those scoring in the 40's the per cent rose to 70%; while of those with the most neurotic-like score (20–30) 88% had either noticeable symptoms or complaints. Although obviously not conclusive these data provide some evidence supporting the test and indicate that our community groups are certainly not symptom-free. There is also a suggestion that for our screening purposes possibly two cutting points rather than one, may be desirable, with a "Doubtful" or "Don't Know" category between the "Well" and the "Ill."

Validation by Psychiatric Examination

In order to push validation a step farther than the evidence from the Interviewer's Observations, it seemed desirable to get a psychiatric appraisal of a sample of the people tested in the county. To this end a psychiatrist visited 64 (11%) of the community individuals tested, interviewed each in the trailer for half an hour, and evaluated the subject's mental health status. This evaluation was done without any knowledge by the psychiatrist of how the individual had scored on the HOS nor of what impression he had made on the HOS interviewer. The results of this evaluation can be seen in Table II, where the psychiatrist's assessments are compared with the scores achieved by the same individuals on the HOS.

Here it is plain that twin cutting points rather than a single one are essential, for under these circumstances it was not possible for the psychiatrist to categorize 23 subjects as definitely neurotic or definitely non-neurotic. He simply could not place them with confidence on either the "Well" or the "Ill" side of the scale. The psychiatrist estimated his error to be between 10% and 15% of those he rated. He was obviously working under difficulties in that the surroundings were certainly not like the usual clinical situation and, more important, the persons he was interviewing lacked the familiar motivation of coming to him for help. Moreover, half an hour is a very short time for making such an appraisal (though considerably longer than is usual in military assessment interviews). In all probability, a proportion of his "Don't know's" could have been placed in either the well or the sick group if he had had more time to interview them.

Table II shows a high correspondence between the psychiatrist's assessment and the HOS test score; that is, nearly all the persons that he considered well had high HOS scores, and nearly all that he thought sick had low HOS scores. In other words, as far as it goes, the psychiatric clinical assessment tends to validate the HOS as a means of screening the neurotically sick from the well. It tends, further, to indicate that a number of the county residents actually had recognizable neurotic symptoms as well as neurotic HOS scores.[4] There is a total difference of 14% between the psychiatrist's assessment and the designa-

[4] Four of his "Well" and two of his "Sick" had HOS scores in the doubtful range. (Of his doubtfuls 6 scored from 79 to 62; 1 in the 61–59 range and 16 were 58–20). There are no false-negatives. That is, he did not consider Sick anyone who had a high (or "Well") HOS score; but there are 3 whom he considered Well who made a Sick score, while 4 of his Well and 2 of his Sick appear in the doubtful-score group.

TABLE II. Validation Experiment—Psychiatrist's Assessment Compared to HOS Score

Psychiatrist's Assessment	HOS "Well" Range					?	HOS "Sick" Range			
	91–86	85–80	79–74	73–68	67–62	61–59	58–53	52–47	46–41	40–35
Well I	N N N	N N N N N	—	N(Pp?)	N N N N N	N	N(Pc)	N	—	—
Well II	N(Ps)?	—	N Pc Pn	Pn Pn Ps Ps	—	Pc Pc? Pn?	—	—	Pn	—
Sick IV	—	—	—	—	—	PP PC	—	PN PN	PC PN	PN PN
Sick V	—	—	—	—	—	—	PN PN	—	PC PN	PN

Psychiatrist's assessment: Well I, appears quite well; Well II, minor symptoms but not disabling; Sick IV, appears to need help with problems; Sick V, definitely needs help.

Psychiatrist's diagnosis: N, normal; Pc, Slight Character Difficulty; Pn, Slightly Psychoneurotic; Pp, Slightly Psychotic; Ps, Slightly Psychosomatic. If a second code letter of any pair is also a capital, this indicates strong evidence for the diagnosis. A diagnostic code followed by "?" indicates "questionable."

Note. The psychiatrist's "Don't knows" included 6 in the HOS well range, 1 in the "?", and 16 in the sick range, which are not shown in the table.

216

tion by the HOS scores. This indicates that, where the picture is reasonably clear from the clinical point of view, there is an excellent chance that the HOS screening test will categorize the person in the same way as the clinician in gross terms of "Ill" and "Well."

Discussion

While these results are probably indicative of a usable devise, certain cautions must be observed. For example, it may be that the validation by the psychiatrist was a matter of chance and that in another trial his assessments would fail to agree with the test scores because of the unfamiliarity of the situation to a clinician. Furthermore, the test needs a much more extensive try-out in different types of communities and in various cultures in order to see what modifications are required under various socio-cultural conditions. Our experience with and modifications of this test in Stirling County will be reported elsewhere. While its use in Stirling County provides a limited opportunity to test the effect of translation into another language, the full significance of language and cultural differences for the HOS also remains to be explored. Further work is being done with the HOS data with latent structure and factor analysis, as well as an attempt to derive a psychotic index as a complement to the neurotic index reported here.

Supposing further trials substantiate the apparent promise of the HOS as a means of screening neurotics from non-neurotics, some of its potential uses might be: (*a*) to obtain an estimate of the degree of need for psychiatric services in specific communities, industries or institutions; (*b*) to compare the variation of need across a region (country, province, state, county, etc.) in order to plan the most efficient use of scarce psychiatric resources; (*c*) to measure the effectiveness of mental health programs by reassessing the prevalence of psychiatric symptoms from time to time; (*d*) to designate individuals for psychiatric appraisal in educational, industrial or military contexts; (*e*) to provide a time-saving general overview of a patient's symptomatology for the busy physician; (*f*) a wide variety of research uses.

REFERENCES

1. Leighton, A. H. A proposal for research in the epidemiology of mental disorder. In *Epidemiology of Mental Disorder,* Milbank Memorial Fund, New York, 1950.
2. Leighton, A. H. Psychiatric disorder and social environment. *Psychiatry, 18, 4* (1955).
3. Macmillan, A. M., and A. H. Leighton. People of the hinterland. In *Human Problems in Technological Change,* edited by Edward H. Spicer. Russell Sage Foundation, New York, 1952.
4. Leighton, Dorothea C. The distribution of psychiatric symptoms in a small town. *Am. J. Psychiat., 112, 9* (1956).
5. Mackinnon, Donald W. Facts and fancy in personality research. *Am. Psychologist, 1953, 8* (4) 138–45 (1953).
6. Stouffer *et al. Studies in Social Psychology in World War II.* Vol. IV, Measurement and Prediction, 1950. Pages 162–66.
7. Eysenk, H. J. *Dimensions of Personality.* Routledge and Keegan Paul, London, 1948.
8. Rimoldi, H. V. A. *Behavior Inventory.* University of Chicago, personal communication.
9. Kreidt, P. H., and K. E. Clarke. Item analysis versus scale analysis. *J. Appl. Psychol. 33,* 114–21 (1949).
10. For others who have published on this subject since the preliminary analysis was undertaken see: Valentine Appel and David Kipnis. The use of levels of confidence in item analysis. *J. Appl. Psychol., 38* (4), 256–59 (1954); Jane Loevinger. Some principles of personality measurement. *Educational and Psychological Measurements, 15* (1), 3–17 (1955).
11. Grinker, R. R., and J. P. Speigel. *Men Under Stress.* Blakiston, New York, 1945.
12. Myerson, A. Neuroses and psychoneuroses, the relationship of symptom groups. *Am. J. Psychiat., 93* (1936).

DISCUSSION

DR. MILTON TERRIS: Dr. Macmillan's paper is significant on two counts: first, because of its application to a civilian population of the neuropsychiatric screening methods developed in World War II, and second, because of its concern with the problem of validation, a subject which needs a great deal more discussion and exploration than it has hitherto received in epidemiologic studies of mental disease.

The Neuropsychiatric Screening Adjunct (NSA) used in World War II was developed on the basis of studies comparing a cross-section of the Army and of psychoneurotics in station hospitals. It was found that questions relating to psychosomatic complaints differentiated most sharply between the known psychoneurotics and the Army cross section. Ninety per cent of the former had critical scores for this group of questions as compared with 27% of the latter. Dr. Macmillan, using a screening test with items the majority of which are of the psychophysiological complaint type, and the balance dealing with social relationships similarly found that 22% of his county population sample had critical scores as compared with 92% of neurotics in hospitals and clinics.

The Army psychologists further attempted to validate their psychosomatic complaints questionnaire by administering it at one induction station and comparing the results with the independent diagnosis of the station psychiatrists; 18% of the men found acceptable for service had critical scores as compared with 82% of those rejected for psychiatric reasons.

When the results were studied for all induction stations, it was found that 22% of the men found acceptable for service had critical scores as compared with 70% of the men rejected for psychiatric reasons and 81% of those rejected for psychoneurosis.

However, while the NSA results were relatively stable, this could not be said for the psychiatric rejection rates which varied from ½% in one station to 51% in another. And while, for the country as a whole, 40% of all psychiatric rejects were diagnosed as psychoneurotic, the percentages varied all the way from 3 to 90% in individual induction stations. It might be argued that this enormous variability in diagnosis reflected variations in actual prevalence, but unfortunately, the variations were as great within regions as between regions. In Pittsburgh, 24% of the men examined were psychiatric rejects, as compared with only 7% in Philadelphia. In Detroit, the percentage was 22%, but in Chicago, only 8%. In Seattle and Portland, it was 16%, but in San Francisco, only 5%.

Similar variations occurred in the proportion of psychiatric rejects diagnosed as psychoneurotic: it was 58% in Boston as compared with 25% in New Haven; 63% in Albany and Syracuse, and only 33% in Buffalo and Rochester; 30% in Pittsburgh, and 3% in Philadephia; 69% in San Francisco, but only 23% in Seattle and Portland.

It is true that the psychiatrists working in the induction stations had extremely limited time available for examination of each individual, although the figures quoted are for August 1945, a relatively quiet period in the induction stations. Also, rejection was based on two psychiatric judgments, one of diagnosis, the other of the effect of the diagnosis on suitability for Army duty. The variations which occurred reflected differences with respect to both these judgments. Nevertheless, the differences were almost fantastic. It is not surprising, therefore, that the Army psychologists concluded that: "Until, however, psychiatric diagnosis is better standardized than it is today, it is likely that the predictability of psychiatric screening tests will fall far short of ideal."

Any survey of health status which relies only on interview methods runs a serious risk of error. In the Hunterdon County chronic disease study, for example, Trussell and his co-workers found that only 22% of the total conditions discovered by careful clinical evaluation had been reported in a previous, rather exhaustive, family interview. For diabetes, the match was 64%; for heart disease, 39%; for mental, psychoneurotic and personality disorders, 22%; for genitourinary diseases 11%, and for neoplasms, 10%.

In prevalence studies of mental disease, reporting by the individuals under study is widely recognized to be relatively unproductive, not only because the individual may not have been previously diagnosed or informed of the diagnosis, but also because he may be ashamed to report the presence of mental illness.

The substitution of a symptom inventory such as the Army's NSA or Dr. Macmillan's screening test has the advantage that the connection with mental illness is less obvious. Instead of being asked whether he is psychoneurotic or has a "nervous condition," the individual is asked whether he often, sometimes, or never has trouble with sleep, trembling hands, fainting spells, nervousness, heart beating hard, pressures or pains in the head, dizzy spells, nail biting, shortness of breath at rest, sweating hands, sick headaches, upset stomach, nightmares, and cold sweats. But this technique does not entirely remove the problem of inaccurate reporting because of fear of the stigma of psychoneurosis.

As Stouffer has said, "There are ample grounds for warning

against the danger of carrying over blindly into civilian research the direct questioning techniques used. . . . For example, the Neuropsychiatric Screening Adjunct may have worked as well as it did because a man who was motivated to escape duty stood at least a chance of being rewarded if he displayed psychosomatic symptoms. But if the same items were used to screen applicants for employment in a department store, it is likely that the applicant would expect to lose out if he admitted to psychosomatic symptoms."

That the problem of accuracy of response may well be a serious one was recognized by Hunt and Stevenson, who state that "The military recruit taking the test is under tremendous impulsion to tell the truth since the consequences of lying to military authority may be severe.

"As a result, the military psychologist often gets the truth where a civilian psychologist would not. Moreover, the recruit accepts the situation in a serious vein. Military service is a serious matter; it is undertaken under strong personal tensions, and these factors also tend toward truthfulness in answering the questions."

How can we validate the results obtained by such tests as the NSA and Dr. Macmillan's screening test? Clearly, this requires careful clinical evaluation such as that performed in the Hunterdon County study. And here is where we get into difficulty. For the clinician searching for other types of disease has a much more complete and effective diagnostic armamentarium at his disposal. In addition to a history of symptoms, he can observe and examine for physical signs and, most important of all, he has an extensive battery of laboratory tests, radiological examinations, and instrumental adjuncts, such as the sphygmomanometer, ophthalmoscope, sigmoidoscope, and electrocardiograph to help him.

In the Hunterdon County study, for example, there were 11 laboratory and radiological tests performed for every person examined.

In the case of psychoneurotics, however, the situation is quite different. As Hunt and Stevenson have pointed out, screening tests such as those used by the military services and by Dr. Macmillan are merely printed psychiatric interviews. Dr. Macmillan's validation procedure, then, consists in the substitution for a 20-minute standardized interview by a largely untrained person, of a 30-minute unstandardized interview by a clinician. The two procedures, the screening test and the psychiatric interview, are not really independent, since undoubtedly the psychiatrist asks many of the same questions used in the screening tests. It would be very interesting in this connection to obtain records of some of the 30-minute psychiatric interviews used in Dr. Macmillan's validation study and to compare them with the screening test.

Hunt and Stevenson believe that the screening test may even have some advantages over the clinician, since it may be a better instrument than the clinical judgment of some psychiatrists and since it never forgets to ask all the questions. On the other hand, the psychiatric interview has the important advantage over the screening test in that it adds the factor of skilled observation of signs of psychoneurosis to the symptom history. But this is about as far as the psychiatrist can go. There are no instruments to help him, no x-rays, no reliable laboratory tests. We remain, therefore, in the clouded area of clinical judgment, and both the military experience referred to previously and experience with psychiatrists in civilian practice indicate that there are wide differences in diagnostic criteria for psychoneurosis, differences which are largely determined by the training of the clinician and the viewpoint of the particular school of psychiatry to which he belongs.

The uncertainty of diagnostic criteria was well expressed at the 1952 Annual Conference of the Milbank Memorial Fund, by Dr. Frederick Redlich, Professor of Psychiatry at Yale, who said: "My own feeling is that at the present time we cannot say what a case is. We have no good criterion. That is too bad. Our friends in public health are quite distressed about that because they know, or believe they know, for instance, in infectious disease, what a case is or what a carrier is. We are not in this fortunate position. Certainly, they know at least much better than we do. They have better operational criteria for their opinion. What the normal and the normal neurotic is, we don't know. However, I believe the difference is not between the various shades of gray in the neurotic scale, where we can draw a line, but the difference is between the severely ill on one side, and between the normal and the neurotic on the other side.

"Freud is actually responsible for all this terrific confusion, because he introduced the notion that the normal is the abnormal, and that the abnormal does not have any strict boundaries. In our dreams, we are all 'way off.' We are very close to the schizophrenic, and so on.

"Because there is a fluid line between the normal and the abnormal, everybody becomes abnormal."

Does the existence of wide differences in diagnostic criteria mean that validation of screening tests such as that developed by Dr. Macmillan is impossible? I don't think so. What it means is that such tests cannot be validated by a single psychiatrist, or even by several psychiatrists belonging to the same school of psychiatric thought. It means that the whole problem of validation has to be studied and explored, and that psychiatric procedures, definitions, and diagnostic criteria have to be standardized on a scientific basis. Unless this is done, I am afraid we can expect little but confusion from epidemiologic studies of psychoneurosis and other mental disorders.

DR. OSKAR DIETHELM: I would like to ask three questions which have to do with the same topic, the limitations of the test which were just discussed.

1. As far as I can see, the test does not tell us about the degree or intensity of the psychoneurosis or of the psychosis. It may only tell us about certain aspects of it.

2. He stresses the influence of the emotion of anxiety, but, in the physiological field, if that emotion is not of an outstanding component of the psychoneurosis, will the test still tell as much from that special point of view?

3. Since the test could not bring out any facts which have to do with ethical values, it would not bring out problems which are so commonly caused by psychoneuroses, such as alcoholism, promiscuity, and dope addiction.

I wonder if we know enough about the limitations as well as the assets of it.

DR. GRUENBERG: I want to express my personal gratitude both for Macmillan's paper and for Dr. Terris' brilliant discussion. I think that personally this represents one of the greatest advances in the case findings methods in the field of psychiatry that has yet come forward.

I don't disagree particularly with any of the precautions that both doctors mention, but there is one that Dr. Terris mentioned that I would like to bring out for discussion. I disagree with the implication that he made regarding the relative qualities for an examiner to come in contact with manifestations of disorder and of illness in the person being examined, and personality disorders as contrasted to physical disorders.

It seems to me that the emphasis he placed on instrumentation and examining techniques in physical disorder is misplaced. In fact, instrumentation is needed in order to examine disorders of functions, physical disorders of functions, because the disorders are hidden from the examiner by the skin, by overlaying tissues, by the fact that disordered function is not manifested on the surface immediately observable to the examiner.

Stating my thought on a question dogmatically (I hope somebody will disagree with me) it seems to me that psychological disorder does not exist unless it exists in psychological functioning and that psychological functioning is directly manifested in the interview situation.

Now, although it is perfectly true that different kinds of interview situations bring forward different aspects of the physical function, there is no skin between us and the patient except the skin created by the nature of our interpersonal relationship. Consequently, I cannot conceive of any more ultimate criterion ever developing for the presence or absence of psychological disorder than manifestations of disordered functioning in the presence of a trained observer.

DR. ZUBIN: I very rarely disagree with Dr. Gruenberg about these matters, but here is a point I want to take issue with him. I am caught in between his extreme faith in the interview and the extreme opposite point of view where you can get the results by simply asking the person to answer a questionnaire.

I am very much excited about the interview. In fact, we are trying to develop techniques for measuring affects through the interview, focusing the interview on specific functions of the individual. I think if you had this (maybe in ten years from now you can get the thing worked up), we will be able to have focused interviews on anxiety, depression, and general affective levels.

We don't have them now except through the general interviews, and you see from the report given by the discussants that they varied in terms of evaluation from over 3% in Philadelphia to 90% somewhere else.

First of all, these psychiatric inventories were born out of sheer hunger back in 1937, when Woodward was requested by the Surgeon General to develop a technique for screening out the recruitments who would fall before they even got to the front line. That was the beginning of the inventory. He went through all the textbooks of psychiatry and he picked off those things which characterized people before they became sick. Then he said that anybody who has these characteristics in his background, in his past, is eventually going to become sick.

No one ever tested that hypothesis. It got lost in the shuffle. We don't even know now today whether, from the history of an individual during his youth, you will be able to tell whether he will break or not.

Primarily, the people that came into the Army were not in the hospital. They were ready to go to war. It was a question of whether they would break down in the future. As a result of the lack of time, and as a result of the fact that the war ended before they could try out this interview, this became available after the war and was used in industries. Colleges became the guinea pigs for testing it out. Finally, it became a test which was accepted as a method for finding out how well the person is mentally.

The trouble with the way those tests have been developed—and I think Dr. Macmillan's approach to it may suffer from the same difficulty—is that it is a category of quirks and of deviations, while the assets of a person are thrown out.

Take, for example, these two items: "I'm afraid of high places," and "I never go to high places."

Now, item "I never go to high places" may be washed out. It will not differentiate between neurotic and normal, and it gets thrown out. But I think if a person says, "I am afraid of high places, keep away from them" (even though that is still a little peculiar), this represents a different kind of personality from the one who says, "I am afraid of high places, but I do go to them, I am forced to go to them."

The fact that we take this blind approach to differentiating items, whether or not they differentiate, throws off the inventory, and I am surprised we get the differentiation we do get. It seems to me that if, taking the pattern of response into consideration, starting all over again and taking both assets and liabilities into account for each person, we might be able to get some kind of figuration which differentiates.

Now, a score of thirty, whatever it is, means that it is a critical score. But that score of 30, say, if it were a hundred items, could be gotten in about 90 trillion different ways. I am asking to find the pattern which characterized each one of these individuals who finally break down and those who do not in order to see whether you can make a new scoring device depending upon the structural pattern that gave that score. Then perhaps you can get something closer to the individual.

But aside from that, I think that dependence on conceptual behavior to the exclusion of physiological sensory, perceptual, and psychomotor behavior is going to lead us into trouble. Very often the same conceptual deviation may be given by a person who otherwise functions well, or by a person who does not function well. What we are doing now is trying to get screening tests that will actually tap each of these areas, the physical, the sensory, the perceptual, the psychomotor. Then we can get an implicating pattern to characterize the total individual. That is, in itself, a difficult test to give. Once you work it out to the point where it is applicable, however, people will take a perception test and a psychomotor test in much the same manner as people take x-rays. This is bound to give us a much better way of screening than depending only on the interviewer or the person interviewed.

DR. P. V. LEMKAU: To attack Dr. Gruenberg's points a little bit, while in a laboratory test you don't usually mix the serum of the patient with the serum of the examiner before doing the test, in the interview situation you do. The attitude of the examiner can contaminate the experiment, as has been pointed out, many, many times.

Dr. Terris' discussion of the various psychological problems relating to the motivation of people when they are answering questions, either in an interview or on a questionnaire paper, is certainly one that has not been solved at all to my satisfaction.

I do know that Dr. Robin Williams, Jr., who was involved with the later phases of the NSA used in the Army, recalls having a distinct impression that a good many of the "bad" answers to the psychosomatic questions were obviously a matter of "goldbricking."

Since any of you who have been in the services knows what that means, I believe that this aspect of the Army test situation is one of the reasons why the Army found the "quasi" scale as reported in the *American Soldier,* Volume IV. Of course, we didn't get any such scale. Obviously our community population was differently motivated—"goldbricking" did not apply.

On the point of how to validate the study: This paper, of course, is a report on an attempt to transfer the same kind of test used in the Army to a civilian population. Since there was no civilian-standardized test available to us, we went ahead and built one and standardized it. This is not a conclusive instrument at all, and I have serious doubt as to its wider application until it has been tried in many other areas. As I said in the beginning of the paper, it is, at this stage, just a question of exploration.

With regard to Dr. Terris' point that he would have liked to have seen a record of the validating psychiatrist's examination, we were able to tape record two of them entirely. (A third was attempted but the machine broke down.) These examinations are typed, but they have not been examined to compare the interview content with the content of the HOS questionnaire. That is a very interesting suggestion.

I quite agree with the belief that validation by one or more psychiatrists would not be feasible. I have done some exploratory work on this problem, with this same questionnaire, and have used a panel of 7 psychiatrists, the "extra comments" of our respondents, and the answers to the HOS items. These extra comments were presented to a panel of psychiatrists who were asked to evaluate them in terms of whether they were possibly high in psychological content or purely organic, and so on. The degree of agreement achieved on this exercise was 65%.

As for Dr. Diethelm's questions about limitations, of course I did not stress limitations in view of the short time available for these papers. Obviously, the HOS is a very rough measure, if it is a measure at all. It doesn't give any degree of intensity of psychoneuroses, nor does it give the kind of psychoneurosis. It only indicates some degree of illness of the individual in terms of score span comparing psychoneurotic people with a large number of other community people like himself, who do or do not respond in this way. This is about the way the matter stands.

As for degree of differentiation of psychotics, while still in the field we attempted a psychotic scoring device. I found that the efficiency of detection of psychotic patients from the mental hospital was exactly by chance, i.e., fifty-fifty. So the test as presently scored certainly does not discriminate psychotics as a group, though with further analysis we may be able to differentiate certain kinds of psychotics. I can say, however, that so far as some of the sociopathic categories of illness are concerned, we did not think it feasible to gather certain types of information necessary to make such diagnoses. Nor did we attempt to put items in the HOS which would give indications of manic, melancholic, depressive tendencies, and the like. It is simply not designed for that.

Dr. Diethelm's comment about the lack of information on ethical values that are really necessary to make some diagnoses is pertinent. I might say that while working in the early stages of field activity, while putting together this questionnaire, and while interviewing general practitioners in the research area, I considered introducing items of values. I wanted to introduce a series of about eight or ten questions of this nature which would be appropriate to the local cultural milieu. When I started, however, to refine some of the topics that I had and to explore their application in the two-county research area, I found that in order to have reasonably applicable questions I would need to spend an entire summer doing research on this topic alone, which would delay the field work for another year. So I had to abandon that part of the HOS questionnaire.

I would like to follow up on the idea sometime, nevertheless. Following along the line of what Dr. Zubin said, we would like to put together packets of questions which we may hope obtain in ten, fifteen, or twenty-five years some degree of validity.

I heartily agree with Dr. Zubin's comment that a major loss comes from a failure to obtain information on the positive or supportive side. In a good many of these kinds of approach to research in the community, the assets of the individual appear to be lost sight of, and it is only the negative aspects that are seized upon by researchers. We, in the Stirling County Study, have been aware of this and are trying to deal with it. As far as this HOS questionnaire is concerned, we have undoubtedly overplayed the negative or pathological without a counterbalance of assets.

I also agree with the idea of types of patterns of response, and this in terms of the problem of validation, too. This is the reason we are exploring the latent structure type of analysis, because this kind of analysis, in effect, does away with criterion groups and differentiates the people themselves without any subjectively derived criterion group.

It is the wide variety of patterning of complaints that people have which has been the subject of great interest to a good many psychiatrists. Recently, at a public health meeting in Washington, a psychiatrist made the comment that while it was quite true that many people he saw fell neatly into definite diagnostic categories, on the other hand just as many or more he saw did not fit into one or another. They were ill, they had complaints and so on and so forth, and he was puzzled as to where to place them. It is this patterning of people's complaints that I would be very interested to see successfully differentiated. This just amounts to the selection of empirical types. The task, then, would be to try to "look behind" the empirical types, if that can be done.

I might say that, in discussing the quality of control during the interview, a trailer is an admirable device for the director of this type of a survey. He can stand outside and listen at the window to see if the standard of interviewing is being maintained—also, to pick up certain important procedural hints which had not been anticipated. I checked on my field workers consistently in this way, and they knew that this was my practice. I feel it tended to achieve a much higher standard of interviewing than the usual one where there is little supervision.

Genetic and Demographic Aspects of Disordered Behavior Patterns in a Deaf Population[1]

JOHN D. RAINER AND FRANZ J. KALLMANN

New York State Psychiatric Institute,
Columbia University, New York City

A deaf population affords an unusual opportunity to investigate genetic and demographic variables in the epidemiology of disordered behavior patterns. If epidemiological studies of mental disorders aim at relating their frequency, pattern and distribution to the life conditions of a given population (7), their main objective is to assess the differentiating effect of various outside factors on the etiology or clinical symptomatology of properly defined disease entities. A better understanding of the nature and variable manifestations of a disorder will most certainly be helpful in the management of the adjustive problems of the people forming the paticular population (6, 8).

Persons with total deafness from birth or early childhood share a severe form of sensory deprivation. By interfering with the culture-specific development of speech, it affects the patterning of emotional and thought processes, as well as the potentialities of learning and socialization. Isolated from the hearing world to a greater or lesser degree, the deaf form a society within a society. Out of necessity or choice, they merge into

[1] This report is the fifth in a series on the progress of the Mental Health Project for the Deaf, which is being conducted by the Department of Medical Genetics of the New York State Psychiatric Institute, Columbia University, aided by a grant from the Office of Vocational Rehabilitation of the U.S. Department of Health, Education, and Welfare.

groups that cut across many boundaries, including those conventionally drawn for geographic, ethnic, cultural or socioeconomic reasons.

Hence deaf people are destined to live under the stressful yet peculiarly protected conditions of a minority group, having in common those manifold problems which are in part created by an unknowing or apparently unsympathetic world around them. The presumed lack of sympathy, whether real or imagined, is bound to be distressing, especially when reinforced either by a tendency to deny the disabling effect of the hearing impairment, or by the rather common attitude of regarding any form of ill health as a weakness or disgrace (12).

In view of these specific existential contingencies, *demographic* analysis of disordered behavior patterns in a representative deaf population may be expected to provide valuable information about such variations in the prevalence or symptomatology of mental disorders as may be due, either wholly or in part, to one of the following sets of factors: (*a*) difficulties in communication and social interaction; (*b*) frustrations arising from intrafamily disorganization, residential school living, inadequate educational or vocational opportunities, or limitations on the choice of a mate; (*c*) constriction of emotional and intellectual maturation.

The most immediate general questions that come up in a demographic study of this kind are the following:

1. Are there any types of mental disorder which are more likely or less likely to occur in a deaf population than in a hearing one?

2. Is the symptomatology of a disorder which seems to be more prevalent or less prevalent among the deaf than among the hearing essentially the same in the two populations, or are there any particular differences in the expression, recognition, or persistence of clinical symptoms, which may account for observed variations in prevalence?

3. Does the deaf population receive approximately the same

amount and quality of personal guidance and psychiatric treatment as the hearing one, and, if not, why not?

4. Is a deaf population capable of forming a stable subgroup of society with which every member can readily identify himself, or what are the optimum degrees of adjustment the deaf can attain on different levels of intellectual capacity and personality integration? This matter is complicated by the following uncertainties: (*a*) Diagnostic classification of early total deafness is neither clearly delineated nor easily established. (*b*) Deafness is known to result from a multiplicity of causes, each of which may affect personality development in different ways and to a variable extent. (*c*) Irrespective of the diversity of causal factors, the severity of the resultant lag in maturation depends on the age at which deafness occurs.

5. Regarding this variable feature of emotional immaturity, a particularly interesting question is whether it can be considered as specific to the deaf, and how it affects other psychological functions and emotional responses, such as learning processes, anxiety reactions, and illusional phenomena. Under certain circumstances, it is conceivable that the given lack of maturity, plus the relatively inadequate formation of abstract concepts due to difficulty with verbal communication, may confer an adaptive advantage. Generally, however, it is expected to result in a weak conscience structure and somewhat naive attitudes toward family and community responsibilities.

When pronounced, such simplicities of behavior may account for a number of time-worn notions regarding the psychopathology of the deaf, to say nothing of the habit of confusing the psychological effect of hearing impairments developed in later life with those associated with early total deafness. The descriptive clichés include sexual immaturity, asocial behavior, extreme suspiciousness, and a tendency to paranoid symptom formation with concomitant acts of violence.

Generally overlooked in this stereotyped psychodynamic appraisal is the fact that many deaf persons, especially those with deaf parents, show a childlike trust in their fellows, rather than overcautious suspicion. Behavioral imperfections in their social and sexual relationships may often be due to inexperience, rather than to a basic personality deficiency. The consistent finding of a high divorce rate may be as much a reflection of unusual social, cultural, and economic pressures as of friable personal loyalties or immature personality features.

On the basis of our own observations made up to this point in our study, we can only state that much work has yet to be done before any valid generalizations can be reached regarding the psychodynamics and epidemiology of disordered behavior patterns in the deaf.

Genetically, in view of the fact that deafness tends to arise from different causes and is known to accumulate in certain families, especially in the presence of assortative mating trends, it is apparent that the *hereditary factors* operating in this condition represent another set of variables requiring thorough analysis. Actually, one of the unique characteristics of the deaf is a tendency to cluster within families.

It has been estimated that nearly one-half of total deafness cases are genetically determined, that about 47% of the American deaf population marry, and that the majority of the mates comes from the same group (10). According to Best (2), marriages in which one or both partners are deaf tend to be approximately one-half as productive of children as those contracted by a comparable group of hearing couples.

In appraising the genetic aspects of deafness, the following points are most pertinent:

1. While external factors may produce either conductive or perceptive deafness, the hereditary types are usually perceptive in nature. However, the deafness groups classified as apparently "nongenetic" in origin may include some forms that are actually based on a genetic predisposition to deafness that is environmentally induced.

2. A similar syndrome of early deafness may be caused by

the effect of different genes, which can be autosomal recessive, or dominant, or even sex-linked, and may show different degrees of variability in both penetrance and expressivity. As for the specificity of the action of a certain gene, variations apparently depend on the lapse of time from its initial appearance in any one family line.

3. Since the most common form of inherited early total deafness is determined by a recessive gene with a high degree of penetrance, it is certain that consanguineous marriages between carriers with normal hearing, as well as matings between two deaf persons, will raise the frequency of the condition in the population. On the other hand, even two deaf parents with a gene-specific type of deafness may have both hearing and deaf children, if they carry mutant genes of a different variety, or genes with a limited degree of expressivity. Ordinarily, the expectancy of deafness among their children will be 100%. Thus, the emphasis of epidemiological considerations in this sector is to be placed on the evaluation of the mode and degree of transmission of a given genetic component, as well as an understanding of the cultural factors affecting mate selection.

Because of the complex interaction of genetic and nongenetic influences in the epidemiology of disordered behavior patterns in the deaf, our *pilot project,* sponsored since April 1, 1955, by the Office of Vocational Rehabilitation of the Department of Health, Education, and Welfare, has been organized in such a way as to combine the study of two representative samples (5).

Our *first sample* consists of the total deaf population of New York State in the age group of 10 years and over, including a special subgroup which comprises all deaf patients in state institutions for the mentally ill and the mentally retarded. In this sample, the definition of deafness has been extended to all persons in whom the sense of hearing has been "non-functional" for the ordinary purposes of life, and who developed their hearing impairment at so early an age that they required special education (2).

The total number of persons fulfilling these criteria in New York State has not yet been fully ascertained. Variously estimated from 6,000 to 15,000, it probably amounts to a good deal more. No U.S. census data or other official registrations have been available since 1930, and a 1936 New York State law making deafness a reportable condition has never been complied with or enforced. Our own count of names, still far from complete after 21 months of painstaking fieldwork, stands at present at 10,600.

The distribution of this population according to sources of ascertainment is shown in Table I. Compared with the proportion

TABLE I

New York State Deaf Population over Age 10
(End of 1956)

Source of Information	Number of Persons			Per Cent of Total Population	
	Single born	Twins	Total	Expected	Observed
Schools for the deaf	1,045	20	1,065	—	0.064
Schools for mental defectives	306	2	308	—	1.56
Mental hospitals	236	6	242	—	0.24
General population	8,946	39	8,985	—	0.078
Total	10,533	67	10,600	0.039	0.079

of deaf persons over the age of 10 as published by the 1930 Census (0.039%), our survey to date has already led to the discovery of over twice as many bona fide deaf in the state, namely, a rate of at least 0.079%.

Within the populations of mental hospitals and schools for mental defectives, the proportion of early deafness cases is even greater, from 0.24% to 1.56%. This finding may have any one or all of the following three possible explanations:

1. Our hospital census is considerably more complete at this

point than our census of deaf persons in the general population.

2. The need for institutionalization is greater among the deaf than among the hearing.

3. The average length of hospitalization of the deaf exceeds that of hearing patients.

In relation to the total New York school population over age 10 (11), the percentage of deaf students attending special schools is slightly below the rate for the total population, probably because most of these schools are residential in character. There is no law by which residential school attendance can be enforced, and apparently too many deaf children remain at home. Furthermore, some deaf children try to get along in regular schools, although many drop out along the way.

Apart from the lists of deaf persons provided by hospitals and special schools and their graduate organizations, our method of ascertainment has been based on the cooperation of private and communal clubs of the deaf, church groups, vocational agencies, and deaf families referred to us for guidance. Most groups have been very helpful, although some were at first reluctant to furnish names. In smaller communities outside of New York City, many deaf persons have been ascertained through direct questioning of policemen, county nurses, storekeepers, and the like.

Two groups are particularly hard to find, yet it is evident that both are needed if a complete picture is to be obtained of the levels and techniques of adjustment among the deaf. One group consists of the most poorly adjusted persons outside of institutions, including vagrants, delinquents, and unschooled children who remained at home. The other group is made up of those who may have risen to positions of prominence, such as college professors, scientists, and other highly specialized professional people, but who have never identified themselves with the deaf by joining their clubs or other social institutions. We know of the existence of some of these individuals, but there may well be a good many others.

Of the total population compiled in this manner, some easily accessible subsamples have been used to standardize our interviewing techniques. Of course, all the members of our research staff have been trained in the use of the sign language of the deaf, and most have acquired considerable skill in it. However, the real difficulty in the conduct of our interviews is not connected with the mechanics of this special language, but rather with the limitations imposed by the concrete quality of thought and emotion that can be transmitted by this elementary form of communication.

Nevertheless, our population study has been planned in such a way that the life performance of a deaf person can be rated in the educational, vocational, intrafamily and social areas, and can be related to such factors as age of onset and form of deafness, type and length of schooling, presence or absence of other deaf members in the family, preferred method of communication, desired criteria for the choice of a mate or reasons for intentional celibacy, and the special problems of parenthood planning. In institutional cases, particular attention will be paid to the difficulties encountered in the diagnosis, general care, psychiatric treatment, and early rehabilitation of deaf patients.

Our *second sample* consists of deaf twins of any age and variety from the eastern part of the United States, including the state of New York. Planned with a view to complementing each other, the two studies will make it possible to combine cross-sectional and longitudinal methods of investigation under controlled conditions, from a demographic as well as a genetic standpoint.

For demographic purposes, twins represent an easily ascertainable random sample of a population, constituting 2.19% of an American population at the time of birth, or 1.9% of those who reach the age of one year (1). An additional advantage is the fact that twins, apart from being conspicuous, tend to be more cooperative than the average research subject. Few families are averse to being questioned about their private affairs if the original contact is made in reference to twinning—something regarded either in a neutral light, or even as a mark of distinction.

From a genetic point of view, of course, twins offer a unique opportunity to study variations in clinical symptomatology and personality integration in genotypically like and unlike individuals, affected to a similar or dissimilar extent by a severe trait such as deafness. The brief histories of four twin pairs,

FIGURE 1.

taken from our series of 67 deaf twin index cases, may serve to illustrate this point.

The twins in Fig. 1 are two-egg pairs. The girls on the left are particularly interesting because they are conversely discordant for two conditions, congenital deafness and an apparently progressive form of schizophrenia. The deaf girl was always physically and emotionally less mature than her psychotic cotwin, but she is doing well in school and shows no evidence of a schizophrenic personality change. The parents are first cousins with normal hearing, and a brother of the mother is schizophrenic.

The other twins are concordant as to both total deafness and mental retardation, with intelligence quotients between 60 and 70. They come from a large family without a history of early deafness and have reached the same grade at a school for the

FIGURE 2.

deaf, although they differ considerably in their personalities.

The two pairs in Fig. 2 belong in the series of one-egg twins. The girls are four years old and have been reared in a silent home, with deafness in both parents and an older sister. They are strikingly similar in behavior as well as in their intelligence and social maturity levels, despite the fact that deafness manifested itself in only one of the pair. The hearing twin on the left shows a touching concern for her deaf sister and makes every possible effort to interpret for her sake other people's remarks into sign language. On the verbal level, however, both are considerably retarded, although their intelligence as measured by nonverbal scales is normal and their social maturity is advanced.

The boys have been deaf since birth, but they had hearing parents and sibs. After graduation from a school for the deaf, which at that time was rather military in character, they were equally successful in the printing trade. They are now over 60 years old and not very cooperative. Their wives are deaf, apparently due to a nongenetic cause, since all the children have normal hearing.

Of similar epidemiological interest, at least at this stage of our study, is the distribution of mental disorders observed in the subgroup of 242 mental hospital cases (Table II). The most striking feature is the unusually high proportion of deaf patients classified under psychosis with mental deficiency (25.6% of

TABLE II

Distribution of Mental Disorders Among New York State Mental Hospital
Patients (101,581 in 1954)

Mental Disorder	Number of Deaf Patients			Per Cent of Hospital Population	
	Male	Female	Total	Deaf Patients	Hearing Patients
Schizophrenia	60	42	102	47.5	57.2
Psychosis with mental deficiency	28	27	55	25.6	3.4
Senile and arteriosclerotic psychoses	5	12	17	7.9	14.6
Cycloid and involutional psychoses	1	11	12	5.6	9.1
Organic psychoses	13	3	16	7.4	12.2
Other behavior disorders	7	6	13	6.0	3:5
Undiagnosed	15	12	27	——	——
Total	129	113	242	100.0	100.0

215 cases that had been given an official hospital diagnosis at the time of this analysis). This excess may be due in part to the fact that many deaf persons who are actually mentally defective tend to become psychotic and require hospitalization. Most of them fall into the "episode of excitement" subcategory, suggesting that the added stress of total deafness on a mental defective calls for further study.

It may be mentioned in this connection that the relatively high number of deaf persons in schools for mental defectives is largely due to the fact that many of these cases represent syndromes in which deafness and mental defect are incidental to the organic damage. Another group may be formed by deaf persons of borderline intelligence who were found to be uneducable in schools for the deaf and, for want of better facilities, placed in institutions for defectives.

On the other hand, the presumably retarded deaf patients in mental hospitals seem to include a relatively large group, at least one-quarter and possibly as many as one-half of the total, in which the diagnosis of psychosis with mental deficiency represents a "wastebasket" classification for any deaf person who, at one time or another, shows signs of emotional disturbance. From histories and many personal interviews, we have gained the impression that the term "mental deficiency" in such cases is simply a relic of the time when the deaf mute was considered a defective, and the "episode of excitement" diagnosis served as the most convenient description of their otherwise unexplainable behavior at the time of admission.

It may be assumed, therefore, that the category of deaf patients labeled mentally retarded includes many who, had they been hearing persons, would have been placed in a more precise psychiatric classification, and that these inaccurate diagnoses account for much of the deficit observed in the other categories. This observation is especially true of the schizophrenia group, which is the largest in the deaf as well as in the hearing, although the respective rates vary from 47.5% to 57.2% (9).

Regarding the diagnosis of schizophrenia in the deaf, it should be noted that the usual diagnostic criteria in terms of disordered thought and emotion are grossly obscured by difficulties in communication. Only in the more advanced stages do catatonic, hebephrenic, or paranoid symptoms in the deaf show no significant difference from those typical in the hearing.

Even auditory hallucinations are found in many of these patients, including those who have been deaf from earliest infancy. While it is true that most of these hallucinations are "vibratory" rather than auditory in nature (such as machines operating in the basement), or are hallucinations expressed in sign language, there are some instances in which totally deaf persons insist they actually hear voices. Figure 3 shows a drawing by a 32-year-old schizophrenic male, deaf since the age of 13 months, and acutely psychotic at the time of his recent admission. He made the drawing during an interview to explain his suddenly acquired ability to hear voices in both ears, especially the voice of God speaking on both sides, albeit through wires leading from his arms and legs.

A special affinity of deafness to the development of paranoid delusion has been postulated. However, despite the recent report by two English investigators of a significant increase in paranoid manifestations in a group of 40 deaf hospital patients (3), this supposition lacks adequate substantiation. In our series of 102 deaf schizophrenic patients, 50% have been diagnosed as predominantly paranoid, a rate not significantly higher than that found in hearing schizophrenics.

It is among the deaf with indeterminate behavior deviations that the diagnosis of schizophrenia poses a particular problem. Intensive genetic and developmental studies will be necessary to answer such questions as the following:

1. What are the signs of early, latent or "pseudo-neurotic"

schizophrenia in the deaf, and do they fall into a definable pattern?

2. What is the significance in the deaf, not only of behavior forms resembling mental defect, but of impulsive or psychopathic

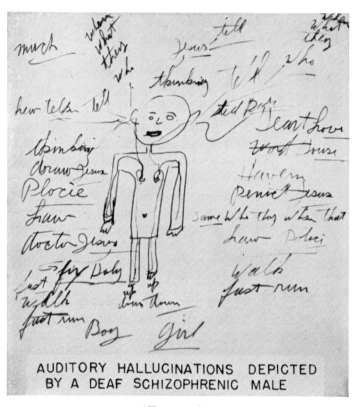

AUDITORY HALLUCINATIONS DEPICTED
BY A DEAF SCHIZOPHRENIC MALE

FIGURE 3.

syndromes? How are they related adaptively to early total deafness, and what connection have they with schizophrenia?

3. What evidence is there that deafness can protect against schizophrenia altogether (4), rather than promote its manifestation?

Apart from these phenomenological and etiological uncertainties in a population distinguished by an unusual combination of stress factors, our study of disordered behavior patterns in the deaf leaves no doubt about the challenging complexities inherent in an epidemiological investigation, which uses both genetic and demographic techniques. We hope that the study will cast some light upon the determinants of mental illness, especially of schizophrenia and with respect to the intricate interaction of genetic and nongenetic components in its etiology. At the present time, it is not even clear whether a stressful condition of the magnitude of early total deafness causes a significant change in the prevalence of schizophrenia in the given population, and whether the change is toward an increase or a decrease in the prevalence of the disorder.

With our incomplete count of 9,321 deaf New York State residents over age 14, one obtains a tentative estimate of 2.5% for the prevalence of schizophrenia in this special population, instead of an expected rate of approximately 1%. It is probable, however, that this tentative figure is an overestimate, and there are various reasons for doubting the causal significance of external stress factors alone if there is a relatively limited increase in the frequency of schizophrenia in deaf family units.

At this time, therefore, the only statement which can be made in this connection is that we have found no evidence for a greatly increased prevalence of schizophrenia in the deaf population of New York State.

REFERENCES

1. Allen, G. Comments on the analysis of twin samples. *Acta Genet. Med. et Gemellol., 4,* 143 (1955).
2. Best, H. *Deafness and the Deaf in the United States.* Macmillan, New York, 1943.
3. Houston, F., and A. B. Royse. Relationship between deafness and psychotic illness. *J. Mental Sci., 100,* 990 (1954).
4. Kallmann, F. J. *Heredity in Health and Mental Disorder.* W. W. Norton, New York, 1953.
5. ———. Objectives of the mental health project for the deaf.

Proc. 1955 Convention of American Instructors of the Deaf,
U.S. Government Printing Office, Washington, D. C., 1956.
 6. ———. Psychiatric aspects of genetic counseling. *Am. J. Human Genet., 8,* 97 (1956).
 7. Leighton, A. H. In R. H. Felix *et al., Epidemiology of Mental Disorder.* Milbank Memorial Fund, New York, 1950.
 8. Levine, E. S. Mental Health Clinic in New York. *The Silent Worker, 9,* 7 (1956).
 9. New York State Department of Mental Hygiene. *66th Annual Report, 1954.* Albany, 1955.
10. Sank, D., and F. J. Kallmann. Genetic and eugenic aspects of early total deafness. *Eugenics Quart., 3,* 69 (1956).
11. United States Department of Commerce, Bureau of the Census. *Census of Population: 1950,* Vol. II, Part 32. U.S. Government Printing Office, Washington, D. C., 1952.
12. Weinstein, E. A., and R. L. Kahn. *Denial of Illness.* C. C Thomas, Springfield, Ill., 1955.

DISCUSSION

DR. ABRAHAM LILIENFELD: Doctors Rainer and Kallmann have presented a rather intriguing plan of study. I think they should be complimented on the very concept of selecting a deaf population for genetic and epidemiological studies of behavior patterns. Epidemiological studies of such population subgroups will no doubt provide some information which will be of importance in elucidating etiological factors.

In view of the fact that most of this paper outlines a plan of study, my comments will be essentially limited to asking questions concerning the plan of study, perhaps with a few comments on some of the data presented.

The authors state that it is known that deafness shows a tendency to cluster within families. "It is apparent that the genetic factors operating in this condition represent another set of variables requiring a thorough analysis."

I would like to underscore the fact that familial aggregation of a disease does not necessarily mean that genetic factors play a role. Familial aggregation may result from environmental factors to which all members of a family are exposed. At our present level of biologic knowledge, a genetic hypothesis can be entertained only after various environmental hosts or factors have been excluded. There are many examples of environment-determined familial aggregation besides infectious disease, which is the most common.

We can recall pellagra, a disease which pragmatically may be considered to be a result of an environmental aggregate, even though there may be possibly an underlying genetic component. Nevertheless, this disease has exhibited a high degree of familial aggregation. In fact, prior to the time when this disease was found to be due to a dietary deficiency, several studies were published from which inference was made that pellagra was an "inherited" disease, when obviously it was a dietary disease, and the resulting familial aggregation was due to the dietary insufficiency being common to all members of the family.

In view of such possibilities, I was wondering if Dr. Kallmann and his associates are planning to investigate possible environmental factors in deafness. It seems to me that this would be a rather important area for research in their study and may be related to the behavior problems in which they are primarily interested.

In relationship to this I would like to mention a study which we have completed concerning familial aggregation and what inference can be made thereof, a study not yet published. We obtained information on the medical students at the University of Buffalo with regard to whether or not their parents had gone to medical school. Looking at the distribution as to whether or not one parent or both parents went to medical school, we were able to fit a very specific statistical test to data, from which one would make the inference that going to medical school is inherited as a recessive gene.

If Doctors Rainer and Kallmann should be interested in looking into the possibilities of environmental factors in deafness, I think it would be rather important to state and specify the kinds of environmental hypotheses they ought to look at.

My second comment concerns the ascertainment of twins. The authors point out that 1.9% of the population are twins. High mortality brings this rate down to say 1½% on the average for all age groups. I note from Table I, out of 10,600 individuals, only about 0.7% are twins. I realize that the survey is not complete, but I was wondering if this indicates an infrequent ascertainment of twins, or that deafness is less common among twins. It would be necessary to select a sample of twin births and follow them for a number of years to determine the frequency of the development of a condition like deafness.

Time does not allow us to discuss the use of twins in genetic studies, but even in twin studies as well as in the familial studies, it is rather important to make genetic inferences with a great deal of caution. We know very little about the biology of twinning. We know very little about the frequency of various diseases, various entities among twins, and until we get more information concerning twins, I think a genetic generalization should not be made with the definitiveness with which it sometimes has been made.

In carrying out the epidemiological study of the deaf population which these two investigators organized, I think it would be very helpful for them to have a control group, that is, a group of non-deaf individuals selected in an appropriate manner from the general population, for further comparisons with regard to such factors as age, sex, social factors, social status, industry, occupation. This would permit a more intensive search for possible etiological factors, as well as a comparison of the deaf population with general types of demographic data that are available to the investigators at the moment. I was wondering if they had given any consideration to expanding the study in such a manner.

Another area for expansion of the study, particularly with regard to familial factors, is the possibility of carrying out a longitudinal study. Once you define your population of families, perhaps the thing to do would be to take these individuals and follow them over a number of years. This would enable you to find out whether or not the result of developing various behavior disorders, deafness, or whatever other factors they are interested in, is greater in the population of families having one or more deaf members than in a control group, that is, in a normal (non-deaf) population.

As I said initially, I think they should be complimented on the very concept of selecting a deaf population for this kind of study, and I am looking forward to the results of such an investigation. However, I think it is rather important that they take very real advantage of this opportunity to carry out rather intensive epidemiological studies in this kind of a population.

DR. RAINER: Of course, the fact that deafness aggregates in families is largely determined environmentally. In many cases, the main reason is that deaf persons tend to marry each other.

As far as the etiology of deafness is concerned, we can go only by what the otologists tell us at this point. We expect to find out more about it in our survey, but current statistics show that about 47% of all cases of early total deafness may be assumed to have a genetic basis. We intend to explore the environmental factors as thoroughly as the genetic ones in the etiology of deafness. We are aware of the fact that in certain cases a complex interaction of genetic and non-genetic factors may be at work.

The intriguing suggestion that there may be less twins among the deaf than among the non-deaf did enter our minds. At the present stage we are inclined, however, to attribute the smaller percentage of twins to imperfections of ascertainment.

It is always hard to collect representative samples of twins. One has to utilize all available assertainment methods. However, it seems to be particularly difficult to find deaf twins, harder than it has been in any of the other twin studies that the department has made.

As to formulating hypotheses based on twin studies, we have always stressed the need for a cautious and broad-minded scientific attitude. This is true for twin studies as well as any other population study deserving of this name. One of the precautions calls for the use of a control population, and we are fortunate enough to have control data available for our final analysis.

Finally, we certainly agree that longitudinal studies of deaf persons are very important, and we do hope to be able to provide long-range data of observation, which can be called "longitudinal" and "carefully collected."

Distribution of Intellectual Potential
in an Infant Population

HILDA KNOBLOCH AND BENJAMIN PASAMANICK

Ohio State University College of Medicine, Columbus, Ohio

The concern with the relative influence of nature and nurture in intellectual functioning is one of the perennial problems of psychology. While most of the recent work has consisted of elucidating the variables involved in the environmental shaping of intelligence, a hard core of belief in the inherent variation of intelligence quotients as a fundamental biological characteristic is almost universally held.

Recently attention has been focused on the lower end of the curve of intelligence, and an increasing number of exogenous factors have been shown to be etiologic. Conditions previously considered hereditary have been shown to be due to environmental influences, and more and more evidence is accumulating that familial aggregation does not necessarily imply genetic causation, but rather may mean exposure to the same environmental agencies. In spite of this concentration on the problems of mental retardation, consideration needs to be given to the entire range of human intellectual functioning in any discussion of the factors influencing behavioral development.

The problem in the area of intellectual functioning is complicated by the question of the definition of intelligence and of what is being measured by the various intelligence tests. Whether the same functions are being measured at all ages is also a controversial matter. Particular attention needs to be directed toward infancy, since it is about this age group that the greatest questions concerning the validity of examinations of intelligence are being raised. Although workers maintain that performance in infancy has little or no relation to later function, we would like to emphasize that, as Dr. Arnold Gesell has stated, the behavioral developmental appraisal can be reliably used as an estimate of the maturity and integrity of the central nervous system. It reflects function as this is related to neural equipment during maturational development. It is the intactness of neuropsychologic functioning which is basic to later integration and learning, and as such offers a reliable estimate of intellectual potential.

Recently evidence has accumulated on various neuropsychiatric disabilities which points to a pattern of the association of central nervous system damage with certain deleterious conditions in the prenatal and paranatal periods, and also indicates that there is a socio-economic distribution of these harmful conditions (1). It leads to the hypothesis that interference with neural integration may be the major factor in disturbed neuropsychological function. The genetic constitution gives man his distinctively human character, and neurologic integrity is basic to the realization of his full developmental potential. In the human organism with an undamaged central nervous system, however, it is life experience rather than hereditary influences which seem more important in molding intellectual functioning.

We propose to report some details of the examination of a large representative sample of an infant population which help to cast additional light on some of these problems.

Method of Study

The data for the present report were gathered during the course of a study of premature infants born in 1952 in Maryland. Because of the bearing on sample selection and the general applicability of the results, some of the details of that investigation are pertinent, and will be described here. They have been reported elsewhere (2) in greater detail, and limitations of time preclude an extensive review here.

The phase of the total Study of Prematures which provided the material for this report was designed to compare the development of a group of Baltimore premature infants and their full-term controls. Certain information regarding each infant was available, which permits adjustment of the findings to give a representative picture of the total population of infants of Baltimore. This information includes the birth weight of each infant and information regarding socio-economic status based on the economic level of the area of residence as determined from U.S. Government census tract data, race, and the education of the mothers and fathers.

The study group examined consisted of 992 infants, 500 prematures and 492 matched full-term controls. It is important to mention that these 992 infants represented an 85% completion of the examination of the original 1,170 scheduled; 3.5% were refusals, while the other 11.5% could not be located.

It was planned that each infant would be examined at 40 weeks of age. This could not always be accomplished, so that age at the examination ranged from 34 to 69 weeks, with 75% being seen between 39 and 41 weeks. In the case of the premature infants, the chronologic age was corrected to make allowance for the estimated amount of prematurity. Physical growth at 40 weeks as well as correlations with later development have indicated that the estimate of prematurity was quite good.

The examinations consisted of a Gesell developmental examination and a physical examination. Almost all of them were done by one of us (H.K.), a pediatrician experienced in this work, who was not told whether the infant was premature or full term, in order not to bias her observation of behavior or her diagnostic judgment, nor was she given any information about the child's history. In some instances this information was revealed unwittingly by the mother. A history was taken from the mother, usually by a person other than the pediatrician and was recorded on a form devised for the purpose. It covered items such as neonatal adjustment, illness, seizures and other neurological symptoms, current emotional behavior, and some parental history.

The pediatrician's Gesell examination followed the procedure outlined in Gesell and Amatruda's *Developmental Diagnosis* (3). A brief interview was conducted including inquiries about the infant's current behavior and items necessary for the Gesell developmental schedules which were not covered by the history recorded by the previous interviewer. The standard examination items were offered, adapting the situations as necessary in the face of handicapping conditions or unusual emotional responses, and a dictated recording of the infant's behavior was made, describing not only the use to which he put the examination materials but his neuromotor patterning as he manipulated them. The infant's performance was recorded on the appropriate Gesell developmental schedule while the mother was undressing the infant for the physical examination.

After the baby was examined, weighed, and measured, a special examination form was completed. This included scaled judgments of the quality of integration, of abnormal behavior patterns, and abnormal neurologic patterns, and of the physical examination results, as well as the assignment of maturity levels for the various fields of behavior, a diagnosis of neurologic status and intellectual potential and a prognosis for future development. Only after the examination record was completed was the history secured by the other interviewer reviewed to see if their were any factors, such as severe convulsions or institutionalization, which might modify the prognosis made. Changes in prognosis were necessary on fewer than ten occasions.

Two-thirds of the examinations were done in the study office, while most of the remainder were carried out at home because the mothers were unable for one reason or another to bring the infant in for the examination. When the examination was done at home, or in a hospital, it was necessary for the pediatrician to take the history also, but this followed rather than preceded the examination and the judgments made.

Detailed definitions of neurologic status as well as some of the comparisons between the premature and full-term infants have already been published (2). The neurologic status is an estimate of the integrity of the nervous system as this was manifested by the absence or presence of impairment in neuromotor functioning and deviations in muscle tonus and control. It was expressed in terminology appropriate to the field of infant neurology which indicated the extent of the departure from normal. The intellectual potential was a clinical estimate of intelligence based largely on the adaptive maturational status of the child. It took into account not only the developmental level but also the quality of the behavior. The concept of intellectual potential is concerned with prognosis and implies that, if nothing happens to damage the infant, organically or psychologically, his future development should be at essentially a constant rate in terms of an overall level of adaptive functioning which is related to but not equated with school age or adult tests of intelligence.

The present discussion will be confined to the general developmental quotients assigned to the infants. The general developmental quotient was usually the same as the adaptive maturity quotient, but it was considered more valuable since it took into account the clinical factors mentioned above in predicting the general course of future development. On the average the developmental quotient was less than one point higher than the adaptive quotient, and the two were highly correlated (.97 for the white full-term infants, for example). The limitations of the procedure of separating quotients from other aspects of clinical judgment must be recognized. It is being done, however, in order to make comparisons with other findings at later ages and to point up some of the implications.

Findings

Since the sample examined was not representative of the distribution of the surviving infant population because of the difference in incidence and mortality between the different birth weight groups, the distribution of the general developmental quotients was adjusted to take these factors into account, by using the incidence and mortality figures for Maryland in 1952. The white and non-white populations were adjusted separately, since the total incidence of prematurity in Baltimore is 6.8% in whites compared with 11.5% in Negroes (4).

The study sample was selected so that the prematures and the controls would be as comparable as possible and there would be no differences between the birth weight groups for economic status; the area of residence was the criterion used in this matching. Education is another measure of social status, and information about this was obtained after the matching when the infants were examined. The fact that there was no difference between the birth weight groups when the education of either the fathers or the mothers was compared indicates that there was adequate control for social status. As in other studies (5), there was a correlation between education and other measures of economic status, and the parents in the two upper economic fifths of the white group as determined by census tract had significantly more education than those in the lower three fifths and the non-white group. However, neither the education of the parents, their economic status, nor their race was related to any significant differences in the distribution of the general developmental quotients. The question might be raised that the samples were too small, when subdivisions were made for all of the above factors, but no trend in the differences was observed. Nevertheless, to make certain that no biases in distribution may exist, since the sample was not equally distributed in the white infants among the economic fifths, the general developmental quotient distribution was adjusted for economic status. The non-white group was considered in its entirety since almost 70% were in the lower two economic fifths by census tract of residence. Also, this census tract method used in assigning economic level does not make the same distinctions within the non-white as within the white group.

An additional final adjustment was made for race, since the Baltimore population is 26.8% Negro. The final distribution of the general developmental quotients, then, is representative of the surviving infant population of Baltimore, having been adjusted for differences in birth weight, race, and economic status.

Table I presents the mean general developmental quotients and standard deviations for the different birth weight and racial groups. It indicates that as the birth weight of the infant decreases the mean developmental quotient decreases for both

TABLE I

Mean General Developmental Quotients in Baltimore Infant Population (1952) by Race and Birth Weight

Weight and Race	General Developmental Quotient		
	Number[a]	Mean	S.D.[b]
Less than 1,500 grams			
White	18	99.2	14.6
Non-white	37	89.4	22.1
1,501–2,000 grams			
White	28	102.0	7.5
Non-white	55	102.3	11.4
2,001–2,500 grams			
White	165	104.9	8.8
Non-white	194	102.5	12.0
2,501 + grams			
White	222	105.4	9.9
Non-white	269	104.5	11.6

[a] Three prematures and 1 full-term infant for whom no quotient was assigned are excluded.
[b] In calculating the significance of the differences, pooled variances were used.

whites and non-whites. The mean general developmental quotient
for the infants with birth weights under 1,500 grams is 99.2
(S.D. 14.6) for white infants and 89.4 (S.D. 22.1) for non-whites;
for infants with birth weights between 1,501 and 2,000 grams it is
102.0 (S.D. 7.5) and 102.3 (S.D. 11.4) for whites and non-whites
respectively. Those infants with birth weights between 2,001 and
2,500 grams have quotients of 104.9 (S.D. 8.8) and 102.5 (S.D.
12.0) respectively, while for the full-term infants with birth
weights above 2,500 grams it is 105.4 (S.D. 9.9) for the whites
and 104.5 (S.D. 11.6) for the non-whites. As was previously
reported, there are no significant differences between whites and
non-whites for any of the birth weight groups, but there are
significant differences between the smallest premature infants
with birth weights below 1,500 grams and the heavier infants.[1]

Table II shows the adjusted distribution of the general
developmental quotients for the white population, the non-white
population, and the total population of Baltimore infants born
in 1952. There are no significant differences in distribution between the whites and non-whites. The most important findings
are that only 1.5% of the infant population has general developmental quotients below 80 and 2.7% below 90. There was a
sharp rise starting at 90 so that more than 90% of the infant
population falls between 90 and 120. These findings differ
markedly from those reported in the literature.

Comment

Before entering upon a discussion of the implications of these
findings, some consideration must be given to the question of
the validity of the infant examination. This cannot be presented
in great detail, and will be covered more adequately at a later
time, but a few points need to be made. Although we believe
that later performance is more influenced by learning, it is

[1] In judging the evidence on this and subsequent questions, the 5%
level of statistical significance was used. Pooled variances were used in
making the calculations.

TABLE II

Distribution of General Developmental Quotients in Baltimore Infant Population (1952) Adjusted for Birth Weight, Race, and Economic Status

General Developmental Quotient	Adjusted Rates, %			
	White	Non-white	Total	Cumulative
15–19	—	0.0	0.0	0.0
20–24	—	—	—	0.0
25–29	—	0.4	0.1	0.1
30–34	—	—	—	0.1
35–39	—	—	—	0.1
40–44	—	0.1	0.0	0.1
45–49	—	—	—	0.1
50–54	—	0.4	0.1	0.2
55–59	—	0.0	0.0	0.2
60–64	0.7	0.6	0.7	0.9
65–69	—	0.0	0.0	0.9
70–74	0.7	0.1	0.5	1.4
75–79	0.0	0.4	0.1	1.5
80–84	0.1	0.8	0.3	1.8
85–89	0.7	1.4	0.9	2.7
90–94	6.5	7.9	6.9	9.6
95–99	18.6	18.2	18.5	28.1
100–104	27.2	24.6	26.5	54.6
105–109	25.2	19.9	23.8	78.4
110–114	9.0	13.9	10.3	88.7
115–119	5.2	3.9	4.9	93.6
120–124	3.0	3.4	3.1	96.7
125–129	0.7	2.1	1.1	97.8
130–134	0.7	1.0	0.8	98.6
135–139	0.4	0.4	0.4	99.0
140–144	0.7	0.4	0.6	99.6
145–149	0.3	—	0.2	99.8
Unknown	0.4	0.0	0.3	100.1
Total	100.1	99.9	100.1	100.1

necessary to state the truism that such later behavior is not independent of the nervous system. There is a substrate of neural integration which permeates the behavior of each individual, and it is the physiologic organization which is the foundation for all learning.

The literature on the subject of infant evaluation has indicated, up to the present time, that later performance cannot be predicted from infant examinations and that the correlations vary from plus .2 down to small negative correlations (5, 6). It has also indicated that approximately 60% of reexaminations differ by more than 15 points from initial ones. Recently workers in the area of adoptions (7, 8) have shown good correlations by the device of using broad clinical categories instead of actual scores in making comparisons. This statistical method normally tends to decrease the amount of correlation found, and one wonders why they did not use the actual scores in presenting their data. We have already mentioned our findings on the reexamination of almost 300 infants at the age of three years in a previous publication, but they require further discussion here since they are basic to a consideration of the present material (2). The correlation between the examinations was plus .5 for the entire group; for those cases with some intellectual or neurologic abnormality it was plus .75. These correlations are similar to those which we found in a group of 53 infants examined in the first year of life and seen again at age seven, when the correlation was found to be .5 (9). They are also similar to the findings in a group of 100 infants seen at the ages of 16, 28, and 40 weeks and 18 months, where the correlations again ranged between .5 and .75 (10). With regard to the data concerning the amount of the actual change in the developmental quotient, 74.2% of the infants examined as a part of the study of prematures changed less than 15 points between the first and second examinations, while 52.9% changed less than 10 points.

While we may appear to be paradoxical if we proceed to discuss differences with later examinations, yet at the same time point to the highly significant correlation with these examinations as a validation of the infant appraisal, we believe that it is psychobiologically sound to postulate that neural factors which operate to mold behavior in infancy continue to manifest themselves throughout the life span and are not completely negated by environmental influences, unless qualitative change is caused in the central nervous system by noxious agents. In other words, providing gross changes do not take place in the milieu of the child which alter major variables of functioning, the damaged or undamaged state of the central nervous system should influence even learned behavior in a predictable fashion. We believe we have, by the use of the developmental appraisal as a clinical neurological tool, demonstrated this continuity.

Let us turn now to a comparison of the present findings with the distributions of intelligence quotients of older children and adolescents as reported in the literature. While the intelligence quotient is influenced by more environmental factors than affect the intellectual potential as diagnosed in infancy, the IQ is obviously related to neural integration. A lowered score may be the result of many environmental factors, physical, psychological, and social, but a higher score can only be the result of learning. A comparison of these two estimates, therefore, may help elucidate the question of how large is the influence of environmental factors on intelligence test scores. Two large samples using the Stanford-Binet test are available. One reports the examination of 873 children born in Scotland on each of four days in 1926 when they were between 8 years 11 months and 11 years 9 months of age, with the loss of only one case from the original group (11). The revision of the Stanford-Binet test was done on a group of approximately 3,000 children selected from various areas throughout this country (12). It did not include children in institutions, and the precise extent of the considerable difference from a more representative population is not clear from the data presented. It included children between the ages of 2 and 18 years. Because the children in these samples were older, in addition to other factors already mentioned which might introduce bias, it seems likely that the majority of the most severe cases of defect, such as the hydrocephalics or those with other congenital anomalies, would have died at an age too early to permit them to be included.

Table III shows the cumulative percentage distributions of the intelligence quotients of the samples just cited and compares them with the findings of the present investigation. The distributions are similar for both of these samples and are in sharp contrast to our findings. Between 4.5 and 5.5% of the cases

TABLE III

Distribution of Intelligence Quotients Reported in Literature Compared with Distribution of General Developmental Quotients in Baltimore Infants (1952)

Quotient	Cumulative Percentage		
	Baltimore infants	MacMeekan (Scotland)	Stanford-Binet
< 35	0.1	0.0	0.0
35–44	0.1	0.2	0.4
45–54	0.2	0.9	0.9
55–64	0.9	1.8	2.2
65–74	1.4	4.5	5.4
75–84	1.8	14.4	14.4
85–94	9.6	39.6	33.6
95–104	54.6	66.1	56.7
105–114	88.7	83.6	78.1
115–124	96.7	93.0	90.9
125–134	98.6	97.5	96.2
135–144	99.6	99.3	98.1
145–154	99.8	99.7	98.7
155–164	99.8	99.9	99.3
165–174	99.8	99.9	99.8
175+	99.8	99.9	100.2
Unknown	100.1	99.9	100.2

have quotients below 75, while approximately 14% have quotients below 85. The corresponding figures for the infant population are 1.4% and 1.8% respectively. The percentages above 125 agree more closely. Additional information from the Stanford-Binet revision group indicates that, as the age of the child increases, the percentage with quotients below 85 increases.

There are 12.2% between 2 and 5 years, 14.7% between 6 and 12, and 15.1% between 13 and 18 years.

The similarity of the distributions of the two samples and the marked excess of cases with quotients less than 85 in comparison to the Baltimore infant population distribution is noteworthy. All three of these distributions differ significantly from the theoretical expectations for the normal curve; the implications of this will be discussed in a forthcoming publication.

The increase in the percentage of children with intelligence quotients below 80 occurs largely in that group called the upper grade retardates, those children with quotients between 55 and 70 who are usually considered intellectually inadequate on a genetic basis (13). Also included is the segment from 70 to 85 which is usually considered part of normal human variation, but again is felt to be due to inferior hereditary endowment. The inverse relationship that has been reported between intelligence quotient and the occupational status of the parents (5) is representative of the nature of the evidence of those who support the genetic hypothesis.

The observations which we have presented in this report would appear to us to lend support to the hypothesis that the measures of intelligence used in later life are greatly influenced by learning and affected by life experiences which tend to limit opportunities of acquiring the kinds of information that the tests seek to evaluate. These life experiences are not only socio-cultural, but also have physiological components. The studies of Klineberg (14) on the changes in Negro intelligence with geographic location, as well as follow-up studies (15, 16) on the later development of morons which indicate that their adult adjustment compares favorably with groups from the same community who tested normally are also in support of this view.

The evidence is far from complete, but there is a great deal of information presently available to support the view that the range of normal human intellectual potential is much narrower than has been thought. The proportion of the population with innate intellectual potential below the range of normal is indeed small, and the majority if not all of these cases appear to be due to organic damage to the brain. Gradually, as we isolate more and more specific factors which tend to damage neural integration, we should be able to narrow this distribution more.

An analysis of the 25 individual infants with developmental quotients below 80 sheds further light on the question of brain damage. In the largest proportion of these infants, a diagnosis of neurologic abnormality was made at the time of the developmental examination, while an additional number had other evidences of organic damage, such as the development of convulsive seizures, or marked undernutrition. In addition, in both the premature and the full-term infants, the median developmental quotient decreased as the severity of the neurologic damage diagnosed at the examination increased. The chronic complications of pregnancy, the bleedings and toxemias, were significantly twice as high in this group of babies as in the total infant population examined, and half of the 17 prematures in the damaged group had birth weights less than 1,500 grams, compared with a representation in our total premature population of only 5.7%.

We have already mentioned the association of socio-economic factors with certain possible precursors of neuropsychiatric disorder, the prenatal and paranatal complications of pregnancy. While the incidence of disturbance in neural function, or at least some of its precursors, is socio-economically distributed, in undamaged children early in life these socio-cultural factors appear to be without important effect statistically in a total population of infants. This is manifested by the observations that differences in education of the parents, economic status, or race, do not significantly affect the distribution of the general developmental quotients in infancy. By three years of age, as the reexamination of part of the study group indicates, these factors are already beginning to exert an influence, since the average quotient for the white controls reexamined rises significantly to 111.2 while it falls to 98.9 for the non-whites.

Other variables about which information was gathered during the course of the investigation will be examined in order to test our general hypothesis further, and the complete results of the follow-up examination at three years of age which is currently in progress will undoubtedly be of great interest.

Man has apparently reached the stage in evolution where change does not take place on the structural level. Because of his tremendous plasticity in psychologic functioning, behavioral variation occurs as a result of exogenous injury or from the few rare hereditary clinical entities. So heavily do these psychosocial factors seem to outweigh any genetic behavior variation that it seems extremely difficult to find any definitive evidence for the importance or even the very existence of the latter.

Even though there are lacunae in the evidence, the patterning of almost all the recent studies, ours as well as others, points the total picture overwhelmingly in one direction. The geneticists will need to give more than post hoc data and will require experimental or better controlled epidemiological studies than have previously been offered to support their views. Otherwise, scientific parsimony seems to lead one to the conclusion that at the present time the most useful theory is that while man's fundamental structure and consequently his basic functioning is genetically determined, it is his socio-cultural milieu affecting biological and psychological variables which modifies his behavior and, in the absence of organic brain damage, makes one individual significantly different from the next.

REFERENCES

1. Pasamanick, B., H. Knobloch, and A. M. Lilienfeld. Socioeconomic status and some precursors of neuropsychiatric disorder. *Am. J. Orthopsychiat.*, 26 (3), 594–601 (1956).
2. Knobloch, H., R. Rider, P. Harper, and B. Pasamanick. Neuro-

psychiatric sequelae of prematurity: a longitudinal study. *J. Am. Med. Assoc., 161,* 581–85 (1956).

3. Gesell, A. L., and C. S. Amatruda. *Developmental Diagnosis: Normal and Abnormal Child Development: Clinical Methods and Practical Applications.* Paul B. Hoeber, New York, 1941.
4. Rider, R. V., M. Taback, and H. Knobloch. Associations between premature birth and socioeconomic status. *Am. J. Public Health, 45,* 1022–28 (1955).
5. Anastasi, A., and J. P. Foley. *Differential Psychology: Individual and Group Differences in Behavior.* Macmillan, New York, 1949.
6. Tizard, J. The prevalence of mental subnormality. *Bull. World Health Organization, 9,* 423–40 (1953).
7. MacRae, J. Retests of children given mental tests as infants. *J. Genet. Psychol., 87,* 111–19 (1955).
8. Simon, A. J., and L. Bass. Toward a validation of infant testing. *Am. J. Orthopsychiat., 26* (2), 340–50 (1956).
9. Nash, E. H., H. Nash, B. Pasamanick, and H. Knobloch. Further observations on the development of Negro children: Status at seven years of age. Unpublished data.
10. Johns Hopkins University School of Hygiene and Public Health. Maternal and Child Health Division. Baltimore, Md. Unpublished Data.
11. Macmeeken, A. M. *The Intelligence of a Representative Group of Scottish Children.* London University Press, London, 1940.
12. Terman, L. M., and M. A. Merrill. *Measuring Intelligence.* Houghton Mifflin Co., Boston, 1937.
13. Benda, C. D. *Developmental Disorders of Mentation and Cerebral Palsy.* Grune and Stratton, New York, 1952.
14. Klineberg, O. *Race Differences.* Harper, New York, 1935.
15. Fairbanks, R. B. The subnormal child—seventeen years after. *Mental Hyg., 17,* 177–208 (1933).
16. Kennedy, R. J. R. *The Social Adjustment of Morons in a Connecticut City.* Hartford, Conn., 1948.

DISCUSSION

DR. ANNE ANASTASI: As a psychologist, I cannot help but be impressed with the importance of the research we have just heard reported and with its far-reaching implications. With regard to the hereditary-environment problem, the chief value of such a study lies in its bringing us a step closer to answering the question, "How?" By tracing relationships between socio-economic factors, prematurity, neurological damage, and subsequent behavioral development, such an investigation helps to disentangle the chain of events leading up to individual differences in intellectual functioning.

My first specific comment pertains to possible misunderstandings which may arise from the use of certain terms and from one or two statements in the paper. Discussions of heredity and environment have been traditionally burdened with so many misperceptions that it seems wise to avoid terms which arouse associations that the authors may not intend. An example is provided by the very title of the paper, "The Distribution of Intellectual Potential in an Infant Population." This would probably convey to many psychologists the impression that the investigators are concerned with the organic basis of individual differences in intelligence over the entire range of variation, on the superior as well as the subnormal end of the scale.

The same implication appears to be carried by statements such as the following: ". . . the behavioral developmental appraisal can be reliably used as an estimate of the maturity and integrity of the central nervous system. It reflects function as this is related to neural equipment during maturational development. It is the intactness of neuro-psychological functioning which is basic to later integration and learning and as such offers a reliable estimate of intellectual potential." Statements in the same vein occur in a few other parts of the report.

Unless I am reading my own misperceptions into the report, I believe the authors make their actual meaning quite clear in other parts of the paper. In their concluding statement, for example, they suggest that, in the absence of organic brain damage, it is the socio-cultural milieu which makes one individual's behavior different from the behavior of another. This is essentially the concept of minimal structural prerequisites, minimum organic conditions which must be available for normal intellectual development—but once these pre-requisites are met, which is probably true in the large majority of persons—further individual differences in intellectual functioning cannot be traced to organic etiology.

My second point concerns the data in Table I, covering differences in developmental quotients with regard to race and birth weight. I assume that these data were not submitted to an overall analysis of variance, with race and birth weight as two criteria of classification.

Had this been done, I am wondering whether some of the differences which now fail to reach statistical significance because of the smallness of the samples might have proved to be significant.

Thirdly, I have a series of questions and comments centering around the predictive validity of infant tests. The investigators report no significant differences in developmental quotients with regard to parental education, economic status, or race. Such results are, of course, in line with the lack of correlation found by other investigators between infant tests and parental or home characteristics. This lack of correlation has usually been attributed to the low reliability of infant tests and to the restricted nature of the functions measured. A noteworthy point in the present study, however, is that, although no correlation between socio-economic status and developmental quotient was found in undamaged infants, the frequency of prenatal and natal complications was greater in lower socio-economic levels and greater among Negroes than among whites.

Also relevant are the retest correlations found by the present authors. The remarkably high correlation of .75 is reported between examinations in infancy and at the age of three years among children with intellectual or neurological abnormalities. Other correlations between tests administered from 16 weeks to 7 years range from .50 to .75. It is not clear which of these correlations were obtained on undamaged cases, which on the entire group, and which on damaged cases. If correlations as high as these with infant tests were obtained on undamaged cases, they are far out of line with previously published studies and would seem to call for explanation. It would also be useful to know what measuring instruments were used in the retests, for example, at the 7-year level.

It is of considerable interest to ascertain whether retest correlations are consistently higher in the neurologically damaged than in the undamaged group. Such a finding would suggest that infant tests may be good predictors of behavior deficiencies resulting from neurological damage while they are of little or no value in predicting individual differences in organically normal cases.

My fourth point deals with the distribution of Stanford-Binet IQ's and of Yale Developmental Quotients given in Table III. The authors draw important conclusions from the fact that the frequency of low IQ's is much smaller in infancy than among older children. The hypothesis they propose on this basis seems to me extremely promising and very likely to be correct. However, it must be noted that such a distribution of quotients is not independent of the scaling procedures employed in developing the tests. The Stanford-Binet was constructed so as to yield a standard deviation of approximately 16 points in IQ. Comparable data are not readily available for the Yale Developmental Quotients. At least, I have not seen a record of standard deviations in the standardization data for that test. It may be available. To some extent, the range and form of the distribution of quotients is influenced by such artifacts of test construction. When making comparisons between different tests, we cannot be sure that differences in the distributions result from conditions extrinsic to the tests themselves.

A fifth point regarding which this discussant would like further information has to do with the subsequent development of premature infants. Have these cases been retested at later ages? If so, do they retain their intellectual inferiority?

Finally, I should like for one moment to play the Devil's Advocate and raise a question on behalf of hereditary interpretations of behavior. It is reported that most of the infants with developmental quotients below 80 showed evidence of neurological disturbance. Did all such instances of neurological damage have a clear environmental origin? How was the possibility of hereditary etiology ruled out in these cases?

In closing, I should like to repeat that I think this is an extremely important type of investigation. I have tried very hard to pick flaws in it so that the flaws may be cleared away and the results might have the impact which they deserve to have.

DR. ALAN D. MILLER: Rather briefly, I should like to ask a question.

I certainly think by training that I am very much in sympathy with the notion of scientific parsimony. Certainly, as a result of medical school training, you were always told to make one diagnosis, if you possibly could, never to make two if you could possibly make one, and so on and so forth. I wonder sometimes, however, whether this approach is really appropriate at this time, and whether sometimes we are oversimplifying by trying to handle certain kinds of variables without reference to other kinds of variables. Now I refer specifically to my question and the data in Table I, wherein the differences between the developmental quotients of the children at forty weeks were noted, the differences between the prematures and the normals.

It is certainly clear that the prematures are a very different group from the normals, and it is almost certainly as sure that their life experience during that first forty weeks may have been signally different from the life experience of the normals, perhaps as part of the fact that they were prematures.

As you cited later, in noting differences in intelligence between children of different socio-economic groups at later ages, their life experiences were reflected in their different test performances. I think, as you said, that they had different life experiences which the tests seemed to evaluate.

I wonder whether those things which the developmental quotient evaluates at forty weeks might not be in part a resultant of an interaction between the fact of prematurity and their life experience, which necessarily grew therefrom. Do you find any data about some of the crucial variables in this life experience during the forty weeks past?

How may the fact that the children were premature affect the amount and kind of various human interactions? Were they picked up as much? Were they played with as much? Were they given the same kinds of things to do? Did they have as much room to play? Were they immobilized more?

I think there is a long list of variables which may conceivably reflect themselves in the kinds of things the quotient would evaluate at forty weeks.

DR. F. J. KALLMANN: I think I would like to ask the investigators why they think that the demonstration of neurological damage precludes the operation of genetic factors. In order to exclude genetic factors in a study of this kind, one would have to have a genetic analysis, or one would have to search for evidence for or against the operation of heredity. I don't think that any such attempt has been made in this kind of a study.

DR. ZUBIN: If you take this study at its face value, what has been done is that we have a new model for explaining intelligence. Instead of going to the older model, in which all of us thought that intelligence is a multifactorially determined variable, they start off with the assumption that men are born equal, that only experience eats away at the granite of the original foodstuff of which man is made, and that the attainment of adult life is the result of the eating away of experience at this pretty firm and constant inheritance.

If they can make the data stick, if they can assume all available data on intelligence, development of children, twin studies, and so on and so forth, and if they can make that model conceptualize and include with it all these data, I think that they have made a tremendous contribution.

DR. KNOBLOCH: I would like to start with something that Dr. Zubin said, namely, that we are presenting this as a working hypothesis for further investigation and not as a finished product. As a working hypothesis it should be examined seriously in an effort to determine how hereditary and environmental forces each influence development.

We would need to make one correction to his comment, however. We don't say that men are born equal. We say that they are conceived so, and a great many things happen in the course of pregnancy as a result of environmental forces that definitely influence development.

I would now like to try to answer some of the questions that Dr. Anastasi raised, although I don't think I will be able to cover all. In the first place, we would agree with one of her first statements; we feel that there is a minimum structural prerequisite that is necessary for normal development.

After submitting the data to an analysis of variance, no further significant differences were demonstrated.

The correlation of .5 was obtained on three different groups: first, on nearly 300 infants in the premature study who were examined at 40 weeks of age and reexamined at 3 years of age; secondly, in a normal group of Negro infants who were initially examined between 16 and 52 weeks of age and reexamined at 7 years of age; in the third group were infants receiving complete medical supervision who were examined at various intervals between 16 weeks and 18 months.

The correlation of .75 was obtained on the "damaged" group in the premature study. In this group there were 48 children who had varying degrees of neurologic damage or intellectual defect. For the remainder of the infants who were undamaged the correlation was approximately .39. While the correlation is exceptionally good in abnormal cases, it is also highly significant in those children who were organically normal and much greater than what has been reported in the literature. While it is true that the inclusion of abnormal cases would tend to improve the correlation, assuming that the instrument actually detects abnormality, as this examination does, this criticism is not particularly pertinent to the matter under discussion. In the first place, we have been trying to point out that the number of individuals with significant damage in an infant population is indeed small. In addition, we question whether it is really permissible to take a selected group of infants rather than a representative sample, and then be surprised that some measuring instrument does not give as much information as one would like to obtain.

Both the Gesell and Stanford-Binet tests were used at 3 years of age. The correlation reported here is the correlation of the Gesell test at 40 weeks with the Gesell test at 3 years of age. The correlation of the Gesell infant examination with the Stanford-Binet test at 3 years was also high, being .48, while the 3-year Gesell and Stanford-Binet tests correlated with a coefficient of .86. At 7 years of age both the Stanford-Binet and Arthur performance tests were used.

Parenthetically, at the 3-year examination a very careful procedure was followed to prevent the results of the infant examination from being known prior to the completion of the latter evaluation.

The data for the standard deviation of the Gesell developmental examination as it was finally constructed are not available, it is true. If we look at our adjusted sample of controls, however, it would seem that 12 is not too bad a guess, although it might actually be a little high. There is restriction at both ends of the scale, but it is much less at the upper end, with 1.4% in the infant group compared with 2.5% and 3.8% in the curves for the older children. At the lower end of the scale there is a steep rise in the infant curve which is not observed in the others. Although this restriction may perhaps be an artifact of the test, we think it just as likely that it is a part of the picture that we are trying to present. Incidentally, neither the Stanford-Binet distribution nor our distribution is a normal one. Both deviate from the theoretical expectations of the normal curve, ours more than the Stanford-Binet.

We cannot answer completely the question of the later development of these children and whether or not the prematures retain their inferiority. It is planned to follow these children as long as possible in order to answer this and other questions. None of the children with birth weights under 2,000 grams was called superior at either examination. The high correlations obtained in the damaged group indicate that these children who are handicapped in infancy retain their handicap, and the developmental examination is an effective clinical tool. We also know, of course, that only a few retarded children become so as a result of postnatal disease; most demonstrate their retardation from birth. It should be pointed out that prematures, particularly the small ones, make an insignificant contribution to a total population. Our total sample was distorted by containing more than 50% prematures, and even within the premature group there was an over-representation of the light-weight babies.

It is true that no real genetic investigation was done on those families where the infant had a developmental quotient less than 80. None of them had those rare clinical entities known to be genetically transmitted. In three of the families there was evidence that some other members were affected, although in only one was there clear evidence that environmental factors might not be considered sufficient to explain the findings. In addition, 2 or 3 of the infants recovered from their physical disease and became normal.

These questions were also raised by Drs. Kallmann and Rainer. We might go on to indicate that almost all our infants with neurologic damage had greater or lesser degrees of cerebral palsy. The question has been raised, but certainly not taken very seriously, that cerebral palsy is genetically transmitted. The important point to stress, it appears to us, is that the effect of heredity in this type of situation cannot really be assessed until the clear environmental inequalities are eliminated.

It is quite true that monozygotic twins are more alike than dizygotes, and we would be willing to extend that similarity down to the period of infancy. It is, however, not as facetious as it might sound to say that there is a more comparable exposure to environmental deviations, even in utero. As evidence for this, perhaps, is the fact that both types of twinning are associated with socio-economic status and that there is a higher mortality rate as well as a higher incidence of neuropsychiatric disability in monozygotic twins. The real question is not so much how alike are monozygotes, but rather how significantly different are dizygotes and siblings, and even unrelated infants. When considered in the frame of reference of the contrast between the Baltimore Negro and white upper economic groups, the similarities are more striking than the differences.

The question that Dr. Miller raises should also be considered in relation to this point. While conceivably in the very small prematures there may have been differences in the amount of handling that the infants received, it is hard to imagine two socio-cultural milieus within our present structures very much more widely disparate than those to be found in Baltimore. Furthermore, the data in Table I indicate that it is only the very small prematures who are different. Since about 50% of these infants had some degree of neurologic damage, environmental differences in management would not appear to be a logical explanation for differences in behavior and in intellectual potential. In a supplementary comment to Dr. Miller's discussion, another individual raised the matter of the importance of mothers nursing their babies happily. While teleologically it is soothing to think that anatomical structures were created for functional reasons, the evidence that breast feeding, or in fact any other child-rearing practice, has any long-term effects on the development of personality and behavior has not yet been presented.

In regard to the variability of test scores, we can only say that our experience has impressed us with the lack of variation and with the constancy of performance, even in the face of illness. This appears to be true not only from day to day during the period of infancy, but also in the interval from the first to the third year. Perhaps abstract concepts of reward and punishment have not yet developed sufficiently at these tender ages to have much effect, but will exert more influence as the child grows older.

We are sure that another comment that was made was not meant to imply that most examiners are either so unskilled or so unperceptive that they can accept fluctuations from 80 to 120 without raising questions about procedure. Neither do we feel that we have really been accused of making our diagnoses on the basis of physical appearance rather than behavioral performance.

One final point in regard to the fact that prematures have to "catch up." When the amount of prematurity is disregarded, there is a differential in performance between the premature and full-term infants which is directly related to the degree of prematurity. We would like to restate the fact that we examined the premature infants at their corrected chronologic ages rather than at their actual ones. Amounts of prematurity which ranged from zero to 116 days were assigned, depending on the birth weight and gestation history, in order to take this factor into account.

An Investigation of Seasonal Variations
of Mental Hospitalization for Old Age Psychoses

JOSEPH DOWNING,[1] ISABEL McCAFFREY,
AND EUGENE ROGOT [2]

Mental Health Research Unit,
New York State Department of Mental Hygiene,
Syracuse, New York

The problem of increasing numbers of mental hospital admissions of the aged has been a matter of concern for some time. As shown by Malzberg, (1, 2) Goldhamer and Marshall (3) and others (4), this trend has been taking place over a long period of time and is believed to be the result of increasing rates of admission as well as increasing numbers of older persons in our population.

The extent to which such increases in rates may reflect increasing pressures for hospitalization rather than a real rise in the incidence of psychoses of the aged is a matter of conjecture at the present time. The number of hospitalized cases alone, however, representing only one segment of the total problem of mental disease among the aged, is sufficiently large and important to justify continued study from many different points of view.

Mental hospital admissions of the aged, therefore, are being studied by the New York State Mental Health Research Unit in Syracuse as one phase in a continuing series of investigations with the hope that a useful body of information relating to the total problem will be accumulated in time. In the course of these studies, systematic patterns of hospital admissions within the

[1] Present address: San Mateo County Department of Public Health and Welfare, San Mateo, California.
[2] Present address: National Institute of Mental Health, Bethesda, Maryland.

273

city of Syracuse (5–7), consistent with those reported by Faris and Dunham (8), as well as systematic differences in the rates of admission from different communities (6) have been observed and reported. More recent findings relating to seasonal distributions of mental hospital admissions of persons 65 or more years old in upstate New York during the seven-year period, 1944 to 1950, are reported at this time.

Upstate New York includes the entire state except New York City. The total number of state and licensed mental hospital admissions of persons 65 or more years old with diagnoses of cerebral arteriosclerotic and senile psychoses during the seven-year study period was 13,800. Of this number, 6,550 were males and 7,250 were females. The seasonal pattern of rates of admission, computed on an average annual basis for two-month perods beginning with January-February and ending with November-December, was markedly different for males and females. There was a single peak (32.5 per 10,000 of the population) for females in the July-August period, whereas the rates for males appear to have had a higher level in the first three than in the last three study periods of two months each. It is the belief of the authors, that there was a high degree of consistency in the patterns from year to year despite the smallness of the differences noted.

Interest in this unexpected finding for upstate New York led to a more detailed study of the records of admissions of persons 65 or more years old to the Marcy State Hospital during the seven-year period 1949 to 1955.[3] The Marcy State Hospital was chosen for this purpose because of its accessibility to the Syracuse Research Unit. The hospital, itself, is located in Oneida County in the east central portion of the state. The hospital district, however, includes Onondaga, Oswego, Madison, Hamilton, and Warren counties as well as parts of Oneida and Herkimer coun-

---

[3] We wish to express our appreciation to the staff of the Marcy State Hospital, Marcy, N.Y., and to Dr. Newton Bigelow, Director, for their courtesy in making these records available for study.

ties. It had an estimated total population approaching 600,000 in 1950. Approximately 60,000 were 65 or more years old. Half of the total population of the district lived in metropolitan Onondaga County, which includes the city of Syracuse. There were five other cities in the district with populations of 10,000 or more in 1950, the largest of which was Rome with a population of 42,000.

The total number of admissions included in the Marcy State Hospital study group was 1,354. The seasonal patterns in the rates of first admissions of old age psychoses from this district are thought to resemble those of the upstate area for both males and females, although the differences between the high and low points in the Marcy district were approximately twice those of the upstate New York area as a whole.

The records were reviewed in the first place, to determine the types of places from which the patients in the study group were brought to the Marcy State Hospital. Fifteen per cent were found to have been patients in general hospitals at the time of admission. Another 26% were found to have been transferred from other local institutions such as nursing homes, homes for the aged, and county homes. Hospitals and local community institutions of the type mentioned, therefore, contributed a relatively large proportion (41%) of the 1,354 admissions in the study group.

Other studies have shown that significant numbers of mentally ill patients may be found in local institutions of these types in New York State and elsewhere (9, 10). It is apparent from the Marcy State Hospital data, however, that a significant number of mentally ill patients in this age group also are transferred from local institutions to mental hospitals. The proportion of the total number of patients in local institutions who undergo such transfers is unknown, but the proportion which they contribute to the total state mental hospital admissions in this age group is so large as to suggest that the policies and practices of local institutions in providing for the supervision of the aged and in selecting patients for transfer to mental hospitals may have a significant influence on the total number of admissions as well as the sex, geographic, socio-economic, and other characteristics reported for mental hospital admissions.

The possibility of such influences is strongly suggested when the seasonal variation of admissions from community institutions is compared with the seasonal variation of admissions from other sources, almost all of which are private residences. There was an excess of male over female admission rates for the group admitted from community institutions. No excess in male over female rates was found, however, for those admitted from other sources. Similarly, the difference in the male and female seasonal patterns was found only in the group of patients admitted from community institutions.

The difference in the total male and female rates of admission from community institutions could have come about as a result of relatively larger male than female populations in institutions such as county homes, as well as the selection by such institutions of males rather than females for transfer to mental hospitals. Other differences in selective factors in mental hospital admissions may be suggested by the difference in the male and female seasonal distributions of admissions from local institutions. The slight decrease in the summer admissions of males is somewhat similar to the distribution that might be expected from an association of mental hospital admissions with terminal physical conditions and disabilities. The increase in summer admissions for females, on the other hand, does not appear to suggest such an association.

Possible associations with terminal physical conditions also were indicated in a group of 139 patients admitted from private residences who died within one month following admission to the Marcy State Hospital. The total number in this group, however, is believed to be too small for conclusive findings relating to small seasonal differences.

In the residual group of 658 admissions, the circumstances

of admission may be said to have been comparable to the extent that they were brought directly from private residences and survived at least one month after admission. The seasonal distribution of this group of admissions was marked with 41.8% admitted in the middle four-month period of May-August. The corresponding figures for the first and last four-month periods were 28.4 and 29.8, respectively, as compared with the 33.3% that might have been expected in each of the three periods if the rate of admission had been constant throughout the year.

Similar patterns of increased summer admissions were found for those admitted from both rural and urban areas (Table I).

TABLE I

Month of Admission to Marcy State Hospital According to Population Size of Community from Which Patients Were Brought

Cerebral Arteriosclerotic and Senile Psychoses, Age 65 and Over 1949 to 1955

(Excludes admissions from community institutions and deaths within one month)

| | | Month of Admission | | | | | |
| | Total Number of Admissions | Jan. to Apr. | | May to Aug. | | Sept. to Dec. | |
Place Brought From		Num-ber	Per cent	Num-ber	Per cent	Num-ber	Per cent
Onondaga County[a]	328	86	26.2	147	44.8	95	29.0
Population of 10,000 or more[b]	126	36	28.6	47	37.3	43	34.1
Rest of district	204	65	31.9	81	39.7	58	28.4
Total	658	187	28.4	275	41.8	196	29.8

[a] Includes Syracuse City.
[b] Excludes Syracuse City, but includes cities of Rome, Glens Falls, Oneida, Fulton, and Oswego.

In Onondaga County, including the city of Syracuse, 44.8% were admitted in the middle period of May-August, as compared with 37.3% for the five other cities with populations of

10,000 or more and 39.7% for the other places in the district with populations under 10,000. Although the summer excess appears to have been larger in Onondaga County than in the rest of the district, the differences were not statistically significant at the .05 level.

The increase in summer admissions also was found for all symptoms and behavior characteristics, except suicide, as recorded by the certifying physicians on the court petitions as the bases for requesting mental hospital commitments. For this purpose, the symptoms and behavior characteristics were classified into eight groups as follows:

1. *Disorientation and confusion,* including statements such as "deteriorated," "forgets," "does not recognize family," "irrational," "rambling," "understands nothing."

2. *Unmanageable and disturbing,* including such statements as "irritable," "needs restraints in bed," "noisy," "screams," "refuses care," "runs away," "wanders," and "uncooperative."

3. *Excitement,* including such statements as "agitated," "sleepless," "restless," and "overactive."

4. *Hallucination and/or delusions,* including statements such as "imagines things," "talks to dead persons."

5. *Depression,* including "apathy," "despondent," "does not eat," "retarded," "wants to die."

6. *Destruction,* including "abusive," "assaultive," "belligerent," "breaks things," "strikes other people," "violent," "throws things."

7. *Paranoia,* including "argumentative," "believes everybody against him," "suspicious attitudes."

8. *Suicide,* including suicidal threats.

The proportions of those with each of the characteristics described (except suicide) who were admitted in the middle period of the year ranged from 47.8% for destructive behavior to 36.4% for depression (Table II). The differences between the observed and expected distributions (33.3% in each four-month period)

TABLE II

Month of Admission to Marcy State Hospital According to Symptom and
Behavior Characteristics Recorded by Certifying Physicians

Cerebral Arteriosclerotic and Senile Psychoses, Age 65 and Over
1949 to 1955

(Excludes admissions from community institutions and deaths within one
month)

Symptom and Behavior Classification	Total Admissions	Per Cent of Total			
			Month of admission		
		Total	Jan. to Apr.	May to Aug.	Sept. to Dec.
Total cases	658	100.0	28.4	41.8	29.8
Destruction	161	100.0	21.1	47.8	31.1
Management	403	100.0	24.6	43.9	31.5
Confusion and/or disorientation	508	100.0	28.5	43.7	27.8
Hallucinations	261	100.0	27.6	42.5	29.9
Excitement	296	100.0	27.7	42.2	30.0
Paranoia	116	100.0	27.6	41.4	31.0
Depression	165	100.0	31.5	36.4	32.1
Suicide	87	100.0	35.6	28.7	35.6

were significant at the .001 level for confusion and/or disorientation, destructive behavior, management. The distribution of the admissions with hallucinations and excitement recorded as a symptom was significantly different from the expected distribution at the .01 level.

Since these findings are based on the 658 admissions brought from private residences who survived more than one month after admission, the effects of possible selective factors associated with transfers from local institutions and terminal physical conditions are believed to have been minimized. Whether the general summer increases in total mental hospital admissions of the psychoses of the aged and groups of symptoms and other characteristics considered separately suggest actual increases in the prevalence and/or severity of the disease in the summer cannot, of course, be determined from these data. The data may be equally suggestive of summer increases in rates of hospitalization due to seasonal changes in transportation difficulties or seasonal changes in problems of home care and supervision.

Of the many plausible hypotheses that might be suggested, however, some are of epidemiological significance in that they are concerned with the natural course of the disease process and its manifestations. Others are of community interest in that they are related to variations in needs for medical, supervisory, and other types of facilities for the care of the aged.

Little is known at the present time about the circumstances determining when the family of a patient will seek care in a mental hospital rather than a local facility or undertake to provide necessary care and supervision in the home. The need for further studies of these factors is strongly suggested as a necessary step to a better understanding of the epidemiological significance of these findings with respect to seasonal variation as well as the many other findings of studies based on hospital populations and other selected groups of patients.

Addendum

Through the courtesy of Dr. E. M. Gruenberg, an early study of seasonal variation in mental hospital admissions has been called to our attention. Quoting from Dr. Gruenberg's communication:

E. Esquirol in his *Des Maladies Mentales considérées sous les rapports Medical Hygiénique et médico-légal* (B. Baillière, Paris, 1838), prints as Chapter I, "De la Folie," an article he prepared in 1816. On p. 26 he discusses the effects of seasons. On p. 27 he prints the following table of admissions to the Saltpêtrière.

He comments that the admissions are more numerous during the months of May-August, decline in September-January. He states that seasons also affect the course of the mental disorders. He then reviews the notion that the moon has an effect which, if any, he attributes to the stimulus of illumination.

Year

Month	1806	1807	1808	1809	1810	1811	1812	1813	1814	Total
Jan.	18	19	18	13	15	13	22	26	18	162
Feb.	23	23	27	26	13	13	15	19	14	173
Mar.	27	27	16	18	22	17	17	27	16	187
Apr.	32	24	15	27	19	13	28	30	18	196
May	26	27	23	26	39	30	29	31	17	243
June	32	28	33	31	22	18	32	26	29	251
July	23	37	21	39	34	24	37	21	29	265
Aug.	20	23	25	32	21	19	29	25	45	239
Sept.	21	24	21	25	16	25	23	26	25	206
Oct.	23	24	16	17	18	18	23	23	26	188
Nov.	23	21	23	27	28	16	16	19	25	198
Dec.	24	19	14	18	18	23	20	25	30	191
Total	292	296	252	299	260	229	291	288	292	2499

The correspondence between this monthly variation and that observed in upstate New York 150 years later is interesting despite considerations of diagnostic, age, and sex variations. Persistence of such a phenomenon over both space and time suggests a basic mechanism which has not yet been explained.

Although some may believe that the most plausible hypotheses are those related to seasonal changes in environmental needs for hospitalization, other hypotheses relating to physical and/or environmental conditions affecting the mental disease process or its manifestations should not be ruled out without further study. At least one vitamin deficiency disease, pellagra, has been found to be an etiological factor in a summer increase in psychoses. It is conceivable that seasonal variations in "subclinical" vitamin deficiencies, subclinical infections, or metabolic states also might be found to be etiological factors in the manifestations of psychoses of the aged.

REFERENCES

1. Malzberg, B. Age and sex in relation to mental disease. *Mental Hyg., 39*, 196–224 (1955).

2. Malzberg, B. Ages at first admission. *Psychiat. Quart., 23,* 344–66 (1949). A statistical review of mental disorders in later life.

3. Goldhamer, H., and A. Marshall. *Psychoses and Civilization.* Free Press, Glencoe, Ill., 1953. Chapters 2 and 3.

4. Kaplan, O. *Mental Disorders in Later Life.* Stanford University Press, Stanford, Calif., 1956.

5. Gruenberg, E. M. Community conditions and psychoses of the elderly. *Am. J. Psychiat.,* 887, June 1954.

6. Technical Report of the Mental Health Research Unit, New York State Department of Mental Hygiene, 1955. Syracuse University Press, Syracuse, New York.

7. McCaffrey, I., and J. Downing. The usefulness of ecological analysis in mental disease epidemiology. *Am. J. Psychiat., 113,* 1063, June 1957.

8. Faris, R. E. L., and H. W. Dunham, *Mental Disorders in Urban Areas.* University of Chicago Press, Chicago, Ill., 1939.

9. Ginzberg, R., and W. C. Brenegar, Psychiatric problems in elderly residents of county homes. *Am. J. Psychiat., 110* (6), 454–59 (1954).

10. Brightman, I. J., *et al.* Proprietary nursing and convalescent homes. *N. Y. State J. Med., 55,* June 15, 1955.

DISCUSSION

DR. A. D. MILLER: In certain respects, this struck me as being a most unusual study, rather unusual in one particular aspect. Furthermore, I think it is deceivingly complex in its structure and in the requirements of the investigators.

The point which particularly arrested my attention in this case was the fact that they considered time as an important variable in an epidemiological study. Time, to my knowledge, has been relatively infrequently considered. Place, whether defined geographically or topologically or sociologically, is a frequently used variable. Time, however, and particularly brief periods of time, are rather infrequently one of the variables examined.

In this kind of a study, time is not considered with a view to identifying trends. Time is part of a necessary description of the epidemiological setting in which various elements in this phenomenon are being considered. Of course, most of the studies in this area have for obvious reasons been prevalence studies, examinations of the state of affairs at a given moment in time. By design time is eliminated as a variable. Where time is used in chronological studies, longitudinal studies, incidence studies, it is part of the definition of the field to be studied. In this case, however, time is used as a variable. This fact raises a number of very serious problems.

What do we want to locate in time? Do we recognize how difficult it is to define onset of various seasons of the conditions we consider? If you talk about onset, it is hard to determine the moment of occurrence. Although, there have been fairly ancient studies of acute mental disorders as they may have occurred in various seasons of the year, chronic disorders such as this one, for example, are very difficult to identify in time.

Using the moment of diagnosis as the event to be counted would be exceedingly difficult because that raises all the problems of the case definition, case finding, case counting, and the identifying of the moment in time when this diagnosis was made.

Some specific aspects of mental illness have been studied—specific events, which are episodes in a mental illness; for example, there have been studies of suicides and their seasonal variations. In this study, first hospitalization is used as the index event, and I find myself, somewhat to my surprise, making a brief aside in defense of the use of first admission rates.

Hospital first admissions are relatively easy to define, easier than other kinds of studies. Their greater ease doesn't necessarily make them useless if we identify them as such, do not confound them with prevalence studies, and recognize the complexities involved. Certainly, when you introduce time as a variable, the problem of mental disease causality becomes extraordinarily complicated. We know how many epidemiological variables "place" alone implies; I would say there is an equal number of crucial variables which are summarized when we say "spring" or "summer."

In this instance the authors have been remarkably successful in reintroducing for our consideration the time variable, in gathering very interesting data, and in interpreting with restraint. They have been explicit about what they have done and what they have not done.

I would like to ask a number of questions about some of the findings, and I will take them more or less as they appeared in the paper chronologically.

The comment is made early in the paper that the pattern has been "consistent" one from year to year. I have always been very concerned about various ways of quantitating "consistency" of this kind, in addition to determining what "very consistent" means.

But for the moment, assuming—and I would assume validly—that a reasonably consistent pattern has been established over the years —is there any fruitfulness in examining the deviations from the pattern, in the years when this pattern was not as apparent?

I relate this specifically to one of the hypotheses which the authors named; for example, their speculation that the severity of the winter may be related to the seasonal variation as we have seen it.

Is it conceivable that—there must be mild winters some times, or relatively so—there is a difference in this seasonal pattern which might in any way relate to climatic variations of a gross sort?

A second question also has to do with the differences between the hospitalization curves of the single hospital, and the statewide curve. I think they are chiefly differences in the amplitude of the curve, as was noted. It is a rather substantial difference in range. In one, I think, the range was five per 10,000 and in the other 12.

Was this due to other patterns in other parts of the state? Is it due to the fact that a whole different time era was being studied, as it was? And can any of these questions help to raise new hypotheses or shed some light on the ones mentioned?

I would like to turn to another point, choosing to examine carefully only the records of those patients who were admitted directly to the mental hospital, rather than those who had a previous stay in another community institution. Was it valid to assume, as you did in this case, that not only was the route of the entering to the hospital different, but that the travelers (or patients) were different? I think this point is particularly crucial in view of the fact that the seasonal variation was different in the hospital group.

I think that you might consider adding a sixth hypothesis to the five mentioned, namely that administrative and professional practice within the community institutions themselves may result in the seasonal curve in the state hospital population.

Further questions arise about the admissions from the community institutions: What is the one-month death rate among this group? When were they first admitted to community institutions? Did these admissions follow any seasonal pattern, and did it seem to coincide? What were the kinds of reasons they were admitted as compared to those who were admitted directly to the state hospital?

Now I would like to mention what I think is the weakest point in the paper, and that is the dependence upon the clinical data from certifying physicians. There is no need for me to belabor here the great many sources of variation which can contribute to what a certifying physician writes on an admission of one of his patients to a state mental hospital. Obviously, only one of these contributing factors is the symptoms which the patient is presenting at that time.

I think what perhaps bothers me more than this, because I think we all necessarily use such data, is not so much that it *is* unreasonable, but that it *may be* unreasonable without me, the reader, having any way of knowing. Therefore, it is exceedingly difficult for me to appraise the quality of this material and to make an intelligent judgment about it. However, having said I don't know whether I can trust it, I will go ahead and reason from it, which is an example of the dangerous seductiveness of this kind of material.

The authors conclude that among the hypotheses they named that they found themselves thinking more and more about the importance of increased social pressures in the summer, as well as similar factors related to the summertime care of the elderly.

Contrariwise, could it not be reasoned that those who are hospitalized in the winter would be likely to be more disturbed than those who were admitted during the other seasons, because it would take that much more disturbance in the home probably to warrant hospitalization, if they really are easier to take care of? Such was not found. Clinical manifestations were level.

Could it be suggested then that since the manifest indications were relatively similar year round, there is a certain level of behavior which may vary seasonally, at which point people are likely to be hospitalized by their families? The frequency, however, with which people reach this level may indeed differ seasonally and may be related to the way of life in the family.

One final brief comment about the concept of the paper which has to do with the data on suicide. As I noted earlier, I am aware of two studies concerning the suicide variation by season. A fairly recent investigation in Michigan, unlike these findings, found that the suicide rate was lowest in the winter, highest in the spring and summer months. This raises another question for me: What is the rate of successful suicide in the area during the winter? We know only that there was a higher rate in the winter of attempted suicide, obviously not successful suicide.

It is possible that the explanation for the higher attempted suicide rate lies in the fact that attempted suicide is more difficult in the winter. I am not saying I think this particularly serious, but I think it is consistent with the data.

Dr. E. M. Gruenberg: I would like to say, first, commenting on Dr. Miller's last statement, that I hope this is not a preliminary report. I hope this is a final report. I think that there are a number of reasons why I think it is a final report, and I suspect that some people think I hope it is a final report because I do not think this question is worth pursuing, as to why these seasonal variations occur.

I think it would be of some value to know why they do occur. I hope this is a final report, because I hope this pattern will disappear from the utilization of psychiatric facilities for the care of elderly people, ill people, since these patterns reflect the situation in which patient psychiatric care is available for people only in state hospitals, and I realy feel there is no need to add further hypothetical explanations for these seasonal variations, but I am sorely tempted to add one.

I should like to illustrate one reason why this pattern should disappear in the future—one reason—and psychiatric care should become available to elderly people as well as to younger people in the communities where they reside and not in communities exclusively many miles from their home.

I would like to add another hypothesis to the long list already discussed. Emphasis has been placed on attempting to explain why it is suposedly easier to provide home care in the winter rather than in the summer months for elderly people who are moderately lacking in mental functions. I would submit to you that if we have or if we had been shown the same graphs with the peak in the winter, we would have had equally good hypotheses to explain why it is harder to take care of elderly people at home in the winter than in the summer months.

Now, I think that in fact we do have a situation in the winter months when physical movement must be restrained in this climate to some extent for everybody. I would suggest that the interesting features of these graphs is the decline about the middle of the summer in both sexes, just when the harvest is about to come in and fresh foods become readily available again.

I would suggest that perhaps in the winter months we have people confined to home, not getting as much fresh food as they get the rest of the year. Because they are confined at home and somewhat restless, under sedation, I would suggest the hypothesis that this increase represents, not only increased social pressure for hospitalization, but also possibly an increase in confusional states that arise as a result of accumulated use of sedatives during the winter months, and lack of adequate nutrition.

I do think that there is one little item to support this. Although the only statistical difference in symptoms recorded is a decrease in suicide attempts in summer, this leads me to lend some weight to the not statistically significant but present differences of an equal order of magnitude, perhaps, during the summer months of the known depressive syndrome. This is what one would expect if one were getting confusional states along with accumulated malnutrition and sedatives.

DR. A. LILIENFELD: Just another hypothesis: I was wondering what was the seasonal distribution of the death rate in the mental institutions. It seems to me, if I recall correctly, that the death rate is higher in the winter than the summer. Therefore, during the summer, more beds will become available, even crowded as they may be, so that perhaps the first initial admission rate would increase.

DR. P. V. LEMKAU: I would like to ask a question related to one that Dr. Miller raised about the use of the examining or the committing physician's report. Why was this considered to be better than an analysis of the more extensive study after the patient was admitted to the hospital? Although, I realize the environmental situation may not be as easily available there, we are talking about symptoms the patients show. One wonders why the more extensive examination had not been used.

DR. J. DOWNING: First, let us take up why we used data from the commitment forms rather than on the admission writeup? We were interested in the reason why the person went to the mental hospital rather than in his condition on arrival there.

As to whether we would have obtained more accurate data from the presumably more skilled and more consistent report of the admitting physician than the very questionably consistent reports of the committing physician, I am inclined to agree with you.

On the surface, the New York State commitment form, if adequately filled out, would be a very nice research tool for data collection because it specifically asks all these important questions. On the hospital admitting form it is necessary to analyze and to search through a great amount of extraneous material to find the data you want.

The decision to use the commitment form was both a matter of expediency and a desire to find out what the patient was like before he was admitted.

This leads to the next point: what was the nature of the person's illness or their social condition that led them to be admitted to a community institution, as asked by Dr. Miller? We simply have no data on that. This would require the study referred to as "a study of the social use of community institutions."

We were interested, for example, in the problem of duration of illness, a question asked on the commitment form. All too often we could not get adequate consistent data. If the person came from a community institution, the date of illness was also the date given for their admission to that same community institution, obviously unreliable.

Regarding the consistency of the pattern from year to year, it is fairly consistent. Sometimes there are split peaks and sometimes there are one or two months before or after the date of the average peak. The pattern, however, is quite clear. I had not thought to relate it to climatic conditions.

This curve may relate closely to average daily temperatures, but of course there are so many variables as to be of doubtful reliability.

Considering the differences between statewide and Marcy Hospital patterns, we are inclined to believe that metropolitan areas show the greatest seasonal variation pattern. We were lucky in selecting a hospital district in which over half of the district population came from the metropolitan area. This is not true for all state areas, which might explain the differences.

The fact that the differences in admission patterns might be due to differences in community medical and social practices, I believe we mentioned. This again might be related to the findings of differences between the greater number of Onondaga County admissions and the non-metropolitan remainder of the hospital district. There are more psychiatrists in Onondaga County. We do not know that more of the patients are seen by psychiatrists prior to commitment. However, if more are, the recorded clinical data on the patient prior to commitment might be more reliable than those outside this county.

The problems of data reliability, and so on, have been discussed completely, I think, by people more competent than I.

As to the alternate hypothesis suggested by several persons that the winter group, if sicker, should have been more disturbed rather than less disturbed is equally tenable. Unfortunately, our data are inadequate to examine this hypothesis.

We do not have data on suicide in this population. We do know two facts. First, in New York City the pattern of suicide is similar to that of mental hospital admissions; that is, the suicide rate is highest in the spring.

Second, we know in general that suicidal attempts are highest in this old age group. As shown before, "suicidal behavior" did show a seasonal variation. This suicidal behavior included not only suicidal attempts but suicidal threats such as, "I think I will kill myself."

Incidentally, we consulted with some of the local psychiatrists about how to get people committed. They told us that the quickest way to get a person committed to a state hospital is to say that he has made suicidal threats.

The nutritional basis for admission is an appealing hypothesis we also considered. I will agree that the data are consistent with this; that is, that the persons who because of winter malnutrition are suffering from subclinical case of pellagra or beri-beri psychosis are admitted for this reason in the spring. Possibly, as a result of greater confusion or illness they are put in sedation and admitted. This is possible; I do not know.

The institutional death rate follows the death rate for the state as a whole, except that it is much lower.

Incidentally, if you want to live to a ripe old age become schizophrenic in your youth, go to a state hospital, and remain until you die. The old people in the state hospitals have much less chronic disease and live longer on the average than those out of hospitals.

DR. LILIENFELD: But that is not so.

DR. DOWNING: If I may end with one statement on hospital first admission data, we have done a great deal of work with this kind of data, and we are quite dissatisfied. We feel that we have gained something of value from it, such as this study. However, at the present time we are trying to obtain out-patient mental clinical data, too, so that we can be more aware of patterns in the community. Unfortunately, studies to the present, particularly in this age group, have shown that this age group is not seen in out-patient mental health, mental hygiene clinics. Along that line, I have seen no studies, but it is my impression that there is a summer drop in mental hygiene clinic admissions, which is an interesting commentary on the type of problem that is seen in such clinics.

DR. P. V. LEMKAU: The drop in New York City is practically 60% in the months of July and August. It has to do with vacations by psychiatrists.

Index

Adolescents
  California Personality Test, use in study of, 62
  changes in personality of, 39
  personality change of, relation to intelligence, age, and sex, 63
  study of personality change, 40
Age
  as factor in personality change of adolescents, 45, 63
  prevalence by, of mental disorder, 190
  relation to housing environment, 154
Alzheimer, 23
Anergesia, 7

Baltimore
  developmental quotients of infants compared with other infant quotients, 260
  studies in, 176
  study of infant population, 251
  survey in, 196
  survey of mental disease by race and color, 183
  variations in diagnosis, 177
Beyle, 4
Bleuler, Eugen
  use of term schizophrenia, 16
Blood pressure
  relation to nervous illness during pregnancy, 107
Brodmann, Korbinian, 25
Broken homes
  factor in personality change, 50
Brooklyn State Hospital
  study of schizophrenic patients at, 131

Caesarean section
  relation to patients with history of nervous illness, 111
California Test of Personality, 40, 43, 62, 68
  inventory items, 55, 58
  use in study of adolescents, 62
Calmeil, 4
Cities
  mental disease in, 183
  size of, relation to schizophrenia, 82

Deafness
  relation to mental disorders in twins, 236
Deaf population
  mental disorder in, 229
  in New York State, 234
Dementia praecox, 16; see also *Schizophrenia*
Demographic aspects, 230
  of mental disorders related to deafness, 229
Developmental quotient
  related to birth weight, race, and economic status, 252
Diagnosis
  prevalence of mental disorder by, 191
  variations in, 177
Disease entities, 27

Economic status
  change in, as factor of personality change, 57
  relation of, to developmental quotient, 257

Premature births
  age and nervous illness relationship,
    108
  classification by history of nervous
    illness, age, and color, 110
Prognosis, 119
  adjustment to social roles in family
    and community related to, 132
  difficulties of, 121
  home environment as factor in, 127
  relation to treatment, 122
  specific problems in, 124
  value of background factors for
    outcome of schizophrenia, 128
Psychiatric examination
  validation of, in Stirling County
    survey, 214
Psychiatry
  Kraepelin's research institute for,
    24
Psychological disorders
  versus psychophysiological disor-
    ders, 197
Psychophysiological disorders
  versus pschychological disorders,
    197
Psychoses
  of aged, relation to admission to
    hospitals, 279
  Kraepelin's classification 33
  of old age, classification of, 278
  of old age, seasonal variations in
    hospitalization, 273
  paranoid, classification of, 16
  two groups of Kraepelin, 3

Race
  prevalence of mental illness by,
    183, 190, 193
  relation of developmental quotient
    to, 257
Rinecker, Franz von, 2
Ruedin, Ernst, 23, 25

Schizophrenia; see also *Mental dis-
    orders*
  background factors in prognosis of
    outcome of, 122
  city size related to, 82

Schizophrenia (*continued*)
  consistency of diagnosis, 75
  in the deaf, 241
  hospitalization, ecological and oc-
    cupational rates, 72
  relation of occupational mobility
    to, 79
  relation of occupational statuses of
    respondents and parents, 79
  relation to social structure, 69
  social mobility, effect of, 77
  study of patients at Brooklyn State
    Hospital, 131
  in twins, 237
  variation by occupation, 76
School
  location of, as factor of personality
    change, 46
School mobility
  factor in personality change, 48
Schuele, Heinrich, 5, 6
Sex
  as factor in personality change, 45,
    63
  prevalence by, of mental disorder,
    188
Single-point-in-time study, 145
  differences from longitudinal study,
    165
  disadvantages of, 156
Spielmeyer, Walter, 23, 25
Standardization
  discriminant function analysis of
    groups, 210
Stirling County survey, 203
  validation of psychiatric examina-
    tion, 214
Survey technique, 203
  discriminant function analysis of
    groups, 210
  field procedures, 208
Sympton inventory
  advantages of, 221

Trailer
  layout of, used for interviews, 209
Treatment
  of mental disorders, in metropolis,
    175